0

l

AND THERE WAS LIGHT

AND THERE WAS
LIGHT

The Discovery of the Universe

by RUDOLF THIEL

TRANSLATED FROM THE GERMAN BY

RICHARD AND CLARA WINSTON

NEW YORK   ALFRED A. KNOPF   1957

L.C. catalog card number: 57–13059
© Alfred A. Knopf, Inc., 1957

THIS IS A BORZOI BOOK
PUBLISHED BY ALFRED A. KNOPF, INC.

FIRST AMERICAN EDITION

Originally published in Germany as UND ES WARD LICHT
© 1956 Rowohlt Verlag GmbH, Hamburg.

CONTENTS

LIST OF PLATES

LINE DRAWINGS

IN THE TEXT

Book One

MYSTIC CHILDHOOD

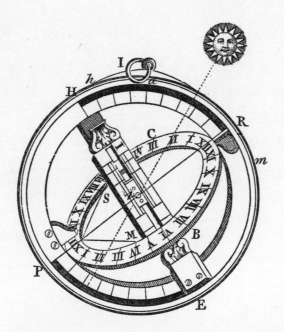

ANCIENT THEORIES

The Displaced Zodiac and the Beginnings of Astronomy

FOR UNTOLD CENTURIES, men believed in the influence of the stars upon human destinies. The particular relationship of the position of the Sun to the constellations of stars at an individual's birth was regarded as having a determining influence upon his character and fate. But the stars, which supposedly governed the lives of man, occupy no fixed position in the sky.

The scientific astronomer of course takes no stock in the intricate horoscopes of astrologers. But he does, among other things, undertake to explain why the stars have shifted their position. The instability of the Earth's axis is at fault. Today the Earth's axis points to Polaris in Ursa Minor; around 3000 B.C. it pointed to the brightest star in the tail of the Dragon. Some 13,000 years ago it pointed to Vega in the Lyre, and 13,000 years hence Vega will once again become the polestar. In other words, the Earth's axis makes one complete gyration in about 26,000 years.

There are twelve constellations in the zodiac, the apparent path of the Sun across the sky, and if observations are made at a fixed time of year, such as the spring equinox in March, long favored by ancient astrologers, the direction in which the axis of the Earth points seems to shift by about one constellation every 2,000 years. This gives us a clue to the origins of astronomical observations.

At the time of the Greek astrologers, the beginning of spring lay

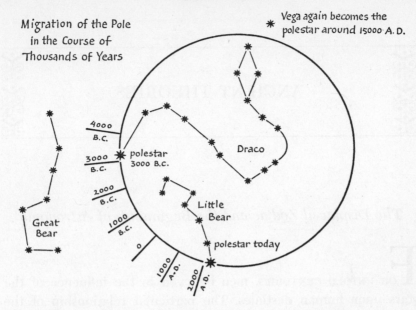

Migration of the Pole
in the Course of
Thousands of Years

Vega again becomes the
polestar around 15000 A.D.

Draco

polestar
3000 B.C.

4000 B.C.

3000 B.C.

2000 B.C.

1000 B.C.

0

1000 A.D.

2000 A.D.

Great
Bear

Little
Bear

polestar today

in the Ram; today it is in the Fish. Some astronomers have classified the entire history of the civilized world accordingly:

AGE OF THE TWINS	6300—4300 B.C.
AGE OF THE BULL	4300—2100 B.C.
AGE OF THE RAM	2100 B.C.—A.D. 100
AGE OF THE FISH	100—A.D. 2300

Probably the oldest civilized peoples were aware of the transitions of the vernal equinox from one sign to the next. They must have followed the course of the Sun through the zodiac with great care. A number of ancient representations of the zodiac bear the note: "The Bull marks the beginning of spring." It is therefore highly probable that astronomical observations were being made as early as 3000 or 4000 B.C.

Possibly such observations were made even earlier. The temple of Dendera in Egypt bears on its dome a magnificent painting of the zodiac. In it, the Twins, not the Bull, stand at the beginning. The temple is not so very ancient; it dates from the late Hellenistic period. But Egypt apparently retained a very old tradition that the zodiac ought to begin with the Twins—which probably means that it was first conceived in the Age of the Twins, be-

ZODIAC FROM THE EGYPTIAN TEMPLE OF DENDERA, 100 B.C. THE
TWINS (JUST BELOW CENTER), NOT THE BULL, HERE MARK THE BE-
GINNING OF SPRING.

tween 4300 and 6300 B.C., and that consequently astronomical
observations must have been made that long ago.

The Duty of the Son of Heaven: Orientation

There is good reason why the human race has been searching
the skies for so long. For astronomy has given us the ideas of
space and time.

It is hard for us to sense what it must have been like for human
beings to live upon an unknown Earth, knowing only that endless

expanses opened out in all directions. For them there were land-marks only in the immediate neighborhood. The world into which each person was born seemed limited by the horizon, "as far as the eye could reach," but the horizon always moved along from one place to the next. The ultimate boundary discovered by the boldest travelers was the ocean, but it too stretched on into infinity. Real stability seemed to exist only in the firmament. The sky appeared to revolve constantly, but its lights again and again returned along the selfsame tracks. The Sun, Moon, and stars alone enabled men to find their way about their world; these alone made possible orientation upon Earth.

"Orientation" originally meant directing oneself toward the east, toward the rising Sun. Direction, in fact, exists only in relationship to the sky; on Earth, all directions were blurred. At first only east and west were taken into consideration—these being the directions of the rising and setting of heavenly bodies. The concept of north grew out of a fairly difficult observation: that not all stars rose and set. Certain of them seemed to turn in a circle in a particular region of the sky. The most noticeable of these were seven bright stars arranged in a curious way. Like seven oxen tramping around a threshing-floor, these stars paraded in a circle every night. The Romans called this constellation the Seven Oxen, and identified the point around which they revolved, the north. The Greeks saw the constellation as a bear—hence the Arctic, the land of bears, came to mean the north. Many other ancient peoples, however, spoke of the Great Wain or Wagon whose path guided them easily and safely toward the north.

This nocturnal signpost was held in special reverence by the Chinese, who have always laid great stress upon the four quarters of the sky. They assigned a center to them: the polestar in the heavens; China herself was the center on Earth—the "Middle Kingdom," around which they conceived a square world. Out of this image sprang a comprehensive world-view, a pattern for all the basic ideas of Chinese thinking.

The Chinese established a system of references to the four cardinal points and their center for such varied matters as the constellations and the planets, the seasons and the time of

day, the elements of matter, the fundamental properties of things, the principal species of animals and plants, the important internal organs of human beings, the chief processes of psychic life, and the major epochs of history under their legendary emperors.

The Sun and the Moon were assigned a special position as the masculine and feminine principles, Yang and Yin. These two could be combined with any single concept within the all-embracing intellectual scheme.

Orientation by the cardinal points was a political problem of the utmost importance. The exact position of the heavenly pole had to be determined for each city. Every temple, every building, every grave had to be aligned with absolute precision in a north-south direction. The emperor's throne, the seat of the master of a house, and the front door of every house, must face strictly to the south. Consequently, Chinese astronomers enjoyed a great prestige. Teachers and scholars par excellence, they chose the right places and the right times for all activities, from battles to hunts, sowing of seed, baths, and even the sweeping of the house. In short, they regulated the entire business of living.

The north-south direction for government buildings was set by the emperor himself, in an involved ceremony. As the Son of Heaven he offered the annual sacrifice at the time of the winter solstice. This rite, performed in the geometrically laid-out temple area on the round hill near Peking, was the most important religious act of the year in ancient China. The sky had a soul-tablet just like a deceased emperor; Sun, Moon, the five planets, and the constellations—the Great Bear being specially distinguished—likewise were provided with soul-tablets. Mandarins sacrificed before these tablets.

Thus there evolved, out of the human need for "orientation," a pure religion of the heavens. Upon this religion a superficial veneer of Buddhism was later set.

During the millennium before Christ, Chinese civilization was based exclusively and thoroughly upon astronomy. The prerequisites for such a development existed also in Egypt. There the art of orientation reached possibly a higher pitch of perfection than in China. The five-thousand-year-old Pyramid of Cheops deviates

only by a few minutes of a degree from the cardinal points. The steep entrance shaft is a "telescope" which pointed directly at the celestial pole.

The Pharaoh called himself Son of the Sun. Like the Chinese Son of Heaven, he established the directions for temples and even made the astronomical measurements with his own hand: "I grasp the stake, seize the handle of the mallet, and hold the string together with the Goddess of Wisdom. I turn my countenance toward the course of the stars. I fix my eyes upon the Great Wagon and stake out the corners of the temple."

But the Egyptians were much too attached to their native beast-headed gods to espouse a religion of the sky. It took the priests of their central shrine, Heliopolis, a long time to establish the doctrine that all local divinities represented mere forms of the sun-god Ra. When, in the New Kingdom, Pharaoh Ikhnaton attempted to impose an abstract worship of the Sun upon the people, he failed utterly. The Egyptians were far more traditional and earthbound than the intellectual Chinese.

No doubt Ikhnaton's famous hymn to the Sun was, for all the reverential spirit it expressed, a purely personal and romantic poem. The Son of Heaven in the Far East would never have addressed the supreme star in such intimate language:

> *Thou shinest so beautifully on the horizon of heaven,*
> *Thou living Sun, who created life.*
> *Thou standest on the eastern horizon*
> *And hast filled all lands with thy splendor.*
> *Thy rays embrace the lands to the very end*
> *Of all thy Creation.*
> *Thou makest the lands subject to thy beloved Son,*
> *Pharaoh Ikhnaton . . . .*

Time Was Once Relative

Time was once relative not in a theoretical, Einsteinian sense, but perceptibly so in daily life. Each hour embraced a different

span of time. At noon the hour was longer than in the evening or in the morning.

Nowadays, hours of different length are almost unimaginable. For us, time flows evenly. Yet human beings once thought otherwise. In fact, all earlier cultures had a sense of time entirely different from ours.

Men are not born with a concept of time. A child lives from moment to moment. The alternation of day and night sets up a rhythm of life to which everyone submits without thinking. In all probability the seasons, with their varying demands upon men, first produced a consciousness of regular, recurrent periods of time. The need to count days, to measure spans of time, coincides with a relatively developed form of life, such as farming. And astronomical observations were ready to hand when men, conscious of passing "time," began dividing up the day.

The first time designation was noon, the moment when the Sun's shadow is shortest. In order to determine it precisely, one of the oldest scientific instruments was invented, the vertical shadow-stick. From this primitive device a logical but probably long and wearisome trail led to the sundial. With the sundial, time was given concrete existence; it became, so to speak, something that human hands could make. The advance of the Sun's shadow across the graduated face of the sundial transformed an unconscious feeling more and more into a "conceptual" idea of a thing that moved, fled away, passed without man's intervention.

But to the Egyptian inventors of the sun clock, this something did not flow evenly; the speed of its passage varied. This may have come about by accident: it is noteworthy that the Egyptians marked out the dial of their sun clock in even divisions. For man does have an instinct for symmetry; when he divides any space, he tends to divide it into segments of equal size. But the Sun passes overhead in an arc, and its shadow therefore passed across the graduations of the dial in different periods of time. The Egyptians made each of their hours a different length; moreover, they also adapted them to the season, the winter hours being one seventh shorter than the hours of summer.

It is evident that the Egyptians had no feeling for time in our

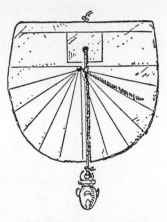

EGYPTIAN SUNDIAL.

sense. We cannot consider the idea of time an elementary component of our minds, or even indispensable for the ordering of our environment. "Time" is a fairly late abstraction, the end product of a long evolution in which the clock played a crucial part. And since the first clock was a sundial, in the beginning "time" moved at a varying, irregular pace.

So rooted did this idea become in the minds of the Egyptians that they arranged their water clocks to register hours of varying duration. Incredible though it seems, they went to great efforts to do so. In the flow of water they had a direct image of steadily flowing time. But with extraordinary skill and ingenuity they artificially produced irregularity in a regular natural phenomenon, in order to make time flow in the only manner that seemed right to them: with the inconstancy of their sundials.

Centuries passed before they succeeded fully, as is evident from the inscription on the tomb of Prince Amenemhet, Keeper of the Seals of the New Kingdom, around 1500 B.C. Amenemhet is there praised for having at last succeeded in building a water clock that kept perfect time. His clock was able to dispense with the several jets of water formerly needed to measure the varying lengths of the hours. Its single stream could even be controlled to change the length of the hours with the seasons.

The probable appearance of this ingenious clock can be deduced from a late Greek water clock—in matters of technology

the Greeks were very dependent upon the Egyptians. The inflow of water in this clock was regulated by a funnel-shaped valve controlled by movable weights, and the length of the hours could be altered from month to month with the aid of a scale mounted on a rotating drum. Every hour a slave had to shift the weights, and every month he changed the position of the drum.

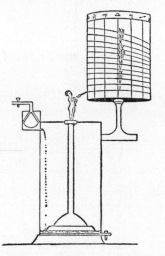

RESTORATION OF AN ANCIENT WATER CLOCK. THE INFLOW OF WATER IS REGULATED BY THE VALVE AT LEFT; HOURS OF VARYING LENGTH ARE INDICATED ON THE DRUM. THE FIGURINE WITH THE POINTER IS RAISED BY A FLOAT IN THE WATER TANK.

Egyptian time-measurement with its relative concept of time remained the model for all of antiquity. Athens, for example, was very proud of her Tower of the Winds, which in addition to a weather vane had no less than eight sundials, visible at a great distance from all directions. They told the time with an error of no more than three or four minutes, we are informed—a type of accuracy which makes us smile. Of course the duration of every hour differed; but the Greeks undoubtedly felt the same confidence in their inconstant division of time as do we in our infallible chronometers whose hands circle the dial with military precision. Human beings can grow accustomed to anything—even to operating with two simultaneous and contradictory conceptions of time. The Babylonians and the Chinese did not fit their

water clocks to their sundials; they let the water flow regularly. They therefore had two different kinds of hours, the one changing and the other regular. As late as 1600, Father Ricci, the Jesuit who introduced pendulum clocks into China, adjusted some of them for absolute and some for relative time-measurement.

The Eternal Problems of the Calendar

Chronology, or calendar-making, is hampered by a relative sense of time. For the Sun and Moon dictate the calendar with absolute authority. Discovering the exact course of these heavenly bodies with sufficient precision to establish the length of the year and the month was one of the most difficult tasks ever undertaken by man's mind. But it was essential; public life, festivals, dates, lists of rulers, everything subject to annual or cyclical recurrence, depended upon the making of a calendar.

Chronology began with the month. The revolution of the Moon, with its changing phases, is certainly the most obvious movement in the heavens. Its duration was easier to establish than the annual period of the Sun. The moment when the new Moon first reappears can be fixed with great precision. That moment was celebrated among early primitive peoples. As late as A.D. 1500 many persons in Europe still prayed to the new Moon, despite the Church's threat of dire punishment for such idolatry.

The month of approximately thirty days provided a measure for the seasons and the year. The Sun required some twelve months to reappear in the same constellation. Hence, the year was reckoned at 360 days. This figure was the product of calculation, not observation. In fact, such observation would have been quite a feat, since the background of the starlit sky fades in the blaze of the Sun.

In Egypt, however, there existed a more convenient measure for the year: the floods of the Nile. These floods came annually with extreme regularity; obviously they had some connection

with the Sun, for at the same time Sirius reappeared out of the Sun's glow—Sirius which, as Homer has it,

> *Among men is called the dog of Orion,*
> *Rising ever in autumn, radiantly glowing*
> *Brighter than other stars, at the dusky hour of milking.*

The reappearance of Sirius from the Sun's glow in the sultry dog days marked the start of the Egyptian New Year. It then became evident that the true length of the year was not 360, but 365 days. This was one of mankind's most painful discoveries. It threw into the discard the neat calculation based on the sacred numbers 12 and 30. The heavens proved to be irrational; they no longer fitted man's mathematical instincts, which had seemed so miraculously confirmed by the calendar.

The Egyptians never fully accepted this disillusionment. Along with the irregular year dictated by the Nile and Sirius, they retained the old, symmetrical 360-day year. Consequently, there were two calendars, a complicated twin bookkeeping system for time. Not in vain was the High Priest at Heliopolis called Observer of the Secrets of the Heavens. He had a great deal to do to make some semblance of order out of this confusion. Festivals shifted, occurring on different days every year, as a result of the conflict between the two calendars.

There was an even more embarrassing complication: Sirius also shifted in relation to the Nile floods, because of the wandering of the Earth's axis. Gradually the Egyptians realized that a year of 365 1/4 days most closely approximated the true annual circuit of Sirius and annual rise of the Nile. There were radical reformers who wanted to introduce such a year exclusively; but Egyptian reverence for tradition won out, and the dual calendar was retained. At every coronation the priests made the new Pharaoh take an oath not to alter the Sirius year, and not to coordinate the mathematical year with the real year by intercalating days.

This method of intercalation which the Egyptians disdained was adopted by almost all other peoples, for it was a highly convenient solution. It had been developed by the Babylonians.

it as to nothing else; the ornaments of their temples were chronologies in stone; calendars were inscribed on every pillar and every frieze. The whole of Mayan public life was guided by the calendar.

As a result, modern historians were able to obtain a remarkably good picture of the history of this buried civilization, for the numerical symbols of the mysterious Mayan script had been deciphered. A clear and comprehensive chronology of Mayan history was drawn up. But until recently, only one factor was missing: a fixed initial date which would permit comparison with our own chronology. The entire building had been reconstructed, but the key which would open the door was still lacking. What was the year 1 of the Mayans?

Vast effort was expended in vain calculations. A solution was reached only after the construction of another calendar superior to all those of the past in convenience, practicality, and range. This was a calendar with all the refinements that could be desired, and which involved no calculation at all: the Zeiss planetarium.

Among the universal dreams of humanity, a dream that has stirred many an inventive spirit has been that of building a model of the firmament showing the various movements of the Sun, the Moon, and the planets. Archimedes constructed one which the Romans took as part of their booty after the capture of Syracuse. The seventeenth-century Dutch mathematician Christian Huygens worked out the mathematics of repeating fractions in order to calculate more easily the dimensions of the cogs in a planetarium he was constructing. Over the centuries there were other efforts, but none compared to the Zeiss planetarium.

Around 1920 the optical experts at the Carl Zeiss works in Jena, Germany, conceived the idea of manufacturing a projection apparatus that would reproduce the complex movements of the heavens with rays of light instead of cogs and levers. A staff of astronomers, mathematicians, and engineers labored for five years on the apparatus, which projects images of the Sun, Moon, and stars upon a smooth, white dome. Such planetaria have been erected in many cities all over the world—modern temples of popular science.

The planetarium projector permits the operator to reproduce the appearance of the sky in any part of the world and at any period of time by throwing a few switches. In 1954 this everlasting calendar was subjected to a test of its capabilities. A group of scientists watched while an image of the firmament in the course of 600 years, between A.D. 300 and 900, was projected above them. They were seeking some unusual cosmic event that might correspond with the presumed initial date of the Mayan chronology. For it seemed a fair assumption that this astronomically minded people would have chosen some astronomical base for their chronology. Near one of the possible dates, May 25, 482, a rare celestial conjunction appeared: near to the Pleiades the Moon, Mars, Venus, Jupiter, and Mercury crowded together in a narrow sector of space.

A conjunction of the Moon with four planets is an extremely rare event. To medieval astrologers such a combination would no doubt have boded a world-wide conflagration. Luckily, it took place when the barbarian migrations were causing such upheavals that no one was paying much regard to the stars. Or, at any rate, if any dire predictions were made, the records have been lost.

The Mayan astronomers in Mexico, however, must have considered the event singular enough to serve as the initial date for their chronology.

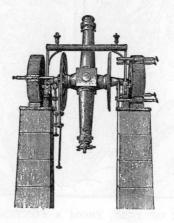

GIFT FROM BABYLON

The Wrath of Heaven

IN THE EARLIEST times astronomers were required to warn rulers and people of impending onslaughts of the wrath of Heaven. It was their responsibility to anticipate any unusual behavior in the celestial signposts of space and time: a colored ring around the Moon; a new star with a tail; an eclipse of the Sun.

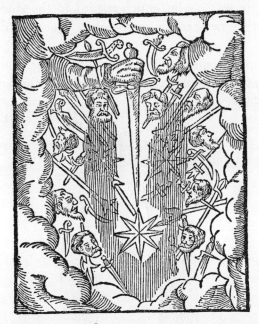

THE GREAT COMET OF 1528, FROM A CONTEMPORARY ENGRAVING. THE SWORD AND SEVERED HEADS WERE DESCRIBED BY AMBROISE PARÉ.

People cared not for the cause; only for the consequence. A comet's tail streaking over half the sky seemed to threaten every living soul. The exact nature of the threat was not so important either. The chief problem was to placate the gods. Therefore the people and their ruler had to be ready in time to do public penance, to pray and sacrifice.

"When an eclipse of the Sun takes place," an old Chinese account tells us, "the Emperor takes no full repast, and has the drums beaten at the altar. All officials lay aside their ceremonial robes; the princes sacrifice pieces of silk; the historian delivers a speech, until the eclipse is over."

Emperor Kuang Wu-ti, of the first century A.D., provided an unforgettable model of how a god-fearing ruler should behave during the Sun's struggle with the Dragon that threatened to swallow it. He made a five-day retreat to meditate on his government. Then he issued a decree: "It is necessary to repair our errors and thus forestall the evil that Heaven is sending. I for my part can scarcely speak; I am trembling over my misdeeds. I do not wish my subjects to give me the title of Ching. I wish the lords of my court to tell me their opinions bluntly, in secret memoranda."

His court astronomer wrote: "According to the rules of starcraft eclipses of the Sun ought to take place only on the first day of the month. This eclipse struck upon the last day; that is because the Moon has speeded his course. The Sun is the image of the Emperor, the Moon the image of the subjects. But the faults of the subjects usually have their origin in the faults of the Emperor."

Such audacious language indicates the remarkable prestige an astronomer enjoyed in China. But mistakes could be fatal for them. In the third century B.C. the court astronomers Hi and Ho sat drinking wine when an eclipse of the Sun began. They were brought to trial for negligence. The verdict read as follows: "The prayer-drums beat, the mandarins mounted their steeds, the people gathered in clusters. Meanwhile, Hi and Ho, like wooden statues, saw and heard nothing. Their negligence in calculating and observing the stars is being punished by death."

BALINESE CONCEPTION OF AN ECLIPSE—THE DEMON KALA RAHU
SWALLOWING THE MOON.

It must not be thought that the emperor or the people expected
astronomers to predict the fearful event beforehand. That this
was impossible had been demonstrated all too often. Even the
best astronomers of antiquity, the Babylonians, invariably missed
in such predictions. Their regular reports to the king of their observations, written on clay tablets in cuneiform script, frequently
contained confessions of their failures.

"As for the eclipse of the Sun, of which my King spoke, it has
not taken place. On the twenty-seventh I will again observe and
report."

"The month of Addaru will have thirty days. On the thirteenth,
and during the night from the thirteenth to the fourteenth, we
made an observation. On the fifteenth, Sun and Moon were seen
together, but no eclipse took place. Seven times I arose, but no
eclipse took place. I will send later the final, decisive report.
Tabu-sil-Marduk, nephew of Inlil-nasir."

Here was an amazing informality and ease in a relationship
with the king. This was possible because the Babylonian kings
considered their astronomers virtually infallible. It was not the

observatory which was responsible for the nonarrival of an eclipse; rather, the blame was Heaven's, which for unknown reasons chose to deviate from custom. Hence the king must do penance—after all, one never knew what Heaven meant by such inconsistency. In the worst case the astronomer might be sent a tablet stating: "The King is tired of his long fast and asks whether the new Moon has not yet appeared." A curious situation: because science blundered, the king had to fast. There is no indication that the astronomer fasted.

Stargazing and Star-Reading

The Babylonian astronomers possessed a charming naïveté and candor, which today enables us to observe the gradual development of star-reading, or astrology, side by side and in pace with astronomy.

It was obvious to everyone that the stars had an influence upon the Earth. By its height in the sky the Sun regulated the seasons and brought drought and rainy months. When the Pleiades reappeared out of the sunshine, about the time of the spring new Moon, there were devastating storms. This effect of the Seven Sisters is described in a very ancient Sumerian hymn: "The winter storms, the wicked demons, engendered in the firmament, raise their heads; mischief they wreak, evil they ponder, day after day; seven their number, heralds of their King Anu; roaring their wrathful hurricane in the sky. Before the radiant Moon they have subsided."

The Moon was itself a weather-maker—and is so considered to this day, despite the lack of meteorological evidence. Certainly the monthly period of women seems to point to some mysterious human relationship with the Moon. The Babylonians believed they had discovered a considerable number of additional ties. A new king, for example, would have a long reign if its first month turned out to be longer than had been calculated, or if two stars set together at the moment the Moon reached its zenith. A ring

around the rising Moon foretold the birth of a crown prince. If a new Moon appeared precisely at the beginning of a thirty-day month, it meant good fortune for the entire country.

Similar influences were ascribed to the planets. The Babylonian astronomers must have been astonished and alarmed when they observed that some of the stars were also wanderers and moved in the same paths as the Moon and the Sun—that is, through the zodiac. Two of these, the morning and the evening star, even revealed themselves to be one and the same planet which was overtaken by the Sun, so that it sometimes appeared on the right, sometimes on the left of the Sun. The Babylonians solemnly appointed it their third principal heavenly body, and frequently depicted it with eight rays, alongside the sickle of the Moon and the disc of the Sun. It seemed obvious that a change in the position of the morning star must have an important meaning. A cuneiform tablet dating from around 2000 B.C. declared:

"When Ishtar [Venus] is visible in the east on the sixth of Abu, there will be rain and destruction. Until the tenth of Nisan it remains easterly; on the eleventh it vanishes and remains invisible for three months. If, then, it glows in the west again on the eleventh of Du'uzu, there will be fighting in the land, but the fruits of the fields will prosper."

Venus, however, had surprises in store for the Babylonians. With their customary honesty, they recorded their consternation on burnt clay: "When the planet Ishtar enters the Scorpion, floods take place, as is well known. This time, however, there were none, for as soon as Ishtar came up to the breast of the Scorpion, she was snatched away. Although she touched the Scorpion, she did not penetrate it."

This was the Babylonians' first acquaintance with one of the great puzzles of ancient astronomical science: the occasional retrograde motion of the planets. Similar motion was observed in the case of the other planets, and with equal surprise:

"Mar-Istar to the King: As to Marduk [Jupiter], I recently reported. My prediction was based on his position in the Anu path [the celestial equator]. I now report: he has been delayed. He has truly run backward; therefore my interpretation was mis-

taken. But it would not have been mistaken if Marduk had remained on the Anu path. May my Lord King understand this."

In any case, there can be no doubt that the path of scientific astronomy led through the fields of astrology in all ancient civilizations. Even the Chinese observed the retrograde motion of Jupiter only because they considered this bright star a harbinger of good fortune. As soon as they discovered Jupiter's inexplicable irregularity, they decided that it was an omen of famine.

The Babylonians surpassed all other peoples of antiquity in the patience, precision, and impartiality of their observations. Not content with the usual interpretation of the stars based upon empirical rules, they created a different, a dogmatic system of astrology.

The Eyes of the Gods

Babylonian astrology became a second celestial religion; but it was quite unlike the first, that of ancient China. In China the stars became gods; in Babylon the gods became stars. To the Chinese the mysteries of the cosmos were so sublime that they degraded their traditional popular divinities to demons and created a cult of the stars without priests, myths, or dogmas. The Babylonians, on the other hand, placed their native divinities one after another in the heavens, and transferred the mythic traits of these divinities to the stars. Here was an amazing evolution: for the first and only time a civilized religion rendered the divine beings visible and calculable by identifying them with the seven wandering stars.

The cuneiform script itself expressed that impulse, for its sign of divinity was a star. An age-old Babylonian legend related that the lord of the Earth, Bel, appointed the three gods Shamash, Sin, and Ishtar guardians of the firmament, which they thereafter patrolled as the Sun, the Moon, and Venus. When four more wandering stars were found in the firmament, the Babylonians made bold to repeat the act of Bel. The city-god of Babylon,

Marduk, became the planet Jupiter; the god of death, Nergal, became the planet Mars; the god of war, Ninurta, became Saturn; and the god of knowledge, Nabu, became Mercury. Mars was called Star of Judgment upon the Dead. The Tower of Babel, which was simultaneously a sanctuary and observatory, was called tersely the Temple of the Seven Transmitters of Commands from Heaven to Earth.

THE TOWER OF BABEL, AS VISUALIZED IN AN OLD DRAWING. THE STRUCTURE WAS AN OBSERVATORY AS WELL AS A TEMPLE.

Thus in Babylon divine worship became equivalent to astronomy, astronomy equivalent to searching out the will of the gods. In observing the movements of the planets and their relationships to one another, the priest was performing the highest rite of his religion. That fact accounted for the enormous power of the priestly class. They did not pray to invisible beings; they associated with them face to face, so to speak. Out of this belief sprang the extraordinarily frank reports of the astronomer-priests to the king, and the king's meek queries as to whether he might end his fast. Moreover, these priests prophesied with a sense of absolute certainty—for *they* did not read the future from deceptive signs; they read it in the eyes of the gods themselves.

The light rays sent forth from the planets were magical glances by which the gods guided activities on Earth. Their influence was predetermined beyond the possibility of doubt by the special traits of the particular god. The system of interpreting the stars no longer depended upon observation and empirical rules amassed in the course of centuries; interpretation flowed simply and directly from the very names of the planets. Each planet's name carried with it the entire body of legend which the old religion had attached to the god.

The transposition of divine characteristics to the wandering planets is the essence of astrology. That is why the position of the planets was held to influence the destiny of individuals. If a child were born while the Moon was rising, his life would be resplendent, long, and happy. If a child were born while Mars was rising, he would be sickly and soon die. If two planets wielded their influence simultaneously, the rising planet operated with greater force. Thus, if Jupiter were rising and Venus setting at birth, a man would have luck in later life, but would abandon his wife. If Venus were rising and Jupiter setting, the man would be ruled by his wife.

Thus the astrological rule was early established that opposition of the planets mutually weakened their influence. Contrarily, in conjunction they strengthened one another, with the higher of the two planets being the stronger. Soon further refinements were added: angles of 60 and 120 degrees, triangles, and hexagons, were considered favorable, squares unfavorable. These various "aspects," multiplied by seven, yielded a complicated doctrinal system which laid the groundwork for a comprehensive craft of prophecy. The aspect of the planets could be consulted for any event in life, for births and the founding of cities, business negotiations, travels, political treaties, battles, harvests, sickness.

Elaborations were added by the Greeks, and in the Middle Ages the *Book of One Hundred Rules* spread knowledge of the arcane science far and wide. Everyone knew his ruling planet. Those who were born under Jupiter presumably possessed a "jovial" character. The children of Mars considered themselves hot-tempered, bold, bellicose, destined for evil deeds. Even physical

appearance was supposed to be governed by the planet. Every planet also had certain natural objects attributed to it, and special periods of influence. Fire, iron, hematite, jasper, the color red, the taste of bitterness, the male sex, the liver, gall, kidneys, veins, and the left ear—all belonged to Mars. Mars also dominated the years of life from 42 to 57, Tuesdays, and the night from Thursday to Friday.

Some of these rules go all the way back to the Babylonians, but most of them only to the Greek astrologers. Like the Chinese, the Greeks connected the principal aspects of thought with the stars. But the relationship which was, for the Chinese, an intellectual pattern, a magnificent synthesis of ideas, became in the West a web work of tangible causes and effects. The difference can be strikingly demonstrated by two quotations. The Chinese *Book of Changes* declares: "The heavens reveal ideas; the holy man takes them as his model." The other conception is formulated in the Talmud: "Everything that is found upon Earth is found also in the heavens; nothing is so trivial that it does not have its correlation in the sky." According to this latter view, it was necessary only to read the celestial signs aright in order to unravel all earthly mysteries.

Such readings, however, would have called for a highly developed craft in observation, which the Middle Ages lacked. But the Greeks apparently foresaw this and established a dogmatic scheme which could be applied in lieu of observation. Every hour of the day was placed under the dominion of a planet. In fixed succession the seven governors of the hours followed one another through an entire week, and then repeated their turns. The system was primitive, but practical. An individual's birth-planet could be determined without consultation with an astronomer.

This arbitrary method also went back to a Babylonian model: the planetary week. Originally the week had had five days because five divided neatly into the thirty-day month. But once the seven planets had been discovered, the number seven became sacred. Babylonian observatories were made seven stories high; state documents were sealed with seven seals. There were seven colors, seven musical notes, seven parts of the body; human lives

were supposed to consist of seven-year periods. In the sky, Orion and the two Bears had seven stars; the Pleiades were called the Seven Sisters, though with the best will in the world only six tiny dots of light could be distinguished. The week was given seven days, awkward as this unit was. And each day was named after and presumably dominated by a single planet. To this day the names of the days retain the system: Sun-day, Moon-day, Tiu/Mars-day, Woden/Mercury-day, Thor/Jupiter-day, Freya/Venus-day, Saturn-day. Although the names of our days derive mainly from Norse mythology, the system can be considered a gift from Babylon, reminding us of the eyes of the gods which once governed the days, the hours, and human destinies with their magical glances.

Picture Writing in the Sky

The most popular form of astrology, fortunetelling by the twelve signs of the zodiac, developed much later than interpretation of the planets. These constellations were preferred above others because they formed the path through which the seven wandering stars moved. They took their names from the figures a patient eye can put together out of the various dots of light.

The Scorpion, with its gnashing teeth and curved tail, could not be missed. The Lion and the Twins could also be recognized fairly easily. Some imagination was required to see the partial outlines of the Fish, the Scales, and the Ear of Grain (later the Great Mother and the Virgin). The Water Bearer, the Goat-fish, and the Crab were real picture-puzzles. And how the Babylonians arrived at the Archer, the Bull, and the Day Laborer (later the Ram), remains utterly obscure. Probably the Oriental impulse to create fables had more to do with the naming of these constellations than anything seen by the eye.

Once these names had been sanctified by use over two or three millennia, they could no longer be considered human inventions. The belief arose that meaningful picture writing existed on the

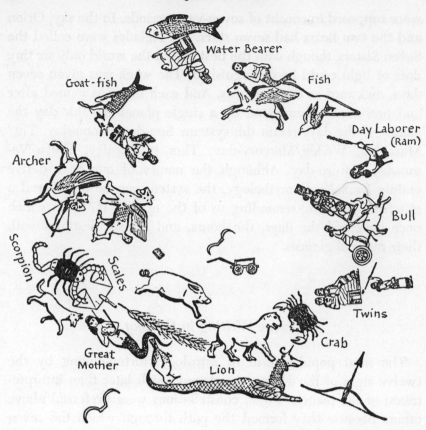

Water Bearer

Goat-fish

Fish

Day Laborer
(Ram)

Archer

Bull

Scorpion

Scales

Twins

Great
Mother

Lion

Crab

LATE BABYLONIAN ZODIAC, SHOWING THE TWELVE CONSTELLATION-
SIGNS.

sky. The Scorpion with his poisonous bite undoubtedly prophesied evil. The Lion would surely have an influence consonant
with his character; the only question was on what this influence
would operate. The Babylonians assumed that its effect would be
felt on the planet that happened to be passing through the Lion.
To them such an assumption was only logical. No one could
deny, after all, that the Sun was strongly influenced by the zodiacal sign through which it passed. When the Sun was in the Fish
or the Water Bearer, there was a rainy season. The seasons
changed; how else could this be explained but that the god of the
daylight employed servant spirits who waited at the various constellations to fire up or dampen his flame, to mix his rays with

heavenly water or dry them out, as happened when he entered the Crab or the Lion?

There seemed every reason to believe that these constellations would have similar effects upon the other "eyes of the gods." The Moon, for example, could just as easily be dried out by the Crab as could the Sun. Formerly, the weather had been an affair of the phases of the Moon; now it could be predicted by subtler signs. If the Moon stood in Cancer, it was not a good time for sowing; farmers had best wait a few days until it shifted into the wet constellations. In many peasant localities this rule is followed to this day.

A small step further, and the picture writing in the sky was ascribed independent significance. If the Scorpion rose on the horizon while some undertaking was in progress, the hour was surely not favorable. Someone born under the rising Lion would undoubtedly be fierce, courageous, and probably extremely strong.

The Greeks took over the Babylonian doctrines along with the zodiac. Without more ado, they attached their own mythology to images in the sky. The Water Bearer they identified with their cupbearer to the gods, Ganymede; consequently, a person born under the Water Bearer was destined to be the favorite of great lords. The Ear of Grain they assigned to the virgin goddess of agriculture; hence the sign promised prosperity, but no children.

Around the signs of the zodiac there now developed a network of relationships similar to the one which embraced the planets, but even more closely woven. All of medicine depended on the stars. The lands of the Earth were divided among the twelve signs. All qualities, senses, colors, temperaments, and humors stood under their dominion. A relentless passion for system seized the learned men of all nations.

The Origin of the Horoscope

The decisive turn in the history of astrology occurred late in the Greek era, paralleling the metamorphosis of the human spirit

in general. The Oriental redemptionist religions began to flourish. There arose profound conceptions of god and devil, good and evil, paradise and hell. A feeling of portentous changes impending was expressed in apocalyptic visions of the end of all things, of Last Judgments, of coming Messiahs, and in the concept that history had a deep meaning, and represented a process of salvation for all humanity.

Persians, Jews, and Chaldeans were the peoples who promulgated this new kind of religion. The Chaldeans, carriers and heirs of Babylonian culture, contributed their astrological beliefs to the new amalgam. Astrology now parted company entirely with its astronomical base, and became mystical speculation. Thus a third and most highly systematized type of astrology came to the fore around A.D. 300.

To determine the full influence upon human beings of the planets and the signs of the zodiac, the astrologer must obviously consider more than the rising and setting planet or constellation at birth. Rather, he must take into account the total radiation impinging upon the newborn child. The Chaldeans thought to accomplish this by introducing a unique device: the twelve zones of influence.

How they hit upon this we do not know. The scheme no longer had the slightest connection with astronomy, nor with any empirical facts. As far as we know, intermediate stages of the idea did not exist. It was simply there one fine day, all complete—a flash of mystical insight.

A circle was conceived, carved into twelve equal zones of influence: a zone for death and a zone for health, for marriage and money, friends and foes, religion and travel—in short, for all the subjects concerning which a person might wish to ask a fortuneteller. This division had no reference to anything in the heavens or on earth; it was purely geometrical, without any demonstrable relationship to anything real.

The planets and the signs of the zodiac radiated upon these twelve zones. The constellation at the hour of birth, the "nativity," could be represented pictorially if the position of every planet were entered on a celestial circle, and the circle depicting

the twelve zones were placed underneath. Thus the celestial disc was superimposed on an immovable circle divided into twelve compartments.

The Greeks gave this contrivance a thoroughly geometrical twist. The angles the planets formed with one another were of prime importance. The signs of the zodiac each occupied thirty degrees of arc, no matter what their true extension in the sky— which happens to be different for every sign—and in spite of their long-since-recognized movement due to the wavering of the Earth's axis.

These paper circles constituted the horoscope, the crown of all the astrologers' efforts. Out of the ominous signs, the roaming eyes of the gods, and the picture writing in the sky, there ultimately evolved this abstract scheme, a pure geometry of fate. It provided the Greeks with endless opportunities for profound speculations. In the horoscope influences and counterinfluences crossed one another to such an extent that there was ample room for interpretation. A science developed which could rival any theological system in its complications. Schools with sharply opposed doctrines sprang up. It was centuries before a unified dogma crystallized out of the conflicting tenets.

A prime subject for controversy was whether the horoscope at the time of conception rather than the horoscope of birth was the true one. Moreover, the Greeks took a view of the zones of influence which differed radically from that of the Chaldeans. They divided the signs into regions, each of which belonged to a specific planet. Even the orbits of the planets were divided into wet, warm, dry, and hot sectors. Two different types of more precise fortunetelling were derived from the horoscope—the so-called "directions." One of these was so difficult that it was scarcely ever applied in practice, and even the other system could be mastered only by formidable mathematicians.

A historical incident suggests how strongly the Greeks believed in their geometry of fate. The tale is that the doctor and astrologer Nektanebos took steps to delay artificially the birth of Alexander the Great until an especially favorable constellation of the planets had come about.

Irresistible Magic

Astrology persisted as the most successful intellectual movement of all epochs. It infected every culture, no matter what the
prevailing religion; it infiltrated all levels of education. It penetrated into dying Egyptian civilization and into the vital, mature
life of the Greeks, the Hindus, and the Chinese, into the flower-
ing Arabic culture and the budding culture of the Occident during the Middle Ages. Believers in Christ and Mohammed, in the
Platonic Eros and the wisdom of Confucius, paid tribute to it. It
affected equally those whose goal was Buddhistic contemplation
and Roman organization. It captured the minds of superstitious
fellahin and sophisticated mandarins, mystics in monks' cowls
and Stoics in togas, Caesars of the second century and popes of
the sixteenth, the visionary who wrote the Apocalypse and the
mathematical genius Ptolemy.

Its conquest of the Greeks was swiftest and most complete of
all. That this should have been so runs exactly contrary to one's
notions. The Greeks of all people would seem to have been im-
mune to such beliefs. They were a daylight people who saw all
things concretely, who cast abstract ideas into tangible form. So
humanized were their gods that a savage fetish would arouse
mystical ideas more easily than such gods. Their cult of heroes
erased the boundaries between god and man, and ended by
building temples for the living. Nothing could have been further
from the minds of the Greeks, it would seem, than viewing the
night sky as ruler of man's soul and destiny.

Of course, the Greeks shared the universal human dread of
the wrath of Heaven, which comets and eclipses patently proclaimed. But Pericles showed his soldiers that they had nothing
to fear from an eclipse by giving them a scientific explanation; he
held a cloak in front of a lamp to demonstrate what happened
during an eclipse. General Nicias was despised by the public for
abandoning a siege because of an ill omen. Aristophanes called
the Moon and Sun "gods of the barbarians."

And yet these very same Greeks developed astrology into a

rigid system of dogma. The stages by which this earthiest of cultures paradoxically arrived at a form of celestial mysticism can be traced step by step. It began with Plato. His universal spirit was open to all suggestions from other realms of the mind. Plato had one Chaldean as a friend, and one as a disciple. Perhaps influenced by them, he took up the idea that hitherto had only been hinted at in the Orphic mysteries: that the stars possessed a divine nature. The stars, Plato went on to teach, consisted of the four elements plus a soul. This wholly un-Greek conception opened wide the gates to Babylonian astrology. Aristotle, ordinarily so critical, spoke with enthusiasm about the stars as animate beings. The Stoic philosophers, in their turn, attributed to them emotion, understanding, and will.

When horoscopes first appeared, the realistic minds of the Greeks objected vigorously. Even the Stoics protested: if man's fate were predestined to the last detail, men would be nothing but slaves of the stars—machines, in fact. Moreover, twins and other persons with exactly the same horoscopes ought to have precisely the same sort of lives. But in spite of these sensible objections, astrology soon became a great fad.

From the third to the second century B.C., Greek culture underwent a transformation. All the Mediterranean lands had been Hellenized; now they won their independence. The distinction between Hellenes and barbarians disappeared; in art and science Syrians and Egyptians had an equal voice with Greeks. The intellectual center of the Greek world shifted from Athens and Pergamum to Alexandria. Economics and technology became more important than literature and philosophy. Greece herself, with her tiny city-states insisting with vain arrogance upon their individuality, ceased to have any political importance. The despised Romans from the West wiped them off the map more easily than they had Carthage or Egypt, carried off the treasures of wrecked Corinth, and made themselves at home amid the charms of Athens.

The feebleness of the Greeks sprang from an inward change. Their faith in the Olympic gods had long since vanished; their mythology had become an object of mockery. In the third cen-

tury only the goddess Tyche, Chance, was really worshipped. In the second century she yielded her place to Ananke, Necessity or the coercion of circumstances. Widespread skepticism paralyzed the energy of the Greeks; they wanted only to know the future, not shape it. Criticism, not creation, was the principal passion of the intellectuals.

The Greek people longed to return to religion. All their old gods came to life once more—as stars. The planet Venus now was seen as Venus herself; the Father of the Gods, Jupiter, stood plainly visible in the sky. He no longer revealed himself in thunder and lightning, as in days of yore, but by direct radiation. He might no longer associate personally with a few chosen mortals, but he wielded direct, magical influence upon every living soul. Astrology afforded a living relationship with the gods, which had formerly been reserved to the mystery cults.

This form of astrology meant infinitely more than mere fortunetelling. It confirmed the supremacy of Ananke above Tyche by providing calculable laws of destiny. Liberated from Chance, life once more acquired a deeper meaning. From the depths of the night sky sounded divine voices; a web of causes and effects linked man to the universe. Man's soul depended on the planets and the signs of the zodiac; the human microcosm represented the image of the animate macrocosm. Man's horror of his solitude in the universe was placated; blind Moira no longer reigned; in faith in the stars, in the demonstrated connection between past and future, men could find inner peace.

That faith overwhelmed the Greeks at the time their own cultural forces were running dry. Once they had restrained their Dionysiac impulses, giving vent to them only in brief, occasional orgies. Now they regarded such impulses as the true lure of life; they abandoned themselves to the dark powers. It was a tremendous experience for them to feel themselves trembling in contact with other worlds, as though invisible threads from these came together within their souls. Precisely because the spirit of mysticism was so alien to their culture, it took hold of them with enormous power as soon as they lost their souls intellectually and politically.

The Romans casually absorbed astrology as they did all other beliefs that came their way. In their Pantheon all the fashionable gods were successively equated with the Sun. They had only a practical interest in astrology, and used it for the crudest sort of fortunetelling. The Emperor Tiberius himself practiced it. Hadrian annually drew up a professional prediction for himself. In Rome astrology became a business. Innumerable "Chaldeans" practiced every variety of it, from the primitive disc of destiny to the weekly horoscope. Juvenal's satirical remarks sound quite modern: "Your dear wife asks the astrologer why her bilious mother-in-law is so slow about dying. She does not follow you to the provinces because Trasyllus' fortune-book advises against it. When her eye twitches, she finds the right medicine in her horoscope, and Petosiris tells her when she must take it. For a trip as far as the next milestone she has some woman friend choose the proper hour from her much-fingered yearbook."

It was not Christianity that spelled the end of Greco-Roman culture; it had been undermined far earlier by Chaldean magic.

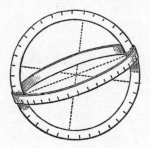

THE GREEK COSMOS

Theories of the Universe

THE EGYPTIAN'S CONCEPTION of the universe was naïvely anthropomorphic: the goddess of the heavens, Nut, arched her starry body over the solid Earth and let the ship of the Sun glide over her back. When the Sun sank below the horizon at night, it

EGYPTIAN GODDESS OF THE HEAVENS, NUT, ARCHING HER STARRY BODY OVER THE EARTH. THE SHIP OF THE SUN IS SHOWN BOTH AT THE BEGINNING AND END OF ITS TRIP OVER HER BACK.

disappeared into the realm of the dead beneath the Earth; next morning, newborn, it began its day's journey once more. Out of this childlike myth, however, there evolved something permanent and great: nothing less than faith in the resurrection of man.

The Babylonian view was far more realistic. It attempted to explain natural phenomena. The sky was a bell-shaped dome constantly whirling around, pasted with stars, and enveloped in a mantle of water that extended down below the Earth. These were the waters over which the spirit of God hovered before the Creation, and out of which the Deluge poured when "the windows of heaven were opened." The universal waters also trickled through the Milky Way to feed the clouds. The Jews took over this idea, called the dome the "firmament," and reasoned that the Tower of Babel had been built in order to bore into the sky and see whether it was of clay, bronze, or iron.

Men of the Middle Ages in Europe apparently had no comprehensive picture of the universe. They borrowed one from the Arabs, nomads who conceived of the sky as a great tent spread out overhead. In processions Catholic priests carried an image of this tent, a canopy of black velvet with stars sewed onto it.

The three impulses underlying the formation of myths—anthropomorphism, the urge to interpret natural phenomena, and the storytelling impulse—were present in remarkable equilibrium among the Greeks. Their view of the universe was founded upon realism, upon frank delight in the visible world. The sky was a curved, brazen shield, but it was not enveloped in a mantle of water. Rather, it was surrounded by primal fire which blazed through innumerable holes of different sizes, sometimes flamed in the lightnings, and shone milky-white through the crack between the two arched halves of the shield. The Greeks took it for granted that rain came not from the sky but from nearby clouds. The clouds rose up from the sea, Oceanus, which bounded the round disc of the Earth and at the distant horizon touched the shield of the sky.

The poetic imagination of the Greeks soon added colorful anthropomorphic details, animating this picture with fabulous and symbolic ideas. The Milky Way became the trace of the heavenly

conflagration Phaëthon had unleashed when his father Helios
gave him permission that one fateful time to drive the wild steeds
which drew the chariot of the Sun. The highest mountain that
Greek seafarers observed at the rim of the inhabited world became the Titan Atlas, forced by Zeus to hold up the vault of
heaven, the same Atlas whom Hercules had briefly released so
that he could steal the golden apples of the Hesperides.

In this concept the stars' relationship to human beings persisted, but exerted no magical influence upon them. For every
newborn child a tiny light was ignited in the sky, and this light
went out at his death.

The Greeks had as great a talent as the Babylonians for im-
agining recognizable figures among the stars. They found such
shapes in a whole segment of the sky—the one which was important for their seafaring activities. The Swan, the Lyre, and the
Eagle formed the summer triangle; along with the Crown, the
Arrow, and the Dolphin, these are unquestionably the constellations most easy to distinguish. Once they have been identified as
such images, they cannot be seen otherwise.

To each figure the Greek poetic spirit linked a character out
of mythology, or else created a new one. The Twins could be
none other than the classical brothers Castor and Pollux, sons of
Leda by the Swan. Castor was mortal like his mother, Pollux immortal like his father Zeus. The two brothers were inseparable,
underwent all adventures together, and even renounced possession of the beautiful Helen rather than leave one of them unsat-
isfied; instead, they preferred to kidnap the two daughters of
Leucippus. Castor was killed in this adventure, and the immortal
Pollux, refusing to accept a seat beside his father on Olympus, followed his brother to Hades. Moved by this loyalty, Zeus placed
the two, in close embrace, in the firmament.

Remarkably, the capacity for creating myths was never entirely extinguished in Greece. In the post-Alexander, Hellenistic
period, when the Babylonian zodiac and astrological ideas had
become current among the Greeks, more myths of the stars were
devised. They were more than fables; they were religious poetry
whose themes were illustrated by examples from the heavens.

Almost everyone knew and loved these myths. The poet Aratus filled the entire firmament with demigods and their beasts, and his verses were quoted and recited everywhere. Never again were the stars at once so transfigured and brought so much down to earth. With a unique combination of brashness and reverence, the Greeks transformed the universe into a picture book.

The Greek temperament, however, was also capable of confining the multitudinous characters of the mythology within a neat, coherent system. This they did in their most unique creation: their cosmogony. Since the days of the Babylonians a myth of the origin of the world was a necessary part of a complete picture of the universe. Among the Greeks, a poet rather than an astronomer set forth the cosmogony. Alongside Homer, the Greeks had their Hesiod, the Dante of the Hellenes, who sang of the origin of all things.

For Hesiod, divinity was not the beginning. While the Babylonians started with their trinity, "Lord of the Sky, Lord of the Earth, and Lord of the Underworld," Hesiod considered the maternal womb of Earth as the alpha and omega. "I invoke the Earth who generates and nourishes and takes back to herself all things, like the ocean its waves." According to Hesiod, Earth arose first out of chaos, and was at first dark and bare. Longing for light, she let herself be fructified by Eros, the creative principle, and then gave birth to the sky. It is noteworthy that this culture, the most human culture that ever existed, saw generation as the principle of creation and believed that even the sky could arise only as the result of love.

The newborn sky bent down to the maternal Earth, and out of their passionate embrace came the Titans, creatures intermediary between god and man. There were also born two spiritual beings, Themis and Cronos, female Order and male Time. This conception, too, sprang from a typical Greek impulse: to confer tangible form upon ideas, and to suggest that two of the most abstract ideas preceded everything else, including the very gods. For Zeus, Father of the Gods, descended from Mother Earth in the third generation. He had to overcome the Titans in order to win dominion, and dethrone Time in order to become immortal.

This cosmogony rivals the Judaeo-Christian in profundity. For all its sensuality and earthiness, it gave a spiritual cast to the traditional beliefs in a whole horde of gods. It made Order and Time the ancestors of the gods, and assumed that even the sky was of later origin than the creative principle of love.

Harmony of the Spheres

A verse of Homer's remarks that the Great Bear is the only constellation that never bathes in Oceanus. The Great Bear is so close to the polestar that it always remains above the horizon during the daily revolution of the heavens.

But in Egypt that is not the case. There the Great Bear sinks into the sands of the desert for a short while every night. The Greek philosopher Thales must have observed this when he was in Egypt, for his disciple Anaximander drew the conclusion that the Earth could not be a flat disc; if it were, the Great Bear would be everywhere equally high above the horizon. Hence, he argued, the Earth must be a sphere floating freely in the universe, with the sky, itself spherical in shape, at an equidistance from it on all sides.

This was one of the most momentous conclusions in all antiquity. Throughout thousands of years not one of the Babylonian astronomers had thought to extend the dome of heaven into a sphere, even though the constellations plainly traveled in circles overhead, night after night. It is difficult indeed for human beings to recognize what they see.

To conceive of even the Earth as spherical required a degree of intellectual freedom which Greek culture alone was capable of. As a matter of fact, Anaximander's bold insight was not accepted by the populace. Even scholars at the time of Aristotle questioned the theory. But when it was first conceived, around 600 B.C., it was intoxicating. This was the age of the Greek Renaissance and Reformation. The long-banished Dionysiac cults were penetrating into Greek life, and along with them Oriental art

forms. Awareness of personality awoke, and the urge toward independent thought about God and the world. The theory of the roundness of the Earth meant as much to the Greeks as the theory of Copernicus to us. It was the germinal cell of all later sciences. It provided a new picture of the universe, incomparably more fertile than the mythological picture. All at once the climate of different countries could be explained by the higher or lower position of the Sun. Oceanus could no longer be imagined as a ring of water; the ocean became a part of the globe of Earth, itself spherically curved. What demands such a concept made upon the imagination—for was it not contrary to all experience? The Greeks began pondering whether antipodes existed on the lower half of the sphere, and wondering what force prevented them from plunging into the abyss. They reveled in the pleasure of having discovered that the purest geometrical form, the sphere, was fundamental to the structure of the universe. And the spherical heavens were but an image of the spherical Earth. Here was perfect order, absolute harmony, a "cosmos."

Pythagoras, the Newton of antiquity, soon extended the idea of the cosmos into a "harmony of the spheres." Pythagoras realized that it was not enough to have a star-studded heavenly sphere circling around the Earth; seven other spherical bowls must be circling within the firmament. The Babylonians had discovered that the Sun, the Moon, and the five planets moved through the zodiac at differing velocities. In a harmonious cosmos, however, no single factor could wander about of its own sweet will. Consequently, Pythagoras conceived a spherical container for each of the seven wandering stars, and in addition a ninth sphere, outermost and immovable, which provided the motive force for all the others in some inexplicable fashion, by a divine principle.

The universe, then, resembled an onion, with one skin inside the other, each moving at a different velocity. Pythagoras had hoped to prove that all the movements of this universe resulted in the harmony of musical tones, which he had discovered. For Pythagoras had learned that the strings of a lyre could produce octave, fifth, fourth, and third by subdivision. His discovery rep-

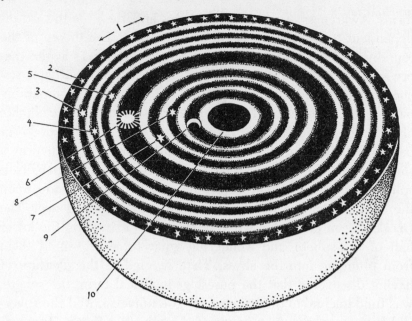

GREEK CONCEPTION OF THE SPHERICAL COSMOS: (1) PROPELLING
SPHERE—INVISIBLE, IMMOVABLE; (2) STAR SPHERE (CARRIES OTHER
SPHERES WITH IT) PERIOD OF REVOLUTION: 1 DAY; (3) SATURN
SPHERE—PERIOD OF REVOLUTION: 29 YEARS; (4) JUPITER SPHERE—
PERIOD OF REVOLUTION: 12 YEARS; (5) MARS SPHERE—PERIOD OF
REVOLUTION: 2 YEARS; (6) SUN SPHERE—PERIOD OF REVOLUTION:
1 YEAR; (7) VENUS SPHERE—PERIOD OF REVOLUTION: 6 YEARS; (8)
MERCURY SPHERE—PERIOD OF REVOLUTION: 3 MONTHS; (9) MOON
SPHERE—PERIOD OF REVOLUTION: 1 MONTH; (10) EARTH SPHERE—
IMMOVABLE.

resented one of man's first triumphs over nature: the invisible
fluid of sound was revealed as hidden mathematics. The kinships
that man's ear recognized were nothing but relationships among
numbers, the harmony of vibrations. The human ear proved to
be in tune with nature, linked with nature by a mathematical
mystery.

Pythagoras guessed that this mystery might also be revealed
in the universe; the differing speeds of the eight spheres, and possibly also the diameter of the spherical shells ought to bear the
same numerical proportions to one another as the harmonics of

musical notes. If this were so, the cosmos would be a structure of beautiful orderliness making music for divine beings, a harmony of the spheres.

He did not succeed in proving that this was so, and the labors of his disciples were also in vain. The more men learned about the movements of the planets, the more irregular these seemed to be. There was the problem of the curious retrograde motions, which had baffled the Babylonian astronomers. Then it turned out that Mars sometimes moved slowly, sometimes faster. For centuries the Greek philosophers strove to find the solution to these problems.

Gradually, the Greek spirit in general turned against Pythagorean astronomy. Socrates was willing to concede the usefulness of astronomy for calendar-making and direction-finding, but he considered it arrogance for man to attempt to grasp the secrets of the heavens mathematically. Plato came only slowly and reluctantly to the conclusion that such an undertaking was justified, even though hopeless. All his life Plato remained convinced that the philosopher alone could fathom the true harmony of the universe, and this by intuition. He formulated his conception of harmony in Anaximander's sense: the sole admissible form for heavenly bodies was the sphere; the globe of the Earth rested in the center of the universe, with all other bodies revolving around it at equal velocities. If the mathematicians succeeded in explaining the planetary motions according to these rules, all very well; but Plato did not think they would succeed, since divine ideas were inaccessible to mathematical reasoning.

Nevertheless, Heraclides, one of Plato's disciples, was able to grasp one of the ideas underlying the motions of the planets. He discovered that the retrograde motion of Mars was in fact a regular revolution in a circle. For Mars is constantly deviating slightly upward or downward from its prescribed orbit. With a little imagination it could be seen that the planet was in fact moving toward us and then away again, that its path, in other words, formed a loop. Jupiter and Saturn could also be observed to perform the same ring dance annually. Their orbits became regular

if Jupiter were envisioned as passing through twelve loops, and
Saturn through twenty-nine.

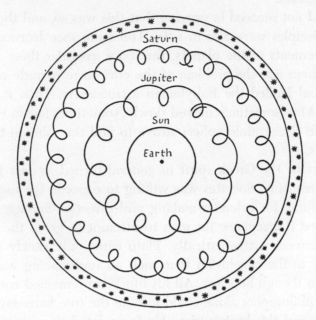

**HERACLIDES DESCRIBED THE IRREGULAR PLANETARY MOTIONS AS
LOOPS, 300 B.C.**

Another disciple of Plato tried to develop this idea into a
scheme that would reveal the whole harmony of the cosmos. For
each of the planets he assumed several spheres whose axes inter-
penetrated one another, and which circled about the Earth in
various directions and in varying periods. This complicated system of spheres within spheres actually succeeded in explaining
to some extent the observed irregularities of the heavenly bodies.
But it did not establish enough regularity of motion to allow for
calculation and prediction. In the end, twenty-six spherical shells
were arrived at. Aristotle increased this number to forty-seven—
and concluded that he had finally established the harmony of the
spheres.

But astronomical problems cannot be solved by reasoning
alone. Neither Platonic intuition nor the ingenious models of

Plato's disciples sufficed. Only exact, unbiased research could lead to truth in this realm.

The Birth of Science

By the time Aristotle rounded out the Greek view of the universe, Greek tragedy and Greek sculpture had already passed their peak. A culture had reached its goal, had brought to fruition its evolutionary potentialities. Its age of poetry was over. With the march of Alexander the Great began what we call Hellenistic civilization. Literature turned to prose, sculpture to realism rather than harmony. The great dimensions architecture had to deal with led to the solution of technical problems. Science was preoccupied more and more with sober facts and tangible results. By 250 B.C. the change was complete. Three names epitomize this new spirit: Euclid, Archimedes, and Eratosthenes.

For posterity the most impressive product of the period is Euclid's geometry: so perfect a logical structure that it has served mankind for thousands of years.

Archimedes was the first real natural scientist, the creator of physical science. He applied the laws of mechanics, which he had discovered, to construct war machines that staved off the Roman conquest of Syracuse for two years.

Eratosthenes, the director of the famous library of Alexandria, accomplished the feat of measuring the Earth's circumference. He knew that in the city of Syene on the upper Nile the summer Sun at noon shone to the bottom of a deep well, while at Alexandria the Sun was never perpendicular to the Earth. By establishing the angle between the Sun's rays and the vertical, he was able to calculate the fraction of the Earth's surface represented by the distance between Alexandria and Syene. Eratosthenes then had this distance carefully measured with ropes and arrived at a figure of 24,647 miles for the circumference of the Earth. His figure was accurate to within 240 miles, for the latitude of Alexandria.

This measurement of the Earth was a triumph of reasoning which made Eratosthenes' name immortal. For the first time the human mind had conquered an inconceivable, conjectural, cosmic magnitude. In performing this, Greek civilization outstripped the entire past, gave birth to science in the proper sense, to objective investigation free of prejudice, myth, and metaphysics. Greek civilization went a step further and presented to the world the first genuine astronomer. His name was Hipparchus.

The time was around 150 B.C., when the Romans were simultaneously overthrowing Carthage and Corinth, and when Chaldean astrology reigned supreme. Hipparchus, a young Greek from Nicaea in Asia Minor, observed a star in the sky where no star had been previously. "Therefore he began a blasphemous undertaking," wrote a contemporary, "namely, to count the stars and measure their positions, so that posterity could determine whether stars are born and pass away." Hipparchus' contemporaries considered his undertaking not only blasphemous, but also stupid. The future, not dreary figures, was what men read in the firmament.

Hipparchus, however, observed that the vernal equinox as established by the Babylonians no longer occupied its old place in the Ram. He detected the displacement of the zodiac, and concluded that astrology was a highly dubious matter. Its astronomical basis had to be checked, he decided, and undertook to do so personally with excellent measuring instruments which he himself devised. So accurate were they that he was able to determine the length of the year within six minutes of the true figure. He discovered that the diameter of the Sun and Moon changed, and concluded that they must sometimes be closer and sometimes farther from the Earth. The average distance to the Moon he determined at 33 Earth diameters—only 3 too many—and he even tried to estimate the distance to the Sun by the size of the Earth's shadow upon the Moon during a total eclipse of the Moon.

His principal accomplishment, however, was establishing the longitude and latitude of no less than 1,080 stars. He also classified their brightness in six magnitudes. This one man did more than all the Babylonian astronomers who had preceded him; he

alone solved problems to which centuries of astronomical work had been devoted. He alone in all of antiquity had the patience and discipline to spend his entire life, night after night, making observations solely for the sake of knowledge.

That Hipparchus was an exception among the Greeks became evident to later scientists when they began checking the data of Ptolemy. For, three hundred years after Hipparchus, Ptolemy based his system on data that were held to be a miracle of exactitude, and which remained unsurpassed until about A.D. 1600. It was long taken for granted that Ptolemy had been a first-class observer. But all his data on the Sun and the Moon were drawn from Hipparchus. Probably he also took the positions of the stars from Hipparchus' catalogue, merely recalculating them for the displacement of the zodiac which had since taken place. It has been demonstrated that Ptolemy read the ascension times of the stars from a celestial globe, and he took his geographical co-ordinates from Roman military road maps. In short, the famous theoretician probably never made any significant observations, certainly none that could compare with the remarkable work of Hipparchus. Before the days of the Dane Tycho Brahe, Hipparchus was the only true astronomer in our modern sense.

We must realize what an unnatural activity scientific observation really is. Any number of people have watched a spider drawing spirals around the spokes of its web. But for most, one or two rounds are enough. To wait out every turn, to study the mechanism of the work in order to determine the movements of each of the eight legs, is a task that scarcely one person among many thousands is willing to undertake. Astronomical observation requires precisely this uncommon kind of patience. Again and again one must look at the known, seeing more precisely something that has been repeated an infinite number of times, recalculating a known figure for the hundredth time.

The true Greek ordinarily left such spadework to his slaves. The great philosopher Aristotle and the priestly Pythagoras might well have despised Hipparchus because he did not preserve his free man's dignity, because he attempted to fathom the cosmic mysteries with instruments, not with the mind. And the

old sages might well have muttered warnings of a coming Neme-
sis.

They would have been right. For with the observations of Hipparchus, the Greek view of the universe was robbed of its meaning.

The Triumph of Theory

The thorniest problem of astronomy was explanation of the apparently varying velocities of the planets, a phenomenon that
was especially striking in the case of Mars. Even the Babylonians
had observed that Mars ran its course irregularly. Every month
for half a year it covered a larger distance; thereafter, the distances diminished from month to month. The Greeks took it for
granted that this could only be an illusion, for the harmony of the
cosmos would allow only the most perfect form of motion, circular motion at unchanging velocity.

The task of Greek astronomy, therefore, was to eliminate these
apparent irregularities. Yet the greatest thinkers among the
Greeks consistently failed to do so until about 250 B.C. Then
Apollonius of Perga, a mathematician who had supplemented
Euclidean geometry by establishing the laws of curves such as
the ellipse, the parabola, and the hyperbola, succeeded in reducing the irregular monthly distance of Mars to equal arcs by means
of a geometrical construction. In other words, Apollonius showed
how an irregular motion might derive from a regular motion.

The solution was not very difficult once the center of the orbit
of Mars was no longer considered to be identical with the center
of the Earth. By shifting it slightly to one side, an eccentric circle
resulted in which the monthly distances were all equal. Thus
Apollonius performed what Plato had thought impossible, and
thus he provided a mathematical rationale which satisfied the
Greek craving for perfect harmony.

His success was so satisfying that the Greeks were willing to
swallow the bitter pill that went along with it—namely, that the

planets circled around an assumed point, instead of around the center of the Earth. After all, the Earth remained the center of the universe as before, and all the planets and stars revolved eccentrically around it. This was not exactly true, for in fact they revolved eccentrically around an empty point in the void. But what did this matter, since the irregularities had been shown to be regular circular orbits? The Hellenistic philosophers could take justified pride in this achievement—until one hundred years later, when Hipparchus began his lowly spadework. He proved that the motions of Mars were even more irregular than had been assumed. Adjust it as one might, the ingenious construction of Apollonius failed. This terrible blow so shocked Hipparchus himself that he abandoned any attempt to solve the mysteries of the planetary orbits. What torment this must have been to Hipparchus: all his precision, all his inhuman discipline, patience, and skill at observation served no other purpose than to destroy a triumphant cosmology. The planets seemed, after all, to have been tossed into the sky by arbitrary powers, solely that fortune-tellers might read fates in them; they were but the counters of incomprehensible magic. To Hipparchus, the Roman victory over Greece may well have seemed a symbol of the collapse of the whole cosmos. The gods had turned their faces away from men; the universe could no longer be understood by the human mind.

Three centuries passed. Then, in the second century A.D., came Claudius Ptolemaeus, an Egyptian—the great Ptolemy who was to be the uncontested monarch of astronomy for a millennium and a half. He restored the harmonious cosmos Hipparchus had shattered. Ptolemy was a theoretician of such superior qualities that only Newton can be considered his peer. A universal mind, he perfected Greek mathematics and Greek natural science in general. His achievement appears all the more impressive when we compare it with the ordinary science of his time, which was hopelessly bogged down in speculation.

Ptolemy called his principal work on astronomy the Great System (*Megale Syntaxis tes Astronomias*, later known as *Almagest* from the Arabic translation). This somewhat arrogant title was fully justified, for he had examined every problem in astronomy,

and solved every one with Euclidean precision. Ptolemy created the first complete scientific system—a structure so vast and coherent that not even the comprehensive mind of an Aristotle could have conceived it, let alone worked it out.

Toward the solution of the chief problem, the apparently irregular velocities of the planets, he made a crucial discovery. Ptolemy drew an overlapping circle near Apollonius' circle; the distance of its center from the Earth was twice that of the center of Apollonius' circle. By this means the monthly variations in distance could be equalized. These second circles came to be known as Ptolemy's epicycles. From the center of the epicycle the motion around Apollonius' eccentric circle appeared to be uniform. The system was extremely complicated, but it worked; Ptolemy could use it to calculate any future position of Mars, say, with fair accuracy. (See diagram below.)

Ptolemy could justly boast that he had laid the keystone of Greek astronomy. "Whosoever thinks my construction too artificial should remember that uniform motion in a circle corresponds to the divine nature. To reduce all apparent irregularities to such motion may well be called a feat. Thereby, the ultimate goal of philosophy and science is attained."

Mathematically speaking, this was true; henceforth, everything was calculable—although Ptolemy did have to make slight alterations in some of Hipparchus' figures. But what had happened to the meaning of the whole, to the Greek cosmology? The planets now traveled in loops, that is to say, around an imaginary point that for unknown reasons itself revolved around the Earth. But even this imaginary point did not revolve precisely around the Earth; the center of its circle was a second imaginary point alongside the Earth. Since this, too, did not yet result in uniform motion, a third imaginary point was needed, from which the motion *appeared* to be uniform!

Such was Ptolemy's ultimate picture; such was the last word in Greek astronomy! Sheer nonsense! What a capitulation for the human mind to accept this sort of mechanics of the universe. What a wretched end for the harmony of the spheres!

It is some consolation that a man named Kepler, fifteen hun-

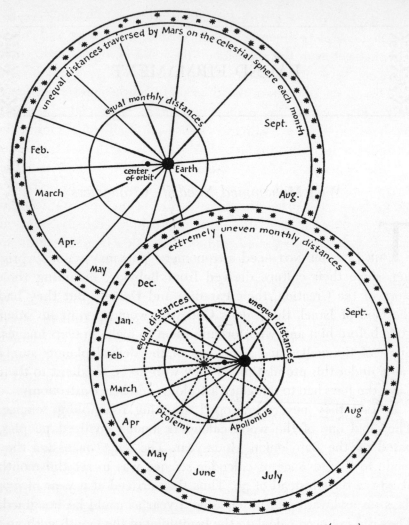

THE ORBIT OF MARS: THE CONCEPT OF APOLLONIUS (TOP), ABOUT
250 B.C., AND THE TRIUMPH OF PTOLEMY (BOTTOM), ABOUT 150 B.C.
PTOLEMY DREW AN OVERLAPPING CIRCLE NEAR APOLLONIUS' CIRCLE,
THUS EQUALIZING THE MONTHLY VARIATIONS IN DISTANCE TRAVERSED
BY THE PLANET.

dred years after Ptolemy, at last was able to refute the last word
of Greek astronomy, and overcome the mathematical sovereignty
of nonsense by even more exact mathematics, which once more
made everything meaningful.

FADED FIRMAMENT

Why Mohammed Needed Astronomers

T HE JEWS DID NOT need astronomers. This may seem surprising, since their culture derived from Babylon, including their story of the Creation, their Paradise and Deluge. But they had the God of Israel, the jealous God who would permit no other gods before him and who forbade them to make graven images. Signs of the zodiac and likenesses of the deified planets surely came under this prohibition. If they were to be obedient to their Law, the Jews had to renounce astrology, and hence astronomy.

In fact they never developed anything resembling science. They had one of the worst calendars among civilized peoples, based on the Babylonian Moon-year. The only concession they made to the advance of calendar science was to set the month at 29 1/2 days instead of 30. Thus they arrived at a year of 354 days—as awkward and unscientific a year as could be imagined. They did not even calculate the beginning of the month with any precision; the Great Sanhedrin established it on the basis of statements by witnesses that the new Moon had emerged from the Sun's glow.

To this day our Easter and Pentecost are governed by the Hebrew Moon calendar. The date for the Resurrection of Christ was established by Passover, which the Jews celebrated on the first Sabbath after the vernal full Moon. The beginning of spring was the vernal equinox, about March 21; the next full Moon might occur as much as a month later, and the next Sabbath a week after

that. Consequently, the highest festival of Christianity oscillated in the Sun calendar, and its calculation caused a good many headaches. That it was managed at all was due to the "golden number" of the Babylonians, which harmonized the positions of the Moon and Sun in periods of eighteen years.

This lasting memento of the astronomical backwardness of the Jews is, however, simultaneously a memorial to one of the greatest events in the history of the world: the overthrow of the religions of the heavens which for several thousands of years had dominated the civilization of man. The tiny nation of Israel was chosen to replace belief in the stars by belief in a single Creator without visible shape. The Hebrews allowed no image of the Divinity to be made. Nor would they permit the development of a mythology, which might have humanized their God. They also forestalled abuse of his name by insisting on the employment of circumlocutions. This spiritualization of religion was worth a certain sacrifice—and sacrifice there was. For a millennium and a half the firmament faded in importance, and science stagnated.

In addition to Judaism and Christianity, there were other religions born of the same spirit. There were Zoroastrians and Manichaeans, and for centuries the Christians were split into three mutually antagonistic churches, the Roman, the Greek, and the Nestorian.

Mohammed, the reformer, borrowed some of their elements and set in motion a wave of conversions that swept over large areas. In the course of a scant century Islam overwhelmed the existing civilized world from Spain to India, and penetrated even into China. This miraculous spiritual campaign was not waged by "the Arabs," but by the followers of the Prophet Mohammed, which included Persians, Jews, and Christians. An international religious community united under the sign of the Crescent.

Mohammed instituted a calendar based on the lunar year only. He was not concerned with astronomical achievements, and coolly declared in the fifth sura of the Koran: "Allah has placed the Sun for daylight, the Moon for night light and also as an instrument for reckoning time and counting the years." If it had been up to him, Islam would have had as little traffic with the science

ARABIAN ASTRONOMERS, FROM AN EARLY SIXTEENTH-CENTURY WOOD-
CUT. AN EARTHQUAKE, WINDS, THE SUN, STARS, AND MOON IN THE
BACKGROUND.

of the heavens as with such idolatries as sculpture and painting.

But Mohammed nevertheless needed astronomers because he
had ordered the true believers to prostrate themselves in the direction of the Kaaba in Mecca when they prayed, no matter where
they were, at home or on journeys. In Arab Spain, North Africa, and India, where Islam garnered most followers, it was no
easy matter to fulfill this requirement. The worshipper had to
know exactly where he was in terms of longitude and latitude.
Since precise directions could at that time be read only by the
stars, Arabic astronomy developed; its principal task was the es-
tablishment of geographical position.

The first Islamic observatory was located in Baghdad and functioned for only two years. Others in Cairo, Samarkand, and Mara-
gheh lasted somewhat longer. Observations were made with
newly invented instruments, wall protractors, and quadrants of
considerable size. These observatories were copied, centuries later,
in India, and one of these copies still remains. But nothing more
emerged from these observatories than occasional corrections of
Ptolemy's data. Arabic astronomy, with its purely practical aims,

MOSLEM OBSERVATORY BUILT IN INDIA ABOUT 1700, FROM AN OLD
ENGRAVING.

made virtually no changes in the cosmology developed by the
Greek astronomers. Its forte was calculation. Every important
scholar endeavored to improve the formulas for establishing lo-
cation. The muezzin who announced the hours for prayer
from the minaret had to know something about the art, for from
time to time he instructed newcomers in the proper direction
for prayer. He would call out the time when the Sun's shadow
pointed to Mecca, and the faithful would then mark the direction
on their walls.

The five daily prayers necessitated clocks that functioned well.
Clockmaking was one of the most important crafts in Islam. But
it developed more along lines of pomp and luxury than of science.
The Arabs abided by the traditional hours of varying length. On
the other hand, they contrived to combine measurement of time
with a kind of planetarium. Their finest water clocks were pro-
digiously complicated rarities. Harun al-Rashid presented one

MEDIEVAL CHRISTIAN ASTROLOGERS, WITH SIGNS OF THE ZODIAC.

ture of the Germanic peoples—and encountered their firm belief
in fate. The Teutons thought that even their gods were subject
to fate—as is evidenced by their myths of the Twilight of the
Gods and of the three Norns, whose names meant Past, Present,
and Future and who spun the thread of fate for mortals and
immortals alike. Later times called the thread "the Law," law in
the widest sense, the law of nature and history and individual
life. Christianity could not remain uncolored by these traditional
beliefs. They came to the fore during a second era of development
in Western culture, in the form of a new mysticism and a new
ecclesiastical dogma, that of scholasticism.

That elements of the old Germanic belief in fate had penetrated scholasticism is revealed by Saint Thomas Aquinas's attitude toward astrology. He did not accept the boundary line that
Augustine had drawn, and held that the stars had influence upon
men's bodies and character. Dante conceded them dominion over
our instincts. Nevertheless, the principle of free will was carefully
guarded. The Church could sanction such a belief in the stars so
long as horoscopes and fortunetelling were left out.

But once the narrow portal had been opened, Chaldean magic
penetrated the Christianity of the Middle Ages. It became known
through Arabic literature, and at once flooded the Occident. The
invasion came with the suddenness of a hurricane, and can be
dated almost to the year. In 1108 the Archbishop of York was re-

fused Christian burial because a book on astrology had been found under his pillow. In 1109 Adelard of Bath called astronomy the science of the past, present, and future—equating it, as it were, with the oracle of the three Norns.

From then on there was virtually no further resistance to astrology. Medicine was practiced according to the stars. For simple surgery such as bloodletting complicated prescriptions related every part of the body with a sign of the zodiac, and hence with particular times. Medicinal herbs must be gathered and administered only on certain nights. Even analysis of urine depended upon the positions of the planets. There were propitious hours for signing political treaties, laying foundation stones, waging battles, for receptions, travel, baths, chess, and changing clothes. The astrologer marched out with the army, gave the signal for the cavalry to mount and the infantry to march. The Holy Roman Emperor Maximilian I suffered all his life under the oppressive knowledge of being a child of Saturn, and Dürer attempted to console him with his *"Melancolia"*; every tiny detail of this engraving contains an allusion to astrological mysteries.

Ultimately, even the popes capitulated to astrology. Leo X founded a professorship in astrology at the University of Rome. Julius II had his coronation day set by astrologers, and Paul IV consulted them for the date of every consistory. The Church, ordinarily so watchful of the purity of dogma, was overwhelmed by the ancient mysticism derived from the long-suppressed sky-religion of the Babylonians. Not until astronomical science came along was the freedom of the Christian restored and destiny once more understood as unfathomable.

Cosmic Anxiety of the Middle Ages

The child awakens as a fully conscious human being with a fear of the strange, the unknown, the boundless. Such cosmic anxiety has also accompanied the awakening of whole peoples to culture. Civilization represses that anxiety again. Sometimes when

On the other hand, it was pleasant for a "Ram" to know that his nature demanded three women, "the first a virgin, the second none; the third will love her husband dearly, will have to suffer ill-repute for a long while in spite of honest conduct toward all, and will be likely to fail in giving birth to children."

But what did unfortunate parents feel when they learned from the *Book of One Hundred Rules* that their newborn child was destined to be drawn and quartered because the Sun's position

THE CONSTELLATIONS PERSEUS (LEFT) AND ANDROMEDA, FROM A FOURTEENTH-CENTURY MINIATURE PAINTING.

was near the Medusa's head in Perseus, and Mars was penetrating the Moon in its quartile aspect, without there being simultaneously a star of good fortune in the House of Death?

Before conjunctions of the planets, all of Christendom trembled. The sevenfold conjunction of the year 1186 forewarned of a world-wide tempest of huge proportions. In all countries underground shelters were built. The Emperor of Byzantium had the

windows of the palace taken out and replaced by planks. The Archbishop of Canterbury ordered a three-day fast. When not a breeze stirred on the ominous day, the cynical monk who kept the chronicles of York made the sardonic notation: "We have experienced nothing but the tempest that His Eminence emitted from the pulpit." For several generations thereafter, such prophecies were not in vogue. But by and by came new predictions of catastrophes: there were such for the years 1229, 1236, 1339, 1371, 1395, 1422, 1432, 1451, 1460, 1487. The greatest panic was aroused in 1524 when a popular German calendar noted a whole succession of dangerous conjunctions of planets—the most perilous being that of February 2. Spanish astrologers confirmed the prediction; a flock of broadsheets set Europe to trembling; priests and monks preached, read, spoke, and dreamed of nothing but the coming deluge.

Master of the situation, it appeared, was gloomy Saturn, made

THE CONSTELLATION ORION AS A MAN IN ARMOR. A FIFTEENTH-CENTURY WOODCUT.

even more malignant by Venus, like an old man influenced by a young woman. Jupiter somewhat alleviated matters, but as the star of the clergy, now infected by Saturn, his presence in the conjunction presaged evil for the Church. Still more evil, as it happened, for the Jews, who were cruelly persecuted. The conjunction took place in the Fish, the sign of Christianity, with the Virgin in opposition; consequently the whole of Christianity would be visited by a flood, especially the lands toward the southwest and the north, which were under the influence of the Fish. Since the constellations of the Four Qualities were also grouped, storms and rains of stone might be expected, in addition to terrible cloudbursts; moreover, there would be fire from heaven, falling stars, fiery dragon-spheres and a ravaging comet.

Although God had promised in Genesis i, 6, not to send another flood, everyone prepared for the worst. The Holy Roman Emperor was asked to dispatch orders to his officials everywhere to establish refuges for the people. The townsfolk of Toulouse built and provisioned a gigantic ark. In coastal cities the population was assigned to ships. People sold their furniture, their houses, drew up wills. Epidemics of mass hysteria ensued. Some persons actually went mad. On the day of misfortune the Margrave of Brandenburg, with the families of his court, took refuge on a ridiculous little hill in Berlin, surrounded by howling, lamenting subjects. Not a drop of rain fell. The whole year was cool and rather rainy, but nowhere were there any floods.

Yet experience has little effect upon deep convictions. Within a few decades the world was convinced that it had suffered from catastrophic floods and had been lucky to survive with only trifling losses. Luther's friend Melanchthon, in his lectures on astrology, expressly mentioned that the prophecy for 1524 had been fulfilled in his lifetime—a proof of the power of the stars.

Fortunately, medieval man took too lusty a pleasure in life to be overwhelmed by cosmic anxiety. The firmament with its magical radiations, the horizon that everywhere hid lurking spirits, produced occasional nightmares, but no permanent complexes. Medieval man possessed moral strength, a medicine that worked far more effectively than all his superstitious cures; he did not need

to psychoanalyze his soul, since he was able to win release from the tension of the unconscious by the voluntary act of confession. After confession he could let his strong, youthful, healthy instincts guide him once more through a life ever menaced by illness or sudden violence.

When Melanchthon's arguments were discussed by his students in the taverns of Wittenberg, one of them might very well strike up a wandering scholar's song from the *Carmina Burana:*

> *When Mercury and Jupiter cry, "Salve!" in the Twins,*
> *And Mars and Venus in the Scales kiss away their sins,*
> *Cecilia came into this world—the Fish had hid his fins.*
> *The very same conjunction held the day that marked my birth,*
> *And so the favor of the hours links our lives upon this Earth;*
> *My stars are joined with her star in well-being or in dearth.*

Dawn of Realism

Science came to the Middle Ages from the Mohammedans, not directly from classical antiquity. The threads linking medieval times with Roman civilization had been badly rent during the barbarian invasions. Along with astrology, the Church had also imposed its ban upon astronomy. It called the study of the movements of the Sun, the Moon, and the planets idolatry, since there was always the fear that these pagan idols might once more win power over men's minds. So low had astronomy fallen that at one time the Pope had to send an embassy to Spain in order to find out from the Arabs when Easter and Pentecost were to take place that year.

Thus the germinating culture of the Occident was placed in almost the same position as the three oldest cultures on the Nile, the Euphrates, and the Yangtze Kiang around 3000 B.C. It would have had to acquire the most elementary types of scientific knowledge anew, had it not been able to draw upon the mature civilization of Islam, whose great cities rimmed the borders of Christen-

dom. Long before the crusades, Germanic chieftains and kings as far north as Sweden bought Arabic weapons, jewelry, and tools from Mohammedan merchants who felt immeasurably superior to these Christian barbarians. They had reason to feel superior, for their greatest treasures were admired merely as ornaments; their true value was not appreciated.

That was the case with the above-mentioned astronomical clock that Harun al-Rashid had sent to Charlemagne. The Frankish nobles stared openmouthed at it, but not even so scholarly a courtier as Einhard knew what to do with it. Einhard drew up documents and decrees, wrote the King's biography, and taught him what astronomy he knew. In the royal annals kept at Charlemagne's court eclipses of the Sun and the Moon were noted with indifferent accuracy. Only once, in 807, were singularly exact data given—and never repeated. That was the year the Arabic clock arrived. Undoubtedly, a scholar came with it to set it in motion and explain how it worked. The unique case of precision in the royal annals probably came from him. As soon as he departed, it turned out that Charlemagne's learned courtiers had understood little. The marvelous clock was placed in the chapel at Aix-la-Chapelle and never again set in motion.

Almost four centuries passed before the Germanic peoples were really ready to learn from the Arabs. In the second quarter of the thirteenth century Emperor Frederick II—who hardly ever resided on German territory—surrounded himself in Salerno and Palermo with Mohammedan and Jewish scholars. In Castile, King Alfonso X followed a similar practice; moreover, he kept a commission of fifty foreign astronomers employed for ten years calculating planetary tables. He was so surprised at the difficulty of this undertaking that he burst out: "Had God consulted me during the Creation, I would have recommended a simpler structure to Him." His son used these blasphemous words as a pretext to force his abdication. But Alfonso's tables became the basis for all astronomical computations during the later Middle Ages.

These tables fitted in neatly with the newly awakened interest in astrology. Astronomical research altogether served the purposes of astrology. The works of Ptolemy and other astronomical

THE TWO MAIN ASTRONOMICAL INSTRUMENTS OF ANTIQUITY AND
THE MIDDLE AGES: ARMILLARY SPHERE (CENTER) AND ASTROLABE
(LOWER RIGHT), WHICH PTOLEMY IS SHOWN USING. THE POINTING
WOMAN IS "ASTROLOGIA." FROM AN EARLY SIXTEENTH-CENTURY
WOODCUT.

books were translated from the Arabic. Arabic numerals and
methods of reckoning fractions, Arabic algebra, and the Arabic
division of the circle were taken over by the Christian West.

In the meantime, Germanic inventiveness was being applied
to astronomical instruction. For teaching material, there were

celestial globes, observation instruments, ingenious paper models that cleverly illustrated the difficult movements of the planets. And as early as 1300 independent science flourished in a few places, often developing ideas far in advance of the times. Bishop Nicole Oresme invented a kind of co-ordinate geometry and studied fractional exponents. William Heytesbury grasped the fundamental concept of future celestial mechanics, acceleration. Albert von Rickmersdorf attempted to measure the increase of velocity of falling bodies. Nikolaus Krebs wanted to determine the weight of the air, and considered the possibility that the Earth might revolve like a planet.

These flashes of insight remained premature lightnings, however. The intellectual leaders of the age, the scholastics, were still discussing the disputes of the Arabic scholars over the merits of Aristotle's planetary theory as against that of Ptolemy, or debating the thickness of the spheres of various planets. All accepted the Principle of Good as the motive force; since Good can stir and move human souls, why can it not affect the heavenly bodies as well?

But in opposition to this dogmatism a basic emotion began to stir in Western man, closely related to his belief in destiny: the urge to capture reality. This urge was far stronger with him than it had been among the Greeks. The Greeks achieved the separation of scientific thought from philosophy only in the mature stage of their civilization; in Occidental civilization, that stage began in the Middle Ages.

Around 1300 there appeared in Italy and England novel clocks, first fruit of the Christian world's independence. The new clocks are praised in Dante's *Divine Comedy:* "One wheel moves and drives the other. . . ." These first clockworks driven by weights instead of water mark the beginnings of European technology. Simultaneously, they established the European concept of time as evenly flowing, for these clocks from the first measured hours of equal length. After 1400 sundials were also changed so that their hours were equal. The Europeans thus broke with an ancient tradition; they demanded that the peculiar law of motion of the Sun yield to a concept of steady time. This was the opening

chapter of the later adventures of Occidental science—a science that demanded something more than understanding of nature: namely, mastery over nature.

Around 1450 astronomers in Florence and Rome were making observations like those of Hipparchus, sober, objective, unprejudiced. They even stated their limits of accuracy. Their instruments had been invented or improved by Johann Müller of Königsberg, who was the first true scientist in our modern sense. He applied Arabic trigonometry to the curved sky, solved mathematical problems which would give pause to a mathematician of our day, and informed the Pope that the Church's calculation of the date of Easter would be incorrect thirty times in the next fifty years. He demanded a thorough reform of the Julian calendar.

At this time it also occurred to someone to check the weather predictions of the astrologers. "All one winter I daily checked the weather according to the astrological calendars. God punish me if I do not say the truth: out of 130 days, the predictions were correct for no more than six." This keen critic was Giovanni Pico della Mirandola. His unusual act in making reality the test of a belief created a sensation. But the astrologers could feel that a higher power had vindicated them in the eyes of all. For at the age of thirty-one Pico died at the very hour his horoscope showed Mars entering the House of Death.

Book Two

HEROIC YOUTH

COPERNICUS THE HUMANIST

An Everlasting Student

A MAN WHOSE uncle was a sovereign bishop, and who has a fat prebend to live on, can afford to spend all his life as a student. Niklas Koppernigk of Thorn in Poland went on knocking about from school to school for a full fifteen years, until he was thirty-three. He studied, mainly in Italy, everything there was to study at the time: Latin and Greek, secular and ecclesiastical law, theology and mathematics, astronomy and medicine. Betweenwhiles he would occasionally show up at his cathedral chapter in Frauenburg on the Baltic, in order to collect his salary and justify the necessity of further studies.

It was good to be a student around 1500, in the age of the humanists. A new world was opening up whose existence a young man's father and grandfather had never suspected. Or to be more exact, two new worlds: the world of books and the world of nature.

Since Gutenberg's invention of movable type, 40,000 printed works had been published within a single generation. No one today can grasp the impact of this sudden wealth. A desert was transformed into a flower garden. The knowledge that had previously been guarded jealously by a few ecclesiastics became accessible to all. The young men at the universities were no longer dependent upon their teachers' words; they could read for themselves, could hear the voice of men of two thousand years before their time distinctly, and see an ancient landscape brilliantly il-

luminated while the days of their grandfathers were already sinking in gray obscurity.

What particularly enthralled a young man was the revelation of a new way of life, one so free, easy, and happy that he awoke from the perennial anxieties of the Middle Ages as if these had been but a bad dream. What a leap from scholastic hairsplitting to the urbane orations of Cicero; from the simple-minded monkish chronicles to the chiseled historiography of Tacitus; from *Till Eulenspiegel* to Ovid's impudent *Art of Love*. Here was a true "revaluation of all values," a rebirth of true humanity, a flight of winged souls into the dawn of a new age.

In the name of humanity an international order sprang up, and held together without bylaws or vows. In accordance with an unwritten law, one entered it by a kind of second baptism, by conferring a Latin or Greek form upon one's name. A Schwarzert became a Melanchthon, a Heussgen an Oecolampadius, a Luther an Eleutherius, and a Koppernigk a Copernicus.

Among the humanists, the distinction between clergy and laymen was eliminated. Future bishops wrote verse that would have made a troubadour blush. Copernicus, the canon-to-be, translated spicy stories by a late Greek and dedicated them to his eminent uncle. From country to country the humanists corresponded with one another, couching their letters in the style of Cicero. An elegant epistle made a man famous overnight, for the humanists' letters were the newspapers of the time, the humanists' judgments the public opinion of the day. The humanist intelligentsia possessed the greatest power intellectuals have ever had. A word from Desiderius Erasmus was enough to make kings tremble. Reuchlin's satires made the theological faculty of Cologne a laughingstock in the eyes of the world. Aretino's pamphlets were bought sight unseen because he was noted for his wit. Emperor Maximilian I honored the poet Conradus Celtis before the assembled Diet.

Professor Codrus of Bologna publicly told his students: "The hereafter is an old wives' tale," and was not prosecuted. Copernicus learned Greek from this radical.

The example of a friend of his uncle, a professor at Cracow, taught him how far a humanist could go. This Italian who called himself Callimachus had advocated the overthrow of the Pope and a revival of the Roman Republic. He had barely escaped with his life to Turkey. Now he was in Poland, making a great career; he became tutor of the princes, was sent as ambassador to Cologne, Venice, and finally to Rome. The city where he had once been pursued like a mad dog now received him with bowings and scrapings.

Such was the atmosphere in which Copernicus lived. He lost none of his piety, for that was too deep-seated; but his environment shielded him from that religious fanaticism which was destined soon to smother humanism. And he acquired from this environment the new insight into nature.

For in the eyes of the humanists, nature too had been transfigured. The lurking demons that inspired terror in the hearts of medieval men had vanished like puffs of smoke. The whole of creation appeared fresh as on the seventh day, waiting only to be discovered, enjoyed, depicted, and explained. Artists now painted the human body as it looked, felt out every line in faces, systematically drew plants, animals, the outlines of cities, and sketched maps—in other words, regarded the Earth from a bird's-eye view. They dared at last to represent the world as a sphere, as the Greeks had done long ago. In Nuremberg Martin Behaim boldly made a "globe" showing countries, seas, plains, and mountains.

The older generation protested against this view of the Earth. As a freshman in Cracow, Copernicus heard the old arguments: on the sphere's underside the rivers would fall from their beds, every stone would drop into space. If the antipodes really existed, the people there could only live in the trees, clinging desperately to the branches, with the frightful depths of space below them. But at Cracow, too, Copernicus heard the stunning news from Spain that Columbus had returned home from his mad adventure. The great serpent inhabiting the universal ocean had not swallowed his ships. And to prove that he had really

found India, Columbus had brought back red-skinned Indians, altogether normal human beings except that they had feathers on their heads instead of hair.

Copernicus made the most of a period of intellectual freedom soon to be ended by the Inquisition, thoroughly enjoyed it for fifteen blissful years. He studied in Bologna, Rome, Padua, and Ferrara, where the greatest libraries could be found and where the stars at night glowed so much more brightly than they did in the misty north. He had always intended to devote himself to the most wonderful of sciences, astronomy.

Ten Thousand Celestial Circles

At the monastic school in Thorn he had learned natural science from Martianus Capella's *The Marriage of Mercury and Philology*. These fanciful verses—only the sections on mathematics and astronomy were in prose—had stood the test of time for a thousand years.

Capella described how the Sun moved: in a gigantic spiral, far from the Earth, but in such a manner that the Earth lay within the spiral as in a bird-cage. The spiral had 182 turns, and the Sun slid down each turn in twenty-four hours. It slid lower and lower, until at the end of 182 days it reached the bottom. Then it turned about—this was called the winter solstice—and climbed up the spiral until it reached the top, at the summer solstice.

There is nothing ridiculous about this; it is, in fact, a precise description of the Sun's apparent motion. "For it never rises where it rose yesterday," Capella quite correctly said. "Every day it passes above us in a different circle. There can be no doubt that in the course of a year it moves back and forth through 182 circles. The planets, too, change their circles daily. Mars moves through twice as many circles as the Sun, Jupiter through twelve times as many, and Saturn through twenty-eight times as many."

Altogether, it turned out that there were ten thousand circles in the clockwork of the heavens. That was the reason Copernicus discarded the medieval cosmology: "It would be altogether unworthy of the sublime Creator to have needed so many circles in order to make the Sun, the Moon, and five planets move around the Earth."

After he learned Greek he was able to seek better knowledge in Ptolemy, the prince of astronomers. But Ptolemy disappointed him; Ptolemy, too, was unable to get around the ten thousand circles. How little the mathematicians were able to explain the structure of the world, he complained. They could not even calculate the solar year exactly; they made every planet move according to different rules, and pretended that the Almighty had created a monster senselessly patched together from the bodies of many different creatures. Copernicus resolved to search old books, to see whether there had been any better ideas. And sure enough, he found Cicero and Plutarch both mentioning that according to some philosophers, the Earth itself moved. The passage in Cicero read: "Nicetas of Syracuse believes that the sky, Sun, Moon, stars, and all else stand still, and that nothing in the universe moves except the Earth. The Earth revolves on an axis at very great speed, thus making the sky appear to move."

Copernicus perceived at once that Cicero had only half understood the matter. Even if one assumed that the Earth spun on an axis, the Sun, the Moon, and the planets must still continue to move; only the starry firmament would stand still. But the Sun, Moon, and planets must move very slowly—and in only a single circle. A circle lasting a month for the Moon, a year for the Sun, twelve years for Jupiter, and so on. The rotation of the Earth produced the daily rising and setting of all the heavenly bodies; this theory eliminated the 182 windings of the spiraling Sun. The Sun must rise in a slightly different place every day only because it had moved a little farther along on its annual orbit. This annual orbit must be at an angle to the Earth's axis, for which reason the Sun rose low in the winter and high in the summer, thus bringing about the seasons.

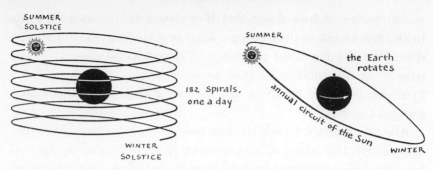

How clear, simple, and convincing this was. There was no need
for the clockwork with ten thousand wheels. Nicetas of Syracuse
was the man Copernicus had been waiting for.

The idea of the rotation of the Earth certainly did not begin
with Copernicus. It was so widely held in antiquity that Ptolemy
thought it necessary expressly to refute it. "Possibly," he wrote,
"events in the sky do not contradict this simplifying hypothesis.
But events on Earth do contradict it. If the Earth actually rotated to the east, winds would always blow westward, clouds always move westward, stones and missiles always fall westward."

Copernicus disposed of this by a single assumption: that in
its rotation the Earth carried its envelope of atmosphere and everything therein along with it. He could not prove this, of course;
it was simply a matter of one opinion against another. It took
Newton to present the possibility of a proof, and an astonishing
one at that. He showed that any falling body which participated
in the rotation of the Earth would have to fall in the opposite
direction—eastward—rather than westward, as Ptolemy imagined. It would have to hasten ahead of the globe, for, before it
was released from a height, it circled in a wider arc than the
surface of the Earth. Paradoxical as that sounds, this was demonstrated in 1791 by very precise measurements.

But Ptolemy had an even more dramatic argument against rotation of the Earth. For the Earth to rotate once in twenty-four
hours, it would have to spin at such a rate that the very ground

would be wrenched asunder; the Earth would long ago have been torn to bits by the force of its motion, and the fragments would lie scattered on the edge of the farthermost heavenly sphere.

Copernicus wondered whether the requisite speed of the Earth's rotation could not be reckoned. He performed the calculations—and was alarmed by the result. It really was a mad whirl: 150 double paces each second. Twenty houses would go flying by in the blink of an eye. How could the body endure such a furious rush? How could a man insist on such a disavowal of appearances: that the Earth turned and the firmament stood still.

Like a man obsessed Copernicus must have stared night after night at the sky and forced himself to believe this seemingly nonsensical idea: that the army of stars above had been at rest since the beginning of all things, and the solid globe beneath his feet was spinning like a nocturnal carriage circling a great city with many lights. Copernicus set out on a voyage through the shoreless ocean of the universe, accompanied only by the shadow of a Greek who had followed the same trail two thousand years before. It was a voyage against all better knowledge, impelled by an urge that may well have seemed of diabolical origin to the explorer himself—until in a happy hour he could cry out like Columbus: "Land! I see land!"

For the answer had suddenly burst upon him. Did Ptolemy fear the Earth would be unable to endure the hurtling motion of its own rotation? Then why did he not have the same fear for the sky? Would not the sky have to spin even faster, since it was larger than the Earth? Would it not then burst asunder? Should not the nine spheres have long ago been torn apart, hurled in all directions, if they were whirling around our Earth in an unimaginable curve at unimaginable speed? If that were so, the daily rotation of the firmament was less comprehensible than that of the globe. Hence it was much more probable that the Earth turned. Hence the Earth must turn.

At the end of that night of insight, when the glowing ball of the Sun rose on the horizon—or no, when Copernicus sped to-

ward it aboard the fastest of all ships—he could open his arms
to greet the day and know that he was no minion of the devil,
but the vessel of a divine inspiration.

Center of the Universe

Ptolemy had also parried another hypothesis proposed by some-
body: that the Earth moved in space. This he settled with an
argument that came down to: "It would be ridiculous even to
imagine such a thing."

Copernicus completely agreed with him. It would be ridiculous, and sinful and blasphemous to boot, to maintain that the
Earth was not the heart of the universe. Man was undoubtedly
the crown and purpose of creation; hence the abode of man
must remain the center of the universe.

Still, Copernicus was interested to know who had proposed so
mad a theory, and why. Perhaps he himself was succumbing to
the devil's temptations after all. At any rate, he searched until
he found the key passages in Plutarch:

"The Pythagorean Philolaus believed that the Earth moves in
an inclined orbit around the central fire, which he called the
hearth of the universe." And again: "Aristarchus of Samos was
charged with impiety. It was said that he would not believe
the Earth to be the sacred center of the world; he averred
that it runs in an inclined orbit and simultaneously turns around
its axis—and that he would have this so in order to be able to
calculate more exactly the phenomena of the heavens."

So Aristarchus of Samos had had the same end in view as
Copernicus of Thorn. And he had thought it necessary to abate
his human pride, to defy traditional belief, and to imagine the
Earth wandering through the heavens—and on a crooked course
at that. Naturally, on the inclined orbit which the Sun supposedly followed. But if the Earth traveled in the orbit of the Sun,
then the Sun must be standing still. And in that case the Sun
stood in the center of the universe. Well, why not? The Sun was

after all the light-giver and nourisher of the Earth. And not only the earth; it illuminated the universe. Come to think of it, the Sun belonged in the center.

There it was, the temptation of the devil, and Copernicus could no longer escape it. The idea became familiar to him; it began to enchant him, and in the end he was overwhelmed by it:

"How could this light be given a better place to illuminate the whole temple of God? The Greeks called the Sun the guide and soul of the world; Sophocles spoke of it as the All-seeing One; Trismegistus held it to be the visible embodiment of God. Now let us place it upon a royal throne, let it in truth guide the circling family of planets, including the Earth. What a picture— so simple, so clear, so beautiful."

This wild enthusiasm still reverberated, a generation later, in his sober mathematical work. Nevertheless, Copernicus did not let himself be carried away by the pretty picture. He gained his heretical belief in a simple, clear, and beautiful world order only after long wrestlings with the adverse opinions of mighty Ptolemy.

Logically least objectionable of Ptolemy's demonstrations was his thesis that the Earth is the exclusive center of the world. Ptolemy's train of thought was as follows:

The horizon constantly divides the vault of the heavens into two equal halves, no matter whether the constellations are turning, rising, or sinking. If the beginning of the Crab lies exactly on the horizon, the beginning of the Goat also lies exactly on the horizon, at its opposite extreme. This also remains the case when the two exchange positions. Consequently, the Earth must un- questionably be in the center of the world—Q.E.D.

Such was Ptolemy's argument in the fourth chapter of his *Al- magest*. In chapter five he used the same example to demon- strate another thesis, which particularly impressed Copernicus: that the Earth is only a point, a mathematical point without any extension. Paradoxical this might seem, yet it was irrefutable. The horizon divides the celestial vault into two equal halves, to be sure—but the horizon does not lie in the center of the world; it lies on the surface of the Earth, quite far from the center, per- haps ten times as far as the distance from Rome, say, to Thorn.

Nevertheless, it seems to lie in the center of the world; practically speaking, the diameter of the terrestrial globe makes no difference. Astronomically, the Earth appears as a point without extension.

Naturally, Ptolemy did not intend this to be taken literally. The Earth's extension disappears only in comparison to the immeasurable distance of the stars. The sky is so far away from us that it does not matter whether the horizon is exactly in the center of the universe, or a tiny fraction to one side.

At this point in the story Copernicus must have started with excitement. For obviously, if a small fraction did not matter, a larger fraction would not, even a fraction a few million times the distance from Rome to Thorn. The Earth might well course around the Sun without its making any difference, astronomically speaking. The horizon would still divide the vault of the heavens in half, no matter whether the Earth were to the right or the left of the Sun at any given time. Ptolemy had refuted his own argument.

From this point on, there was no stopping. Copernicus proceeded to work out the principles of the Earth's annual voyage around the Sun, to calculate the details that were to become the axiom of a new astronomy.

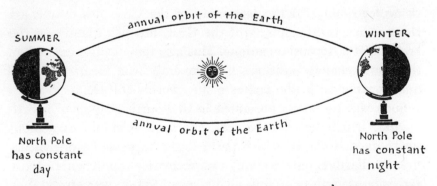

SUMMER annual orbit of the Earth WINTER

annual orbit of the Earth

North Pole has constant day

North Pole has constant night

A PROBLEM FOR COPERNICUS: WHY DOES THE EARTH'S AXIS ALWAYS POINT IN THE SAME DIRECTION?

A difficulty became evident at once. So long as the Earth merely revolved around its axis while the Sun described an oblique cir-

cle around it, the Sun would naturally be high or low at different times of the year, and the seasons would result. But place the Earth on the inclined orbit, and seasons would result only if the terrestrial axis were constantly pointing in the same direction, toward the polestar. And Copernicus did not see why it should do that. He did not consider the simple example of a child's top that has been set going at an angle and continues to spin obliquely, pointing in the same direction, much as the spinning Earth does. As a result of this omission, there remained a flaw in his theory which opponents belabored for generations.

It was therefore not so easy to pick up the ponderous Earth and send it coursing on its way around the Sun. A really convincing, indisputable proof had yet to be found.

The Planetary Loops

At the age of thirty-three Copernicus had to return home, and take up the post of personal physician to his uncle. His uncle ruled the diocese of Ermeland on the Baltic like a secular monarch, holding magnificent court in Heilsberg, a castle in the primeval forests on the very verge of the civilized world, where wolves howled around the gates at night. There he had introduced Spanish etiquette. At the stroke of noon all the inhabitants of the castle stepped outside the doors of their rooms and waited for His Eminence, who first fed the dogs and then, in his full vestments, led the procession to the dining hall. Protocol strictly regulated the seating plan for the nine tables.

No. 1 was for guests of honor, canons, knights, vicars-general, and judges; No. 2 for clerics and chamberlains; No. 3 for the burgrave, village magistrates, jurymen, foresters, and stewards; No. 4 for body servants and pages; No. 5 for indigent dependents; Nos. 6–8 for attendants, servants, maids; and No. 9 for jongleurs, jesters, and musicians.

Copernicus, the bishop's nephew and physician, sat at the first table, by virtue of being a canon, although by rights he belonged

with the jongleurs, jesters, and musicians. A eulogy to His Eminence, the puissant and devout prince-bishop of Ermeland, refers to his doctor as one "who knows how to interpret, with the most amazing explanations, the most hidden causes of things. He examines the courses of the planets and the Moon, as well as the various motions of its brother star."

This was put with great caution; by the Moon's "brother star" the author of the eulogy probably meant the Earth. And the bishop's physician was already maintaining that the Earth moved —even had "various motions." If he were prepared to announce this publicly, even though in veiled fashion, he must have been quite sure of himself. And in fact at Heilsberg he had found the missing proof. He solved the problem that all the Greeks had puzzled over in vain, the prime mystery of astronomy: the planetary loops. And he solved it quite simply by postulating the Earth's revolution around the Sun.

For every planet there came a point in its annual orbit when it seemed to waver, as if it had become uncertain; it then ran backward as if it had lost something, paused again, and resumed its normal direction. While behaving in this peculiar manner, it usually deviated somewhat from its course; the retrograde motion brought it a little above or below its regular orbit. In other words, for the observer on the Earth the planet was plainly traveling in a loop. The Greeks had great difficulty in representing and calculating this loop; they had no adequate explanation for it.

Copernicus explained it by declaring that the Earth was itself a planet. And his explanation was so coherent that it established forever the absolute superiority of his cosmology over all earlier ones.

The Earth's annual journey around the Sun would not affect the positions of the stars, since they were so far away that it did not matter whether they were observed from the right or the left side of the Sun. But the planets, themselves revolving around the Sun, would look different when seen from the Earth's differing positions, just as a jockey's view of a horse race differs from that of a spectator.

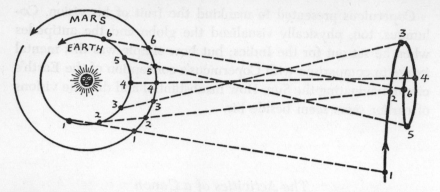

THE TRIUMPH OF COPERNICUS—EXPLANATION OF THE PLANETARY
LOOPS: AS THE EARTH AND MARS MOVE AROUND THE SUN AT THEIR
DIFFERENT SPEEDS, MARS APPEARS TO MOVE FORWARD AND BACKWARD
IN THE LOOP DIAGRAMED AT RIGHT.

Mars, for example, takes approximately two years to revolve
around the Sun. The Earth moves twice as fast along an orbit
half as large. What would happen when it overtook Mars? For
a while it would speed directly toward Mars—and the planet
would seem to stand still. Then it would pass by—and Mars
would appear to run backward. Then it would move directly away
from Mars on its smaller circle—and again Mars would seem to
pause. Then, when the Earth came around the other side of the
Sun and was moving in the direction opposite to that of Mars,
Mars would appear to be racing forward at increasing speed—
precisely what the ancients had observed.

It is plain that Copernicus did not need to make intricate
calculations in order to solve the riddle of the planetary loops;
he needed only to think out the possibilities of the Earth's voyage
around the Sun, to visualize the relations of the planets if such
an annual journey actually took place. Copernicus was a seer of
highly remarkable qualities, one who could cast aside appearances and replace them by a mental image. Such an achievement must not be underestimated. None of the Greeks, for all
their visual gifts and for all their bold imagination, had been
capable of such picturization. No Occidental man had hit on it
in centuries of abstract speculation. Imagination or intellect alone
did not suffice; a synthesis of both was required.

Copernicus presented to mankind the fruit of his vision. Columbus, too, physically visualized the globe and the antipodes when he set out for the Indies; but how simple was this mental image in comparison with Copernicus's conception of the Earth's circumnavigating the Sun. How insubstantial and dim the visions of earlier seers seem beside his.

The Activities of a Canon

At the age of thirty-nine, upon the death of his uncle, Copernicus at last assumed his post in the cathedral chapter at Frauenburg—that is to say, in the "cabinet of ministers" of Ermeland diocese. In this position he demonstrated that he knew more than canon law, medicine, mathematics, astronomy, and Greek. His versatility seems to have had no limits, for he acted for years as administrator of the two largest districts of Ermeland, and proved to be of the stuff of which heroes are made.

There was war with the Teutonic Knights. Frauenburg fell. The canons fled to Danzig and appointed Copernicus commandant of the fortress of Allenstein, in a remote spot on the Masurian Lakes. The fortress became a refuge for all those who were fleeing from the knights. With the cathedral chapter's money, Copernicus bought cannon—and received a sharp reprimand from Danzig for being so spendthrift a patriot. But when the enemy came to lay siege to Allenstein, the chapter begged him to hold this last bulwark for at least three weeks. He held it until the conclusion of peace.

During the next election of a bishop, there were more civil disturbances. The Teutonic Knights sent their own partisans; the King of Poland occupied castles in Ermeland. The cathedral chapter had no alternative but to appoint the defender of Allenstein, who had played so loose with their precious gold pieces, administrator-general of Ermeland. Copernicus drove off the predatory hordes and secured the withdrawal of the Polish oc-

cupation troops. When the new prince-bishop took office, order reigned throughout the diocese.

Copernicus continued to keep busy as a statesman. Among other things, he drafted a plan for preventing inflation. His idea of establishing a standard value for money once and for all was too bold for ordinary men. He could not explain to others what was clear to himself. He hoped that he would fare better with his astronomical system. "The theory of the Earth's motion is admittedly difficult to comprehend, for it runs counter to appearances and all of tradition. But if God wills, I shall in this book make it clearer than the Sun, at least for mathematicians."

God did not so will. The book he labored on for twenty years did not progress beyond the fifth section. His calculations of the planetary orbits failed, and most miserably in the case of Mars, where the theory should have been brilliantly illustrated.

Today we understand the reason for this failure. The planets'

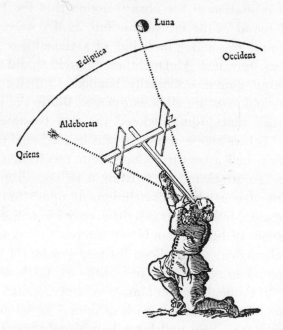

MEASUREMENT OF ANGULAR DISTANCE WITH A CROSS-STAFF OR JACOB'S STAFF, AN INSTRUMENT USED BY COPERNICUS. IT WAS USED IN NAVIGATION UNTIL ABOUT 1750.

orbits are not circles, but ellipses, and the ellipse of Mars deviates most markedly from a circle. But Copernicus could not imagine that the Creator would have employed any but the most perfect form for the orbits of his planets: the circle. It waited for the genius of another man to overcome this prejudice.

For Copernicus, his inability to calculate the orbit of Mars was a catastrophe. He decided not to publish his unfinished manuscript. Nevertheless, word of his new cosmology spread somehow, and since people heard only the theory, not the proofs, it aroused indignation and mockery. In Elbing, a stone's throw from Frauenburg, two fools danced side by side in a carnival procession. One handed out indulgences for whoredom and homicide; the other whirled a pig's bladder in circles, screeching: "I am the Sun; see how the Earth is dancing around me. I am the Sun; fall on your knees and worship me!"

For Copernicus's seventieth birthday a Protestant astronomer sent him a refutation of the absurd notion that the Earth turns round and round in the fire of the Sun, as if it were on a spit. The astronomer was acting on behalf of Melanchthon, Germany's most famous humanist. Melanchthon himself would have liked this dangerous nonsense officially banned. Luther commented: "The fool would overturn all of astronomy. But in the Holy Scriptures we read that Joshua ordered the Sun to stand still, not the Earth." This selfsame argument was leveled against Copernicus for more than a century. Copernicus received it with cold arrogance: "To attack me by twisting a passage from Scripture is the resort of one who claims judgment upon things he does not understand. Mathematics is written only for mathematicians."

The opinions of heretics could not interest Canon Copernicus. But what about Rome? The Pope listened graciously to a lecture on the Copernican system, and one of the cardinals actually sent a secretary to Frauenburg to obtain copies of Copernicus's proofs and tables. "If you fulfill this wish of mine," he wrote in an accompanying letter, "you will learn how deeply concerned I am for your fame, and how I endeavor to win recognition of your deeds. I have closed you in my heart."

This letter was equivalent to official sanction from the Church,

since the cardinal was Chief Censor of the Inquisition. It worked on Copernicus like an elixir. He brought out his manuscript once more, and wrote the final chapters, although they still did not satisfy him. He had barely finished when the cardinal died. Back went the manuscript into its chest.

Copernicus thought of taking it with him to his grave. The days of intellectual freedom were over; the ideals of humanism had gone under in the storm of the Reformation. The humanists had split into a Protestant and a Catholic party; fanaticism was spreading, persecutions were beginning. At seventy Copernicus himself felt the lashings of the rough winds of doctrine. A former schoolmate, who in days gone by had written spicy erotic verses, became bishop in the diocese, and promptly turned more pharisaic than the pharisees. His first decree prescribed the death penalty for the reading and possession of heretical books. He treated the canons who served under him as if they were unruly schoolboys. Although he himself was well known to have a daughter whom he had left behind in Spain, he now drove Copernicus's best friend from his office and the country for having a son who was too much in evidence. Copernicus was sternly recommended to send his niece away because she was too young to serve with propriety as a housekeeper for him. Remembering the bishop's past life, Copernicus could not believe this order was meant in earnest. But after a second admonition he submitted. Then he was ordered to appear before the bishop to justify himself for having spoken with his niece in the market place. That was too much for him; he took flight into the territory of a neighboring diocese where an old-fashioned tolerant bishop was in charge.

This bishop urged Copernicus to publish his great work on the grounds that it ought not to be withheld from the world. Copernicus replied that he believed the theory of the Pythagoreans —that the profoundest doctrines should be transmitted only to the initiate, and only by word of mouth. As if in answer to a wish, a disciple promptly turned up, eager to learn the truth at the source. This disciple had taught astronomy in Wittenberg, and had obediently refuted the absurd Copernican system. But in the course of his refutations he had become interested in the

subject; he had abandoned his post and set out on a pilgrimage to the notorious heretic. The old man basked in the admiration of youth, was persuaded to surrender his manuscript, and the disciple sent it to a printer in Nuremberg.

De Revolutionibus Orbium Coelestium was the equivocal title Copernicus gave to this book which created a new view of the world for the modern age. On his deathbed Copernicus had a chance to touch the printed volume. The introduction to it was written by a Protestant cleric, the author's preface was addressed to the Pope. Here was the true humanist spirit, and Copernican irony: to pretend that the split in the Church did not exist. But fate indulged in an irony of its own. In his introduction the cleric wrote: "The hypotheses of this book need not be true, nor even probable. It suffices if they make possible calculations which fit the observations. We may confidently place them alongside older hypotheses which are no more probable." The Protestant could not, of course, sign his name to a book that was dedicated to the Pope. Consequently, these sentences were thought to express the author's opinion.

For a century and a half antagonists could refer triumphantly to this introduction. "Copernicus? Why, he did not believe in his own theory."

AN OBSERVER AND A PROPHET

Theory and Practice

THE GENERAL CONCEPTION of an astronomer is of a man sitting in an observatory and peering through a telescope. But anyone who is asked to name a great astronomer will mention Copernicus, Kepler, or Newton—men who were basically theoreticians. The names of observers, even those who were famous in their times, such as Tycho Brahe, Hevelius, Herschel, Schiaparelli, are more easily forgotten.

Science itself once naturally inclined toward theory. Greece produced only a single great observer, Hipparchus. Western European astronomy actually begins with the mathematician Copernicus. But thereafter we may witness a striking oscillation between theory and practice. Between 1500 and 1800 astronomical progress was achieved alternately on paper and in the observatory. Every generation the balance swung almost with the regularity of a pendulum.

Copernicus, for example, devoted decades to observation, even making his home in a tower on the city wall for the purpose. But not much came out of his work; all his observational results could be set down on a single sheet of paper. For example, he never saw the planet Mercury; it is so close to the Sun that it can only be observed at dawn or dusk, and on the Baltic coast fog usually obscures its feeble dot of light. Nevertheless, Copernicus could have succeeded in seeing Mercury if he had been determined to do so, for the Dane Tycho Brahe found the task easy

under the same climatic conditions. But Copernicus was not by
nature a practical scientist; he would not stoop to wearisome,
systematic stargazing. Significantly, he was content with a child-
ishly primitive instrument for observation: a stick with two movable crossbars. Ptolemy had filled an entire book with descriptions
of complicated astronomical tools—yet it never occurred to Copernicus to have some of these made for his own use.

This attitude was one of the reasons for his failure to calculate
correctly the orbit of Mars. His data were far too inexact. He
depended entirely on Ptolemy's figures, considering it impossible
to surpass this very summit of observational accuracy. When someone ventured to question this assumption, Copernicus, who ordinarily avoided disputes, penned an angry pamphlet in which
the doubter was taken to task for criticizing the demigod of
astronomy. Not until his extreme old age did he confess to a disciple the greatest disappointment of his life: that he had been
forced to realize that even the Greeks were fallible. He had discovered that the noble Ptolemy sometimes twisted facts to suit
his purposes; his data were accurate only to within twenty minutes of arc. And Copernicus had sufficient respect for facts to add
that a useful planetary theory could never be developed on the
basis of such errors. But when the disciple proposed going to
work to correct the errors, Copernicus demurred. The Greeks
were indubitably the best observers of all time, he said, and they
were so favored by their southern climate that no northerner
could dream of improving on their work. After all, in Greece
books could be read by the light of the stars!

While Copernicus was voicing these counsels of resignation,
the man had already been born who was destined to surpass the
Greeks: Tycho Brahe, the first modern astronomer. He measured
the positions of the stars to within two instead of twenty minutes
of arc, and did this with the naked eye, for the telescope was not
invented until after his death. He used no new instruments; he
merely reproduced the instruments of the Greeks, but improved
them by ingenious methods of sighting and exact scaling. His
results were achieved mainly by his intensive observational technique; he repeated every measurement four times.

Most important of all, Brahe discovered that all earlier data suffered from a basic error resulting from the refraction of light rays in the atmosphere. The light rays of stars are bent as they pass through atmospheric layers of differing density; we see the Sun on the horizon when it has already set. The fact was known before Brahe's time, but Brahe calculated the amount of error for every altitude of a celestial body, and corrected all his observations by a "refraction table"—the first example of modern astronomical precision.

He determined the angle of the Earth's axis to its orbit as 23 degrees, 31 minutes, and 5 seconds. Copernicus had given it as 23 degrees, 28 minutes—three whole minutes' difference! Brahe could scarcely believe the great astronomer capable of such a gross error, and sent an assistant to Frauenburg to check on it. The assistant confirmed the fact that Copernicus had been unable to determine correctly even the latitude of his own home. He also brought back with him the one instrument Copernicus had used. Brahe shook his head and hung the instrument on the wall of his library as a historical memento to a theoretician's ignorance of practice.

But the self-assured practical scientist was forced to learn, for his part, that theory is a calling with its own peculiar tricks, and that a single good inspiration does not qualify a man as a theoretician. Brahe took the greatest pride in his "Tychonic Cosmology," which he imagined would be a considerable advance on Copernicus. As was the case with all his contemporaries, Tycho Brahe's deepest feelings rebelled against ousting the abode of man from the center of the universe and degrading the Earth to a perfectly ordinary planet. For many years, while he labored to make exact measurements, he tormented himself with the problem of reconciling the achievements of Copernicus with human dignity and his inner certainty that God had established the heavenly bodies for the sake of men, and had made them revolve around man's Earth.

One day the solution came to him. It was so very simple, so convincing as soon as it was stated, that he wondered why he had missed it for so many years. Of course: the Earth rested in

the center of the universe; the Sun revolved around it in its annual
motion—but the planets revolved around the Sun! This conception explained the planetary loops as reflections of the Sun's orbit
instead of the Earth's orbit, as Copernicus had it. Human dignity
was restored.

Brahe painted a picture of this cosmology on the dome of his
observatory, and on the walls he hung portraits of the world's
seven greatest astronomers—including one of Tycho Brahe.
Brahe was shown pointing a finger toward the ceiling, while a
little tag bore the legend: *"Quid si sic?*—And suppose it is so?"

It might well have been accepted as so for many generations if
the practical scientist with a pretty idea had not been followed
by a dyed-in-the-wool theoretician: Johannes Kepler. Kepler was
not bound by the *Zeitgeist,* was not the sort of man to be ridden
by inner convictions, did not consider it essential for human dignity that man occupy the center of the universe. He swung the
rudder vigorously back in the direction Copernicus had chosen.

Brahe was forced to watch this happening. He had employed
Kepler as his assistant, but Kepler brashly informed him that he
was not good at observation; calculation was his field. Before long,
Brahe turned entirely over to his assistant the dreary business
of calculation, which he himself did not like. The great astronomer soon discovered that Kepler's mind was altogether different
from his, and so independent and original that it was hopeless
to try to convert him to the Tychonic system. With the aid of
Brahe's observations, Kepler perfected Copernicus's cosmology.
And so it went, from one generation to the next, alternate steps
forward, right foot and left foot. No earlier culture had seen a
development of such rapidity and consistency.

The First Observatory

If any man had been destined to become an astronomer, it
was Tycho Brahe. At the age of thirteen he knew the heavens as

if he had studied them for a lifetime. When an eclipse of the Sun arrived on the predicted day, he exclaimed enthusiastically to his uncle: "To know of such a thing in advance makes a man almost a god."

"That is odd," his uncle replied. "I have known our court astrologer for many years, but it has never struck me that there was anything godlike about him."

He bought the boy the astronomical almanacs Tycho requested, and even an expensive copy of Ptolemy; but he wanted young Tycho to understand that a nobleman could regard scientific pursuits only as hobbies. Tycho replied impudently that while he was still young he did not want to waste his time on horses, hounds, and drinking bouts; he preferred to look around God's beautiful world.

In those days, Danish nobles traveled around God's world for years before they settled down on their estates. Tycho was sent off to Germany accompanied by a tutor whose instructions were to wean him away from his ignoble passion for the stars and lead him to the study of jurisprudence. As a result, the young man slept little, for as soon as he heard his tutor snore, he took a pair of wooden compasses from their hiding place and measured the positions of planets with the aid of a homemade protractor.

The results of his own investigations soon convinced him that the calendar-makers were indeed something less than godlike. One night when Jupiter and Saturn were almost touching, he checked their supposed positions in the tables of King Alfonso of Castile. These tables were a month behind; the Copernican tables were wrong by three days. Tycho resolved to remedy this dreadful state of affairs. Young as he was, he contrived to interest the astronomically minded burgomaster of Augsburg in his plans for superior instruments. The Jacob's staff, the triquetrum, and the other simple instruments of the day were wholly inadequate for accurate observation, he pointed out. What was needed were huge arcs on which minutes of arc could be read off, and the seconds at least estimated. His dream, he said, was an eighteen-foot sextant. The astounded burgomaster protested that such an

instrument would not fit into a room. Tycho replied that a special tower for it should be set up, and coolly proposed a hill in the burgomaster's garden.

Surprisingly enough, the burgomaster was agreeable. A horde of carpenters were placed at Tycho's disposal, and the student constructed a kind of gable roof of oak beams. It supported an arch thirty feet in length, neatly plated with a brass scale. The burgomaster was so delighted that he had a celestial globe made on a similar scale. He promised Tycho the globe if he would settle down as astronomer in Augsburg.

But Tycho went on traveling about Germany for several years, taking an active part in student life, so active in fact, that he had his nose cut off in a duel. Thereafter he went about with an artificial nose which he affixed anew to his face every morning. This defect apparently undermined his masculine confidence, for instead of marrying a noble woman he formed an alliance with a peasant girl who could never become his legal wife, but who nevertheless remained faithfully at his side and bore him seven children.

Back in Denmark he was generally accounted a fool until Landgrave William of Kassel, the most famous astronomer of the time, congratulated a Danish ambassador for having so great a fellow countryman. Amazed, the ambassador inquired about this unknown genius in his native land—and Tycho was one day startled out of his sleep by a royal courier. He had been just about to set out for Basel; the courier handed him a paper solemnly appointing him governor of an island.

It turned out to be Hven, between Elsinore and Copenhagen, an island with white cliffs rising out of the Baltic Sea, some three miles long, containing about two thousand acres of tillable land, a number of fish ponds, and woods. The King gave him this land in fee for his lifetime, "that he may live thereon free of rents and taxes, ever leal and loyal to Us, in all matters concerned to avert ill from Our Kingdom." That is to say, he was appointed Danish court astrologer. He was also given four hundred talers to be used for building an observatory on the island of Hven: the first observatory in the Western world.

BRAHE IN HIS OBSERVATORY, URANIA, ISLAND OF HVEN. HIS FINGER
POINTS TO A SLIT IN THE WALL THROUGH WHICH AN ASSISTANT
(UPPER RIGHT) IS SIGHTING ALONG THE LARGE QUADRANT. IMMEDI-
ATELY ABOVE BRAHE'S RAISED HAND IS A TRIQUETRUM, ONE OF THE
INSTRUMENTS OF COPERNICUS. IN CENTER BACKGROUND ARE THREE
STORIES OF THE OBSERVATORY, WITH ASSISTANTS ENGAGED IN ASTRO-
NOMICAL OBSERVATIONS. THE ENGRAVING IS DATED 1587, WHEN
BRAHE WAS FORTY YEARS OLD.

The four hundred talers were only the beginning, for Tycho Brahe built a palace. Whatever this young nobleman undertook was done with style. His Urania Castle marked an epoch in the architectural history of Denmark. It stood in an orchard and flower garden laid out geometrically, enclosed by fortification walls, and had two stout towers on south and north, with removable canvas roofs. All around were wide galleries that were soon filled with instruments. In the library stood the Augsburg celestial globe; in the main hall was Tycho's invention, the quadrant inscribed on a wall that faced south—the direction in which the Sun, the Moon, the planets, and the signs of the zodiac reached their highest point every night. With these he could measure differences of altitude at various seasons more exactly than any previous astronomer. His determination of the length of the year fell only a few seconds short of the true value.

In addition to the innumerable curiosity-seekers who visited the island of Hven, students also came, remaining for months and years. At one time Tycho Brahe had nine assistants; altogether, he trained more than forty. In each assistant's room there was a bell which Brahe activated by secret bellpulls under the dining room table. He would speak a name softly, and enjoy his guests' astonishment when the assistant he had just referred to promptly entered the room.

Records were kept of observations and the weather. There was a mechanic's workshop and a special group of arithmeticians. The number of types of instruments increased to twenty-seven. One of these Brahe was able to use for making observations while lying in bed. Never since his time has any astronomer lived in such splendor. Kings, dukes, and counts came to visit him. On such occasions he provided enormous banquets, organized lawn games, hunts, and alchemistic experiments. He had huge cages in the dining hall, filled with rare birds. A dwarf capered about the table, catching morsels of food and entertaining the guests with jests and demonstrations of telepathic powers.

The funds to provide for all this magnificence came from seven benefices the King presented to his astronomer. Even these did

not enable him to meet his expenditures, for he spent some 65,000 talers out of his own pocket on the unique observatory.

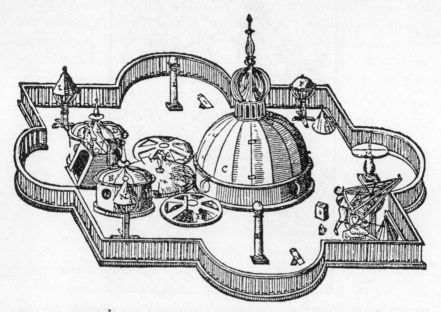

BRAHE'S SUBTERRANEAN OBSERVATORY, A.D. 1590.

A nearby annex was soon added, built underground because Brahe had discovered that the sea wind on the island seriously interfered with observation. This second observatory was also a remarkable sight. It consisted of a cellar with niches along the sides containing beds for the assistants. In the main vault, which was surmounted by a mighty dome, was Brahe's miracle instrument, the equatorial armillary, based on Greek descriptions improved by Tycho. With this he could measure the angular distances of stars from one another with great accuracy; this it was which helped him to produce the crowning achievement of his life, his new catalogue of the stars.

Astronomy needed a new basis. To determine positions, he took the average of fifteen best observations, and in the course of fourteen years of patient work catalogued 777 stars—all new determinations, the first since Hipparchus. These 777 stars served as the framework upon which the entire wonderful structure of

EQUATORIAL ARMILLARY IN THE MAIN VAULT OF BRAHE'S SUBTER-
RANEAN OBSERVATORY.

modern Occidental astronomy has been built. Employing them,
the orbits of the planets could be determined with precision.
Tycho Brahe supplied the exact figures that enabled Johannes
Kepler to create his new celestial mechanics.

Heirs in China

Tycho Brahe was a true *Junker*, imperious, ruthless, and given
to harshness. A tenant who disobeyed him was placed in chains
for three months. He bore down so heavily on his peasants with
forced labor that they several times requested permission to
emigrate. He made enemies everywhere. At court the King was
his only friend, and when the King died, the famous seven
benefices were promptly cut off. The Church condemned his

unsanctified marriage, which it had tacitly tolerated in the past. The court of nobles decided several cases against him. Beside himself with rage and incapable of taking a conciliatory tone, Tycho Brahe threatened to leave Denmark. He knew very well that he was the greatest attraction the country possessed, and the Emperor had more than once bid for his service.

To his surprise, no one tried to hold him. He packed up his instruments, and with a shipload of treasures went into exile. For a year he stayed close to Denmark, constantly expecting to be recalled. He humbled himself in letters to the young King, but received nothing but smart official raps for the arrogant tone he had employed in the past. When he realized at last that through his own folly he had lost his native land, he poured out his grief in elegies:

Denmark, have I deserved this ingratitude of yours?
Have I, my native land, ever knowingly harmed you?
Is not the fault you find with me after all one and the same
With the magnificent glory which through me alone you have
  gained?
Name me but one other man who gave you more richly than I,
Who raised up the fame of your name unto the eternal stars?

Then, with the unrepentant boldness of his age, he waved away the past and his own sins:

Everywhere below this Earth and everywhere on high, the heav-
  ens
Willingly offer a home to the man who stands without fear.

He went to the Emperor at Prague. There, however, he found the situation far less rosy than he had imagined it. The Hapsburg Emperor Rudolf II was a misanthropic eccentric given to passing enthusiasms for all scientific ideas, and all sorts of quackery. His interest in any one subject quickly faded. The observatory planned for Tycho Brahe ended by being nothing but a room in the castle of Benathky. Brahe was unable to make any significant observations. Worn out by endless disputes with scornful officials, he lived only a short time after his removal to Bohemia. But in

that short time his entire personality changed. He put aside his *Junker* arrogance, forgave young Kepler for independence and obstinacy, and took a paternal interest in his needs. Brahe was seeking an heir. He urged Kepler to publish the tables of the planets as soon as possible, and managed to have Kepler appointed imperial astronomer, officially charged with this task. Until the last, he was racked with concern for the future of his lifework. On his deathbed he is said to have groaned repeatedly: "I do not want to have lived in vain." Fortunately he died without having to see all the apparatus he had constructed at the cost of so much money and ingenuity outmoded by a single invention, the telescope. His instruments were never again used for observation, and one fine day they were burned. Nevertheless, beautifully tooled instruments built on the model of Tycho Brahe's were still to be seen in Peking, China, not long ago.

The story of how the great Danish astronomer's bequest found its way to China is a unique episode in cultural history. During the lifetime of Brahe the new order of the Jesuits began sending missionaries all over the world, even to the Far East. The missionaries arrived in China at an exceptionally favorable moment. The new dynasty of the Manchu emperors was engaged in a difficult struggle to hold the throne of the Son of Heaven in the face of passive resistance by the mandarins. The emissaries from Rome, with their superior science, were very welcome. An intellectual *primavera* comparable to European humanism was dawning in China. The Jesuits made a study of Chinese history and philosophy, surveyed the country, and drew up an excellent atlas; they shone as physicians and organizers. One of the missionaries, Father Johann Schall von Bell tutored the crown prince and later became his political adviser and a mandarin of the highest degree. He came within a hair's breadth of winning all of China for Christianity, and probably would have succeeded if the Roman Curia had followed his advice and permitted the sacred Oriental ancestor-worship to continue under Roman Catholicism. Because he was committed to attack this cult, the opposing party won the upper hand at court. Schall was imprisoned.

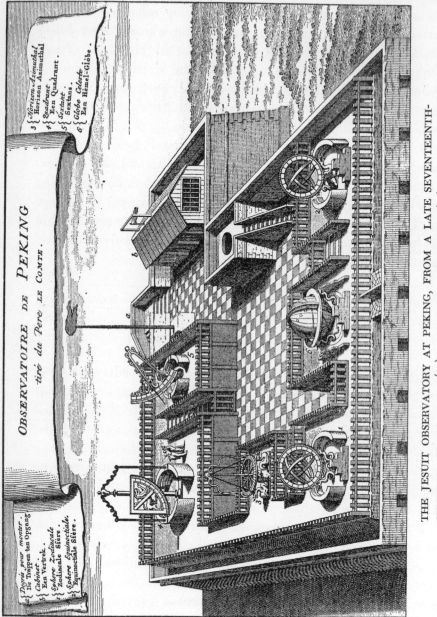

OBSERVATOIRE DE PEKING

tiré du Pere LE COMTE.

1 {Degrés pour monter.
De Trappen ten Opgang.
2 {Cabinet.
Een Vertrek.
3 {Sphere Zodiacale
Zodiacale Siere.
4 {Sphere Equinoctiale.
Equinoctiale Siere.

3 {Horizon Azimuthal
Horison Azimuthal
4 {Quadrant
Een Quadrant.
5 {Sextant.
Sextant.
6 {Globe Celeste
Een Hemel-Globe.

THE JESUIT OBSERVATORY AT PEKING, FROM A LATE SEVENTEENTH-
CENTURY ENGRAVING. (1) ARMILLARY SPHERE; (2) EQUATORIAL
ARMILLARY; (3) AZIMUTHAL HORIZON; (4) QUADRANT; (5) SEX-
TANT; (6) CELESTIAL GLOBE.

With him in prison was an astronomically trained fellow Jesuit who apparently had no hope of ever being released. But after three years of dreary incarceration, during which Father Schall von Bell died, the Emperor sent for him to ask his opinion about a reform of the calendar proposed by the court astronomer, a Mohammedan. The Jesuit said it was inadequate, and offered to prove to all that his rival had miscalculated the positions of the Sun. He was staking his life, for he had only the old, faulty instruments of the Chinese observatory at his disposal. Nevertheless, he succeeded. The Mohammedan was dismissed and the prisoner entrusted with the calendar reform and placed in charge of the observatory. He promptly rebuilt it on European principles and had Tycho Brahe's instruments copied for it. These remained in use for hundreds of years, and have been reverently preserved down to the present time.

The Last Flowering of Astrology

With the passing of the humanistic spirit the medieval temper burst out anew in the sixteenth century. Witch trials became part of the normal order of things in the courts; the devil went about in broad daylight. Black magic, secret sciences, alchemy, and astrology were in demand as never before. Consequently, astrology enjoyed its last great age, its most tangible triumphs. The sixteenth century has left more accounts of successful prophecy than any other era.

Nostradamus of Paris won legendary fame by his oracular rhymes, which purported to predict the future for centuries to come. They were as obscure as the Revelation of St. John, and what few have lent themselves to checking, such as his pronouncement that the papacy would be overthrown, proved to be quite false. But he is credited with having predicted correctly the defeat of the French at Saint-Quentin in 1557. Given at one time the horoscope of a person unknown to him, he foresaw misfortune in a duel. He was laughed at for this, since the horoscope was

that of the King, Henry II, and the King could not engage in a duel, of course. Soon thereafter a tournament took place at court; splinters of a lance flew into the King's forehead, striking him dead.

The son of this prophet informed the Polish King in 1573 that he would wear a prouder crown; in 1574 he succeeded to the throne of France as Henry III. A plague announced for 1580 also arrived punctually, we are told. But when Nostradamus's son predicted a great fire in the city, guards were posted—and the prophet was caught in the act of arson. Thus the extraordinary cases of successful prophecy were suspiciously linked with outright fraud. But the most serious objection to them was that astrology at the time stood upon the most unstable of foundations. In determining constellations of the planets, minutes are all-important; and King Alfonso's tables, which were used by the astrologers, were often wrong by days and even weeks. The accurate figures of Tycho Brahe were needed to test the possible validity of astrology.

Brahe himself made such tests, for he was a passionate believer in astrology. His king had engaged him to "avert ill from Our Kingdom," which meant that he was responsible for predicting good or bad political weather. His annual calendars also included meteorological forecasts for the benefit of farmers. He provided the court with special warnings and advice. At the birth of each royal child he sent a horoscope of several hundred pages, elegantly bound in green velvet. These horoscopes are said to have contained excellent descriptions of character, and occasionally to have hit off a successful prediction. The horoscope of one prince showed an unlucky constellation for the prince's eighteenth year. At eighteen the young man went to Russia to fetch home his bride, and died on the journey.

Brahe's most famous prediction concerned an astronomical event regarded in his time as very rare, although science has since learned that it is of frequent occurrence. On a November evening in 1572 a new star appeared in the northern sky in the constellation of Cassiopeia. It was bright as Venus at her brightest, and could be seen even by day. This new star was neither a planet nor

a comet, for it remained in the same place for one and a half years. From the first it caused great excitement; how could a new star appear upon the eternal firmament, the very symbol of immutability?

Naturally, everyone thought at once of the star of Bethlehem. Ecstatic souls expected the Saviour to return and establish the kingdom of glory. Brahe rejected this interpretation; the star of Bethlehem had been visible only to the Three Kings, he said, and therefore could not have been a heavenly body. New stars, on the other hand, were known, for Hipparchus had seen and recorded them. Perhaps the matter of the Milky Way occasionally coagulated into a star. But any such star would have to fade soon, "for anything that arises after the completion of the Creation can only be transitory."

In this Brahe was right. The most splendid nova of all times shrank visibly, paled, turned yellow, red, and finally leaden gray in color, and after eighteen months vanished away.

What could this strange sign have meant? All his life, Tycho puzzled over the problem. He wrote two fat volumes about it, expending upon the matter an enormous amount of astrological learning. His final conclusion was: a new light would arise in religion, probably in Finland; it would shine from 1593 to 1632 and make the old religion wane. This prophecy was regarded as fulfilled in the personality of Gustavus Adolphus, born at Stockholm in 1594 (Finland was at that time a Swedish province) and killed in battle in 1632.

Brahe's pupil Kepler was the last of the great astronomers to take any stock in astrology, and he was the first and last to attempt to turn astrology into an experimental science. Since a few successful prophecies always tend to make the many failures forgotten, Kepler decided to get to the bottom of the matter by keeping statistics of the highest possible objectivity. His results were not very favorable for astrology.

He was lucky with some weather forecasts. A thunderstorm predicted two weeks in advance arrived so punctually and with such violence that the terrified people screamed in the streets: "The Kepler's coming, the Kepler's coming!" But shortly after-

wards his almanac predictions failed utterly. From then on he kept daily records, checking them against his forecasts—with the result that he soon gave up forecasting.

On the other hand, he had a high regard for character sketches based on the constellations of the planets at an individual's birth. These, too, Kepler checked by analyses written with a psychologist's keenness. He described relations, friends, and himself with ruthless precision and detail. As an example of his view of his own personality, there is this passage from a letter of his: "In me Saturn and the Sun work together in their sextile aspect; therefore my body is small, dry, knobby, my soul suspicious and timid; I reject honors, crouch over books, know no pleasures of life aside from science. All this corresponds to my preference for bitter and sharp tastes, for gnawing bones and hard bread. To toil up mountains, to stumble over fields and rocky slopes—these things delight me. My destiny is similar: where others despair, money and fame come to me, though in modest measure. I meet opposition, and perhaps in the distant future my ideas will continue to meet opposition."

Predictions of personal fate from horoscopes seemed far more dubious to him; his own horoscope had made him very skeptical, since it was identical with his mother's, although their lives had taken very different courses. After numerous experiences he began warning his clients against accepting predictions. His famous horoscope for Wallenstein was prefaced by just such a warning.

The great general wanted direct answers to direct questions: "How long can I go on trusting to my military good fortune? In which countries will I wage war successfully? In which unsuccessfully? What are the names of my enemies; under what celestial sign do they stand? Will I win wealth and offices abroad? Will I die of apoplexy? When and where?"

Kepler's reply was: "Whosoever would have the answers to such questions from the stars alone, without reckoning with the character and the free will of man, has not yet rightly learned to trim the lamp of reason which God has lighted in him. If you would be hoodwinked to your face, turn to the young astrologers; there are many who have the faith and the brazenness to indulge

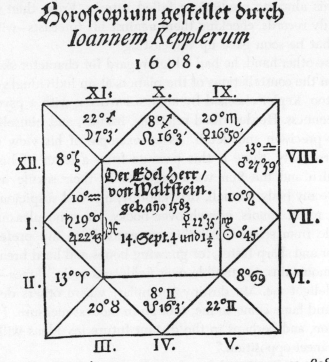

WALLENSTEIN'S HOROSCOPE, CAST BY KEPLER IN 1608.

in such games. True astrology is a holy testimony to God's glorious works, and I, for my part, do not wish to dishonor it."

Since, however, he was dependent upon Wallenstein's good graces, he nevertheless supplied the general with predictions for each year, drawn up according to the astrological rules in which he no longer believed. Most of his prophecies came to nothing: during the supposedly unlucky year of 1627 the general won his greatest victories, and neither his dismissal in 1630 nor his recall in 1631 were indicated by the stars. But the next few years were actually favorable, as predicted, and Kepler's forecast ended with an amazing triumph. For the beginning of March 1634 Kepler deduced from the conjunction of Jupiter and Saturn that there would be "frightful confusion in the land," and he concluded his prediction at this point. On February 25, 1634, Wallenstein was assassinated.

Into Infinity

Contemporary with these astrological astronomers there lived a genuine prophet: Giordano Bruno, the ecstatic herald of the age of science, the man who thought through the Copernican system to its logical conclusion and first revealed its true grandeur.

Giordano Bruno was neither a mathematician nor an astronomer, but a philosopher whose like was not to occur again in the Occident. Bruno was of the stock of Empedocles and Heraclitus, a builder whose only material was pure intellect, who did not define or criticize, only created. Endowed with a seer's vision, speaking a language that had the power of the Old Testament and at the same time the precision of modern science, Bruno was an incredible combination of wild enthusiasm and cool objectivity, a visionary who saw reality instead of mystic realms. He was at home in all the realms of the mind; he could produce with equal facility an impeccably logical essay or a flawless lyric poem, an acid satire or a profoundly religious tract, a saucy farce, and a cosmic vision.

His mind developed within the shelter of the cloister. At the age of twenty-eight he went out into the world. He journeyed through all of Europe, everywhere stirred up the youth, aroused amazement, was wildly hated and intemperately loved, was honored by kings and denounced by Catholics, Lutherans, and Calvinists as the incarnation of heresy. An uncontrollable urge to influence others drove him from place to place; he stayed nowhere longer than three years.

Wherever he went, he preached the Copernican system—in his native Italy, in Switzerland, France, England, and Germany; wherever he went, he represented the Copernican system as the beginning of a new mode of thinking, as a revolution in science, and in the growing consciousness of the human race. Yet to that intellectual revolution he contributed more than any of the astronomers. Copernicus had banished the Earth from the center of the universe; Bruno now did the same for the Sun. Intuitively

he realized that the Sun was only a star, one among millions of other stars.

This second upheaval, even more revolutionary than the first, was in Bruno's time pure prophecy; many generations were to pass before it could be incontrovertibly demonstrated. And yet it sufficed to have put it into words; the idea took permanent root in the minds of all astronomers. Once the Copernican system had won its victory, Bruno's idea was accepted tacitly, without discussion—though it was no more than a belief at that time. The strictest of sciences, the science bound more than all others to mathematical precision, accepted for seven generations a belief whose author was never recognized as a scientist, and scarcely ever mentioned. Science bowed to the word of a prophet.

The idea of the Sun as merely another star had tremendous consequences. For this star was not located upon the celestial sphere like the others, and there was no apparent reason why the others should surround it, all at equal distances from it. What seemed far more likely was that they were distributed irregularly to unimaginable distances. Suddenly the firmament, which had been an absolute boundary even for Copernicus, was rent asunder. Mankind had arrived at the concept of "space" as a boundless universe filled with dots of light.

Underlying Bruno's inspiration was the idea of infinity, the most majestic concept of our culture. That idea was innate in our culture, was embodied in our cathedrals and explorations, in the Vikings, in the circumnavigators of the globe, in the very conception of the Supreme Being as ubiquitous, all-embracing, eternal, without beginning and without end. The spirit of Western man cannot admit any limit to space or time, cannot even imagine such a limit. Instinctively he is driven to ask: what lies beyond, what existed before? The drawing of a boundary is an act which itself presupposes something outside, something beyond. The naïve woodcut reproduced below expresses this characteristic intellectual process: a man has thrust his head through the firmament and sees beyond it an infinity of new worlds.

This basic feeling in our ever-striving Occidental culture was bound, sooner or later, to assume the form of a rational scientific

FANTASTIC REPRESENTATION OF THE UNIVERSE, FROM AN EARLY
SIXTEENTH-CENTURY WOODCUT. THE MAN IS THRUSTING HIS HEAD
THROUGH THE STARRY FIRMAMENT INTO INFINITY.

concept. Copernicus appeared to be the person destined to formulate it, but he exhausted his intellectual forces in the struggle
with the spirit of the Greeks, which had held astronomical thinking in bondage for fifteen hundred years. Someone had to launch
anew on the flight to infinity. Giordano Bruno did so.

Bruno entirely rejected the idea that the cosmos had a center.
He insisted upon the mobility of every celestial body. He proposed the maxims that our earthly laws of nature are applicable
to the whole universe, and that the chemistry of nature is the
same everywhere. In the future science would prove all these
hypotheses, he believed, and he cried out to those scientists of the
future: "Open wide the door for us, so that we may look out into
the immeasurable starry universe; show us that other worlds
like ours occupy the ethereal realms; make clear to us how the
motion of all worlds is engendered by forces; teach us to march
forward to greater knowledge of nature."

That program of his was literally fulfilled. He himself anticipated part of it by describing a universe of countless suns, planets, and earths:

"Sky, universe, all-embracing ether, and immeasurable space
alive with movement—all these are of one nature. In space there
are countless constellations, suns, and planets; we see only the
suns because they give light; the planets remain invisible, for they
are small and dark. There are also numberless earths circling
around their suns, no worse and no less inhabited than this globe
of ours. For no reasonable mind can assume that heavenly bodies
which may be far more magnificent than ours would not bear
upon them creatures similar or even superior to those upon our
human Earth."

This dictum of the probability that innumerable worlds are
inhabited needed only to be pronounced by the prophet to become a basic tenet of Western astronomy. Science was later to
add many cautious amendments: the majority of the stars are
now believed to be ill suited to act as nourishers and warmers of
inhabited planets; some are too hot and some too cold, some
flickering lamps and some too much like flash bulbs. And only
very few of the planets can qualify as possible bearers of life.
They must maintain a certain distance from their sun, and fulfill
many other uncommon conditions. Still, of our nine planets three,
as far as we know, do fulfill some such conditions, and even if
there were only a single Sun-like star among a million stars, and
a single Earth-like planet among a million planets, the simplest
reckoning of probabilities shows that there must still be numberless habitable planets. Giordano Bruno's pronouncement of the
multitudinous possibilities of life in the universe has remained
valid.

The prophet came forward with this vision of a limitless universe at the worst conceivable time, when fanaticism was everywhere reviving, fantasies of witchcraft were beclouding all minds,
and religious persecutions were commencing. Had he stepped
on the stage at the same time as Copernicus, during the golden
age of humanism, he might have set higher goals for the brief era
of freethinking among scholars, might have raised their sights to

"infinity." As it was, he was merely a heretic. And he sealed his fate with a religious perception that was just as heretical as his view of the cosmos. For Bruno matter and God were not contradictory; he saw nothing but Oneness in the All. The Supreme Being was revealed not in the Holy Scriptures, but in everything created. Nature was the only absolute Bruno would accept.

These views led him to the stake. Emissaries of the Inquisition brought him to Rome, where he was kept imprisoned for seven years before he was burned on February 17, 1600. To his judges, he said: "I await your sentence with less fear than you pass it. The time will come when all will see what I see."

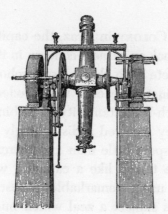

KEPLER THE GOD-SEEKER

Reflection of the Spirit of God

THE PROTESTANT COLONY in Graz, the capital of the Austrian province of Styria, took an earnest concern in its parochial school, which had to compete with three Jesuit schools. Consequently, when a new mathematics teacher was needed, the colony sent for one from the arch-Protestant city of Tübingen, a twenty-day journey distant. They received a disturbingly young fellow, one Johannes Kepler, a spare little man and extremely animated. At his initial lecture he talked like a cataract, waving his arms in dramatic gestures, using remarkable phrases, coining words, and pouring into his subject a zeal which might have been devoted to a better cause. For this man seemed to be converting geometry into a form of idol-worship. It was, he proclaimed, the only genuine science. The human mind had been actually created for the perception of geometric relationships. Man's mind could not truly grasp anything but quantities, and indeed the whole of creation rested upon quantities. God had gone about building up the world like a geometrician; one might almost think that he had had in mind the way men would build after he had created them, with squares, plumb lines, and compasses. Copernicus had demonstrated the wondrous logic of the cosmos, and "this selfsame logic the Creator placed in our minds so that we might share in his very own ideas." Everyone must acknowledge the Euclidean demonstrations; they proved better than any

other testimony that we are indeed God's images, for "geometry is unique and eternal, a reflection of the spirit of God."

After this lecture the school directors held a conference. They were somewhat upset by this queer saint who had been sent from Tübingen, and it was unanimously decided to restrict the number of hours allotted to mathematics. Better for Johannes Kepler to work the youthful froth out of himself. Also he ought to be provided with a wife—one not too young, possibly a devout widow, so that his wild speculations could be drawn back down to the solid ground of Christian reality.

The widow was found; she turned out to be not quite so mature as might have been wished, but on the other hand she had the stable character arising out of the possession of houses and farms. In gratitude for their matchmaking, the bridegroom presented the school directors with a handsomely printed little book entitled *Mysterium Cosmographicum*. It was poorly calculated to reassure them about his future. Kepler's strange conception of God was leading him into ever wilder flights of fancy, it seemed. Now he was invading the Creator's workshop, was endeavoring to decipher God's plan of the universe—and he continued to rely on Copernicus, that flouter of Scriptures.

Since Kepler had first become acquainted with the new cosmology, he had subscribed wholeheartedly to it. But he also posed questions that Copernicus had never thought of. Why, he asked, should there be exactly six planets (including the Earth)? What law governed their varying distances from the Sun? There must be some geometrical principle at work there, since geometry was the reflection of the spirit of God. It should be possible for man to fathom the deeper meanings of the cosmic order.

Kepler would frequently pray for God to enlighten him, to reveal to him the reason for the particular arrangement of the heavenly bodies. And one day, during a class, the reason came to him. He was teaching the last book of Euclid, which contains the demonstration that there are only five possible regular solids. If these shapes should fit between the spheres of the six planets, that would be an arrangement satisfactory to his geom-

etrician's mind. He hastily assigned his pupils a difficult construction, and buried himself with his own calculations. As if a spirit were dictating the solution to him, there came out the following propositions:

Place the cube between Saturn and Jupiter. The cube will limit the orbit of Jupiter.

Place the tetrahedron between Jupiter and Mars. The tetrahedron will limit the orbit of Mars.

Place the dodecahedron between Mars and the Earth. The dodecahedron will limit the orbit of the Earth.

Place the icosahedron between Earth and Venus. The icosahedron will limit the orbit of Venus.

Place the octahedron between Venus and Mercury. The octahedron will limit the orbit of Mercury.

And there resulted the distances between the orbits in the Copernican system.

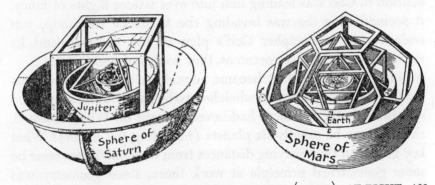

KEPLER'S MODEL OF THE PLANETARY SPHERES (LEFT). AT RIGHT, AN ENLARGEMENT OF THE INNER SPHERES. KEPLER PLACED THE FIVE POSSIBLE REGULAR GEOMETRICAL SOLIDS ONE WITHIN THE OTHER. THIS CONSTRUCTION MATCHED THE DISTANCES BETWEEN THE ORBITS OF THE PLANETS ESTABLISHED BY COPERNICUS, AND THEREFORE INDICATED A EUCLIDEAN SOLAR SYSTEM.

Re-examination confirmed this curious discovery. The Lord God had revealed his Euclidean intentions; the mystery of the structure of the universe was disclosed. And the insignificant schoolmaster of Graz became famous at one blow. "And yet," he

wrote, "I began this investigation only for my own amusement. I am tempted to cry out: Go from me, for I am a sinful man! But henceforth I will be concerned only for His glory, for we astronomers are also prophets of God who preach from the Book of Nature."

Even the chief prophet, Tycho Brahe, praised this idea, although Kepler's conception did not fit into his Tychonic system. He insinuated, however, that the planetary distances given by Copernicus were probably incorrect. Kepler protested that if this were the case, Brahe should publish better figures, not hoard his knowledge.

To obtain the correct figures, Kepler went to Prague. Brahe was friendly to him, but kept his counsel. Only now and then would he casually reveal a few of his cherished figures. But he admitted that he could not solve the orbit of Mars. With the arrogance and exuberance of youth, Kepler wagered that he could master the problem within a week. He returned to Graz with a notebook full of statistics on observations of Mars—and lost his wager. For months he sweated over the rows of figures. He became obsessed with the task; at times it nearly drove him mad. Often he took refuge in the thought that he still did not have enough figures at his disposal. If only he could live with Brahe, could work as his secretary, his mathematician.

His wish was fulfilled in a somewhat rude manner.

At that time the Counter Reformation was beginning. The religious strife pained the devout Kepler. He could not see why he should hate the "Papists." The Jesuit fathers had given his account of the mystery of the cosmos a good reception; Kepler was even dreaming that he might help reunite divided Christendom under the auspices of a profounder knowledge of God. Kepler was an enthusiastic advocate of the Gregorian calendar reform, to which all Protestants were opposed. He affirmed that the Catholics had a superior conception of Christ's divine person, and the Calvinists a better conception of the Eucharist. In the eyes of his former superiors at Tübingen, these were two unforgiveable heresies. They dropped their now famous student. To the end of his life he besieged them with pleas for understanding,

sent long treatises, came in person to swear to them that he was
not a frivolous blasphemer. From childhood on, he declared, he
had trembled at the thought that he might be predestined to correct errors; he was terribly in earnest about all these questions,
but he could not acknowledge the spirit of fanaticism to be a reflection of the spirit of God.

But fanaticism was now the mood of the age. With his tolerance
and his intellectual superiority, Kepler fell between two stools.
The Jesuits kept hoping that some day they would convert him;
his coreligionists considered him weak and lukewarm. When, however, the Protestants were expelled from Graz, he showed that he
did not lack the courage to confess his faith. "I would not have
thought it would be so sweet to leave house and fields, friends,
and kinsmen, for Christ's sake," he wrote. "If leaving this Earth
is much the same, dying must be easy."

His wife lost almost all her worldly goods. The couple turned
up in Prague as poor refugees. Kepler's equanimity, however, was
based upon a compensating factor his fellow sufferers could not
share. For he felt that "religion would have us believe that God
is concerned that men may have knowledge of His Creation. In
Tycho Brahe he has laid a new foundation for such knowledge.
And since by the unalterable decrees of His Providence he has
linked me with Brahe, he no doubt wishes me to build a new
house upon that foundation."

With this theological justification, the mathematician who had
just turned thirty took upon himself one of the most toilsome
and wearisome tasks of research in history.

Ptolemy's Overthrow

Compared to Kepler's achievements, the great works of past
astronomers seem to have fallen out of the sky. The explanation of
the planetary loops came to Copernicus one fine day like a sudden
vision. Kepler groped his way in the dark all along, so that he
had the final result in his hands for years, without knowing that

he had it. Galileo, Newton, and Huygens applied a new principle to a multitude of problems; Kepler tried out half a dozen new principles, and most of them led him into a blind alley. And for each principle he developed his own methods of calculation, solving problems for which mathematics was not ready for generations to come.

The most curious of his blind alleys, and the one on which he expended the longest time, was his effort to reconcile Brahe's observations with Greek astronomy. He devoted three years of work to solving the problem of Mars, which had defeated Copernicus, on Ptolemaic principles; seventy times he carried out the complicated calculations on different premises, until the seventy-first time he succeeded. Tycho Brahe was delighted, but Kepler was not, for he had hoped to refute Ptolemy.

The Greek cosmology could not, must not be true. He felt this. It sullied the honor of God. Ptolemy had mastered the orbits of the planets only by having them revolve around an assumed point in the universe, and this point in turn revolved around another assumed point, so that the equations would work out. But the Architect of the universe could not have caused the heavenly bodies to revolve around a nullity.

Kepler had long since had a system of his own, a virtual revelation which had come to him during his student days. He proclaimed it in his *Mysterium Cosmographicum:* "The Sun not only stands in the center of the universe, but is its moving spirit." He was trying to formulate the one most significant idea in the history of astronomy, to share the Creator's deepest secret by inquiring into the *cause* of celestial motions, and determining the manner in which the Creator impelled what He had created. And Kepler went so far as to remove God as the motive power. "My aim is to demonstrate that the celestial machine is not something like a divine organism, but rather something like a clockwork in which a single weight drives all the gears; that the totality of the complex motions is guided by a single magnetic force."

Here, formulated with full clarity for the first time in the history of European man, was the concept of force. For Copernicus it had not existed. He placed the Sun on its throne and

allowed it to guide a court of planets. Kepler, on the contrary, said that the Sun moved the planets. Copernicus still thought in poetic terms: to him the planets were horses held with reins. For Kepler they were gears moved by the motive power of the Sun.

At this time, to be sure, he could conceive of this force only as rotary force; the idea of attraction did not come to him until later. But this error did not really affect the conclusion he drew: that the planets must revolve around the Sun itself, not around a point to one side of the Sun. And since the planets sometimes moved closer and sometimes farther from the Sun, their orbits could not be circles!

This was indeed unpardonable heresy. The whole of Greek astronomy had been developed about the idea of the circular form. Only the perfect circle could underlie cosmic movements—this conviction had been the starting point for the Greeks, and both Copernicus and Brahe continued to subscribe to it. But Kepler must have doubted it from the first, for otherwise his idea of force would have had no meaning. The trouble was, he felt unable to cope with his own heresy. He did not know how to prove it.

It was not until he had solved the problem of Mars's orbit by Ptolemaic methods that he hit on the decisive test. His was one of the most original of inspirations, a counterpart of the famous dictum of Archimedes: "Give me a place to stand on and I will move the world." Kepler placed himself mentally on a distant star and from this vantage point looked simultaneously at the Earth and at Mars. Mars returns to the same place every 687 days, but by the time Mars has completed its orbit, the Earth is at a different point along its own path. If lines are drawn to the Sun from these chosen points in the respective orbits, the relative distances from Mars to the Sun and from Earth to the Sun can be calculated by triangulation. Kepler did this for several positions of Mars, and each time obtained a different figure for the distance from Mars to the Sun in comparison to the distance of the Earth to the Sun. That was conclusive proof that the orbit of Mars is not a circle, even though no absolute distances had yet been determined.

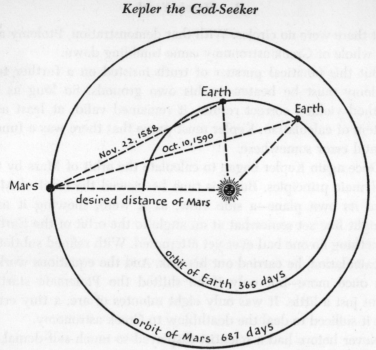

Earth

Earth

Nov. 22, 1588

Oct. 10, 1590

Mars

desired distance of Mars

orbit of Earth 365 days

orbit of Mars 687 days

KEPLER'S INSPIRED IDEA: TO CALCULATE BY TRIANGULATION THE
RELATIVE DISTANCES OF MARS FROM DIFFERENT POSITIONS OF THE
EARTH, THEREBY DETERMINING THE TRUE ORBIT OF MARS.

Kepler had demolished Greek astronomy with its imaginary
centers of orbits. But what a roundabout route he had taken! What
quixotic impulse had made him pay homage for years to principles he did not believe in and which he wanted to overthrow?
The answer is that Kepler himself had the soul of a Greek. He
wanted to see the universe as harmonious; he had a secret yearn-
ing for perfect circles. Janus-headed, he stood on the divide between two epochs. In him the new spirit of modern science was
struggling to emerge, but he persisted in looking backward with
one half of his mind.

What did distinguish Kepler from the Greeks was his modern
impulse to grasp reality. He wanted to know reality firsthand.
That his Ptolemaic calculations worked out might impress a Tycho
Brahe, but not Kepler himself. Whether the orbits of the planets
were truly circles must be established by examination of the sky
itself. And observation plus a little imagination had demonstrated

that there were no circles. With that demonstration, Ptolemy and the whole of Greek astronomy came tumbling down.

But this fanatical pursuer of truth insisted on a further test. Ptolemy must be beaten on his own grounds. So long as his method yielded correct results, it remained valid, at least as a system of calculation. Kepler must prove that there was a fundamental error somewhere.

Once again Kepler began to calculate the orbit of Mars by the Ptolemaic principles. But this time he viewed the orbit of Mars from its own plane—a side view, as it were, showing it as a straight line set somewhat at an angle to the orbit of the Earth—something no one had ever yet attempted. With refined subtleties of calculation, he carried out his task. And the equations worked out once more—but only if he shifted the Ptolemaic starting point just a little. It was only eight minutes of arc, a tiny error; but it sufficed to deal the deathblow to Greek astronomy.

Never before had a scientist displayed so much self-denial, so much inhuman patience. Others had concerned themselves only with their own ideas, had proved them and formed them into systems that achieved better results than earlier systems. Kepler, however, allowed himself this only after he had defeated the Greeks with their own weapons. "Those eight minutes," he wrote, "opened the way for me to renew the whole of astronomy."

Varying Speeds of the Planets

Copernicus had solved the problem of the planetary loops, but had failed to explain the varying speeds of the planets. This phenomenon was most plainly demonstrated by Mars; every month the planet covered a longer or shorter distance. Some months it moved faster, some slower. This was then the thorniest difficulty in astronomy. Because of the varying speeds, the positions of the planets could not be calculated in advance—and such calculation was precisely the task of the astronomers. The Greeks sought to explain away these irregularities, declaring

them to be deceptions, mere illusions. Kepler, however, recognized that they were real and determined to learn how to deal mathematically with varying speeds.

He already had an inkling of how to go about it. His idea about force should come into play here. The force of the Sun diminishes with distance. Consequently, a planet nearer the Sun must move faster, and one farther away more slowly. The planets demonstrated this theorem incontestably: Jupiter was three times farther from the Sun than Mars and therefore ought to take three times as long to make one revolution; in reality it took six times; its average speed was far less than that of Mars.

But the speed of Mars was itself variable. The reason, Kepler decided, must be that it sometimes approached, sometimes drew away from the Sun. Hence its orbit could not be a circle. It should be possible to calculate the variations in its speed from the variations in its distance. But when he tried to do so, he failed completely. On his first attempt to use the idea of force pragmatically, it gave him no help. What next? He still did not doubt the idea, but for the time being he laid it aside and looked about for other approaches to the problem of varying speeds. Few thinkers have possessed a mind of such extraordinary flexibility as Kepler's.

Kepler was deeply convinced that the spirit of God revealed itself most purely in geometry. Perhaps there was some geometrical method for calculating the varying speeds. At last he found one: his law of areas, which remains the basis of all calculations of orbits to this day. Kepler had happened upon two basic truths of astronomy: the orbits of planets are ellipses; and the varying speeds of planets can be calculated because a line drawn from the Sun to a moving planet sweeps over equal areas of the elliptical orbit in equal time.

If ever a man had had a flash of inspiration, this was it. Here was a pure miracle: the method was not mathematically perfect, and yet it worked. Afterwards, Kepler himself did not know quite how he had hit upon it, or how he could prove it irrefutably. He lacked the mathematical tools to deal with his law of areas, and had to employ a laborious process of approximation. He undertook to reckon with every single degree in the orbit of Mars, and

he went over his calculations forty times without getting beyond his approximations. At last, resignedly, he left it to future mathematicians to invent an exact method of calculating with his law of areas. "Kepler's problem," as it is still called, was so difficult that differential and integral calculus were not adequate; it could not really be conquered until the nineteenth century developed the theory of functions.

For Kepler himself, the problem was sheer torture. In vain he sought for some way to deal with the orbit as a whole; always he was forced back upon dealing with tiny segments of the orbit.

After this second defeat he recuperated for a full year by engaging in other research—which resulted in the production of a fat book on astronomical optics. Then he took up the struggle with Mars once more, this time employing a radically different method of attack. He asked himself what the shape of Mars's orbit must be. If it was not a circle, what was it? An oval, of course. The most regular form of oval would be the ellipse. Unfortunately, that seemed ruled out, since an ellipse has two foci, and Kepler could postulate only one, the focal point of force represented by the Sun. If God had provided another, void focus, then the orbits of the planets would once more partly revolve around nothingness—and for the honor of God, that must not be.

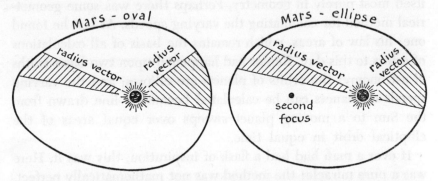

KEPLER'S LAW OF AREAS: THE RADIUS VECTOR PASSES OVER EQUAL AREAS IN EQUAL INTERVALS OF TIME. THE LAW HOLDS ONLY FOR AN ELLIPSE, NOT FOR AN OVAL.

What other choices were there? Aside from the circle, there is only one single regular closed curve with a single focus, the

ovoid. The orbit of Mars, Kepler concluded, must be egg-shaped, flattened on one side and pointed on the other.

Here Kepler was disobeying one of the basic principles of science: he was drawing a premature conclusion. To escape from it again cost him as much labor as he had previously expended on overthrowing Ptolemy. "Hasty dogs litter blind pups," he later said mockingly of himself.

For a long time the idea of an ovoid orbit for Mars underlay all his attempts to deal with the problem of varying speeds. Now he proceeded to the toilsome course that alone was left to him: he measured this ovoid from every possible direction, on the assumption that measurement of enough actual distances from the Sun would inevitably show him the true outlines of the ovoid orbit.

Unfortunately, his result indicated an entirely impossible shape for an ovoid. Kepler was inconsolable, as Copernicus had been before him. His book was almost complete; fifty-one chapters of novelties, full of drawings and proofs as ingenious as any Euclid had ever offered—and all in vain. For he still had no solution to the orbit of Mars.

When he had recovered from his depression, he noticed something extraordinary. His ovoid was too narrow by about as much as a circle would have been too wide. The truth, he concluded, must lie somewhere in between, just as if the orbit of Mars were a regular ellipse. Yet this was the very idea he did not want to admit. Anything rather than two focal points. He tried an alternative whose silliness was a sign of his obstinacy: an orbit with a pair of chubby cheeks that puffed out to the midpoint between ovoid and circle. But then it became evident even to this stubborn soul that an ellipse would do far better. That was, at least, a fine, smooth curve. After all, two foci need not be so incompatible with the honor of God. If he were going to give up the circle, he might just as well accept an empty point.

As soon as he tried this out, everything was fine. "I felt as if I had awakened from a long sleep and were blinking at the bright sunlight," he wrote jubilantly. His calculation of the orbit employing the law of areas worked out beautifully.

It was Easter 1605, ninety-nine years after the great discovery by Copernicus. Now, at last, that discovery was coming into its own. Kepler knelt to greet the risen Saviour. "Dear Lord," he prayed, "who hast guided us to the light of Thy glory by the light of nature, thanks be to Thee. Behold, I have completed the work to which Thou hast called me. And I rejoice in Thy Creation whose wonders Thou hast given me to reveal unto men. Amen."

Trip to the Moon

As astronomer to the Emperor Rudolf II, Kepler had the dreary task of reducing Brahe's observations to planetary tables. This was a matter of dull arithmetic; here was no possibility of making discoveries. From year to year he postponed this chore, and he might never have completed it if John Napier's tables of logarithms had not come his way. Kepler was as happy as a boy at Christmas, and he immediately attempted to fathom the mechanism of the tables, which the Scottish inventor had concealed. In no time at all he had analyzed the underlying principle, and gleefully reported to his former teacher in Tübingen, with whom he still corresponded: "Henceforth there is no need to multiply or divide."

"I find it unworthy of a mathematician to take childish pleasure in a trick which relieves him of work," his teacher wrote back sternly. The old man no longer knew what to make of his former student. He replied more and more rarely to Kepler's detailed, respectful, affectionate letters. "Your questions are ordinarily so subtle that I do not understand them. I dare not allow myself to pass judgment upon your books. Moreover, your high position . . ."

Kepler was quick to reassure him about this last. "My wife complains that the children follow her in the streets, shouting 'stargazer'! I myself am happy when I succeed, after ten requests, in wresting a third of my last year's salary from the court chan-

cery. I despise honors and, if need be, the persons who give them. I do not serve the Emperor, but posterity."

For the Emperor, nevertheless, he devised a fountain, explained the crystalline form of snow, interpreted the appearance of a new star in the sky, and provided horoscopes of Augustus, Mohammed, and the Grand Turk, the sultan of Turkey. He also showed the Emperor an eclipse of the Sun and several comets. Once he virtually dragged the monarch up to his attic observatory to show him a tiny dot on the Sun. He employed no more apparatus than a sheet of paper held in front of a crack in the roof; the round disc of the Sun appeared on the paper, and on it a tiny point "like a dead flea." Kepler thought himself fortunate to be the first to observe a transit of Mercury across the Sun. In reality he was the first to see a sunspot with the naked eye. Five years later the telescope makers, Scheiner and Galileo, were disputing priority to the discovery of sunspots.

When Galileo's achievements with the telescope were made known, Kepler rejoiced in characteristic fashion: "Oh, you omniscient eyeglass, more precious than a king's scepter. Who holds you in his hand is master of the world. Who could remain silent when confronted with such wondrous things? Who could refrain from proclaiming his enthusiasm in word and writing?" And he proclaimed his enthusiasm so unrestrainedly and publicly that he was rebuked by members of the court. After all, it was pointed out to him not everyone was so struck with this marvelous instrument. A good many persons had failed to see these miracles in the heavens.

Thereupon Kepler obtained a telescope from one of the princes to whom Galileo had made a gift, and assembled a committee. Each member wrote down what he had seen; then the statements were compared. The result was a further outburst of enthusiasm, wilder than the first, which came to a climax in a mad fantasy: that ships must be built to sail through the spaces of the universe!

Kepler next withdrew to his study and considered how the magical instrument worked, what made it bring the stars so close.

The paper he wrote was an entirely modern scientific work, completely objective, with not a word of emotion; it contained nothing but geometrical constructions and proofs. Kepler dealt with everything that could happen to rays of light: reflection, refraction in water and in prisms, mirror images and lens images, lens formulas, the path of light rays in Galileo's telescope, and in a superior telescope which Kepler himself devised theoretically.

In short, Kepler virtually singlehanded created the whole science of geometrical optics, with only the law of refraction stated incorrectly. This work he tossed off in six weeks—taking less time to create a science than is needed nowadays to learn it.

With his borrowed telescope he studied the craters of the Moon for weeks, and then fulfilled one of his boyhood dreams: to write about a journey to the Earth's satellite. Kepler's little book with the large title, *Somnium sive Opus Posthumum de Astronomia Sublunari*, was one of the earliest examples of science fiction. And since it was written by a great astronomer, most of the science in it remains valid to this day. In particular, Kepler gives a vivid picture of our Earth as it would appear to the Moon-voyagers—a body four times larger than the Sun. The Moon at night, he relates, is illuminated by a silvery disc the size of a cathedral dome and so bright that it is unnecessary to light lamps. In all probability, the contours of our continents can be seen with the naked eye, and the rotation of the globe recognized. But strangely, the giant globe rotates as if it were turning on a spit; it does not move from its place, is the only body at rest in the revolving universe. Behind it, the starry firmament moves by, the Sun, the planets all spin about; the Earth alone remains in its place, day and night.

That means, moreover, that from any given place on the Moon the Earth is seen at a different angle. If we land at the crater of Copernicus, for example, the Earth appears to be directly overhead. If, on the other hand, we stand on the Lunar Alps, it is seen looming impressively just above the mountains. If we move farther to the south, the Earth touches the horizon, and on the other side of the Moon we would never see it at all.

The Earth also shows phases, Kepler suggested, waxing and

waning in a single day. At sunrise and sunset it is always half illuminated, at midnight always full. Sometimes a small, circular ink spot moves across it for four hours; this is a partial darkening of the Earth by the Moon. During the day, the Earth becomes a pale crescent; at noon it is only a circular line. The Sun ordinarily passes behind it, a little above or below it. Fairly often, however, the Sun sails straight for the Earth, and then vanishes completely behind it for half an hour. These eclipses of the Sun are very impressive; everything becomes pitch-dark on the Moon; only the Earth is marked out magnificently by a golden ring, and at the beginning and end of the eclipse glows a rosy pink.

A visit to the Moon has its unpleasant side. Day lasts two weeks and night two weeks. At noon the ground glows as hot as the lid of a stove; at night it is cold beyond anything imaginable upon the Earth. Kepler did not know the exact figures, but he had a quite correct general idea of the temperature of the Moon. Moreover he drew a highly original portrait of the lunar inhabitants. All the creatures of the Moon are either spherical or snakelike. Their bodies are covered with a thick protective layer, in plants consisting of a spongy, porous rind, in animals of a scaly armor, which in the course of the two-week day peel off in charred fragments. At evening apparently dead creatures, like black pine-cones, lie about, slowly reviving under the mild earthshine and becoming completely restored during the night. Under these frightful environmental conditions their lives are short; most of them are born and die within a single Moon day.

As far as the voyage was concerned, Kepler simplified matters for himself. A spirit transported the travelers, first wrapping them carefully to protect them against cold and above all against jolts, for "in the beginning they were whirled aloft as if shot from a cannon. The spirit had to stupefy them with opium so that they would come through the first part of the voyage alive. As soon as they departed from the attractive sphere of the Earth and entered that of the Moon, he awoke them and released them; they flew of their own accord toward their destination, with increasing velocity. At the end of the journey the spirit hastened ahead and held them back, to prevent a hard impact."

Here Kepler stated a fair approximation of the methods proposed by the most modern theoreticians of space travel. The most remarkable aspect of this account is the manner in which Kepler takes for granted that the Earth and the Moon possess attractive forces; he even speaks of their gravitational fields. In fact he maintained that the two bodies attracted one another and would long ago have united at a point corresponding to what now would be called their center of mass, if they were not held apart and fixed in their orbits by an unknown force.

Here, two generations before Newton, Kepler speculatively approached the idea of gravitation. Kepler even anticipated Newton's best argument: the explanation of the tides by the joint attraction of Sun and Moon. All he lacked was that unknown force which prevented the heavenly bodies from rushing together, and held them in their elliptical orbits. That no force was necessary, merely inertia, was the paradoxical truth which it remained for his great contemporary, Galileo, to discover.

Wife Seeking, Wine-Cask Reckoning, Witch Trial

For eleven years Kepler thrived in Prague; then everything came tumbling down upon his head all at once: war, quartering of soldiers, pillage; his wife caught an infection while tending the sick, and died. His son died; the Emperor died. Kepler took his two remaining children and moved to Linz in Upper Austria, assuming a post as modest as that he had occupied many years before at Graz.

He had promised his wife on her deathbed to provide the children with a new mother by marrying one of her friends. Halfheartedly, he made his proposal; to his relief, the widow refused him. She offered him her eldest daughter; he wanted the youngest, and did not get her. Firmly resolved to keep his promise without delay, he asked the servant maid who had faithfully cared for the children during the journey. She was engaged.

After these three failures, he consulted professional marriage

brokers, but kept spoiling things by his eternal irresolution. He delayed calling upon the parents of one rich maiden until they had picked out another son-in-law. The next girl he decided upon was too fine for him. In the case of another, a distinct beauty, he sent the go-between with instructions to depict him as being altogether undesirable—in order to "try her heart." Her heart did not withstand the test.

Kepler heard that he was being gossiped about—a mild expression for the sensation his continual wife-seeking was causing in Linz. He determined to be more circumspect, and to conduct his subsequent affairs secretly. The neighbor's daughter said yes to him three times and no four times in the course of ten weeks; finally he gave her up. To another he dropped hints so ambiguous that her mother said to him: "You do not seem to know yourself what you want. I will not give my daughter to a man who cannot make up his mind."

In utter despair he rushed once more to the marriage broker, who offered him in turn a ball of fat, a half-fledged gosling, and a notorious half-wit. At this point he threw up the game; he no longer saw any way to keep his promise to his dead wife. Then one fine day he saw again a poor orphan girl who had pleased him the first day he came to Linz. He experienced a sudden awakening akin to the time he had recognized the orbit of Mars as an ellipse; he rubbed his eyes as if coming out of a nightmare, and acted with decision.

The touching aspect of this elevenfold wooing is the manner in which he afterwards described it to a friend—with unsparing candor, self-mockery, and a terrible earnestness which transform the farce into a symbol, a Christian and philosophical experiment.

"Was it divine providence that I lay in wait for more than two years for so many brides, whirling about like a leaf in the wind, or was it my own fault? If fault, then why did the reasoning of my counselors appear to me as so alluringly sensible? Why did God permit me to delude myself with senseless hopes? Or is He not a meddler in our plans; does He only bide His time in order to determine their outcome? Had the stars perhaps exercised an influence? But then how do they operate in such a case? Did

they stir my own impulses excessively? How account for the gullibility, the devoutness, the restless hunt for telling signs and significant acts, the endless analysis of my own mind, the terror of choice? I know well that others go through similar experiences, but perhaps others forget more quickly, do not torment themselves so long as I do. For me, my friend, there is nothing I would so urgently know, nothing I so earnestly seek to understand, as this: Can I find God, whom I trace in the universe, within my own soul as well?"

He celebrated his second marriage as he had his first, by solving a mathematical problem. The problem came to him in the form of a barrel of wine that he bought at the Linz harvest fair. The dealer set the price by measure; he stuck a marked stick into the bunghole, slanting it to reach the thickest part of the barrel, and read off the quantity of wine the barrel contained. But he could not explain his method; this was simply the traditional way of measuring. Kepler considered it his duty to get to the bottom of the matter.

Out of his investigation came something more than precise calculation of the contents of a barrel. Kepler developed the theory of maxima and minima, with applications to ninety-two shapes that had never been dealt with mathematically, among them such tricky figures as the outline of an apple and a pear. This *Dioptrice* became one of the classical papers of mathematics. He introduced his subject in a waggish manner: "The ancient grandmother Geometry long ago distributed all her worldly goods to her children, the architects and artisans and merchants and sailors. Poor as she is, only yesterday she discovered another penny in her favorite spot, an Austrian wine barrel, and charged me to polish it and hand it to the winegrowers with the wish that God may grant them so much juice of the grape that they can sell it henceforth cheaper than they did last year."

The winegrowers gave small heed to the gift. But as a result of Kepler's study, ancient grandmother Geometry was assigned so many new tasks that she had no choice but to undergo a radical process of rejuvenation. In the very next generation René Descartes devised a wholly new method for capturing the reflection

of the spirit of God in numbers and elegantly solving problems even more complicated than the cubic content of barrels.

The newly married and contented Kepler had ample opportunity during the next few years to study the question of all questions: whether Providence is concerned with the individual human being in great and small evils. For this time it was a great evil, no farce like his attempts at marriage, but a matter of life and death. And in so deadly earnest a matter this unworldly scholar showed another side of himself. His irresolution, his timid evasions vanished. He asked no one for advice, did not for a moment consider the influence of the stars. He attacked ruthlessly, abandoned his scientific studies for months at a time, threw his good reputation and his whole existence into the balance, and heroically fought a virtually hopeless battle against the baseness of the times.

For Kepler's mother was brought to trial on suspicion of witchcraft. That was nothing unusual; only recently six witches had been burned in the small Swabian town where she lived, and elsewhere even more. The charges were: a woman had fallen ill after having a glass of wine with her; the schoolmaster had come away with a lame leg after a talk with her, and a butcher with pains in the chest; a tailor's young twins had died because the old woman had rocked their cradle. Besides all this, she had bewitched cattle. Here was ample material for an interrogation.

Her son-in-law, a pastor, raised countercharges against her accusers. But meanwhile the aged woman was caught in an act of flagrant witchcraft: she had brushed by a young girl, and the girl's arm had become stiff for days. There followed a fresh interrogation; in her terror the old woman offered the magistrate a silver cup if he would leave her alone. Her son-in-law packed her off to Linz before the magistrate could obtain a warrant for her arrest.

Kepler plunged into a war of documents which consumed more paper than his calculation of the planetary tables. Then he personally conducted his mother back to Swabia for the trial. He collected a few honest witnesses and obtained a verdict of not guilty. But as soon as he had taken his departure, the magistrate

insisted on a reopening of the prosecution. Frau Kepler was arrested again, but her pastor son-in-law washed his hands of the affair. Kepler heard of this just as war—the Thirty Years' War —broke out, and Linz was being besieged. He arranged to ship his family to secure Regensburg and went to Swabia for the second time to defend his mother.

This time he had the opportunity to study the workings of divine providence for thirteen months. He had to battle with pastors who took him to task for his own heresies, with magistrates to whom one witch more or less merely meant another batch of documents, and with a superstitious rabble who lusted for the spectacle of a burning. He paid almost daily visits to his seventy-seven-year-old mother, kept in chains in the gate tower, guarded by a drunken jailer whose wages she herself had to pay. Kepler barely succeeded in saving her from torture, and at last won her a final acquittal, but she lived only half a year thereafter.

While all this was going on, Kepler was also preparing the planetary tables for the press, writing a book on comets, a huge commentary on the Copernican system, and his beloved and principal work, *De Harmonice Mundi*.

Reform of Astrology; Music of the Spheres

As has been mentioned earlier, traditional astrologers could get little comfort from Kepler. He spoke ill of them, sharply criticized their doctrines, and despised their whole craft as they traditionally practiced it. He manifested great reluctance to having anything at all to do with "the whore Astrology whom her honorable mother Astronomy must nourish." More and more he hated making calendars because everyone expected them to include forecasts. He did not want to provide more food for superstitions other than his own. In regard to the nova of 1572 he commented caustically: "If it meant nothing else, at any rate it notified the world of the existence of the great astronomer Tycho Brahe." When the Emperor wanted his opinion on another nova, he re-

jected all earlier interpretations, but did not voice his own fanciful idea, which was that there would be a general movement from
Europe to America; instead, he closed his exposition with such
vague remarks that the Emperor inquired: "Perhaps you do not
know yourself how to read this sign?" Kepler replied that he was
not employed as an astrologer and did not care to step from the
clean, solid ground of mathematical demonstrations into the dirty
puddles of speculation.

And yet he did believe in astrology, in his own reformed brand
of it, which had practically nothing in common with traditional
astrology. For Kepler discarded the basic concepts of the old
astrology, the twelve zones of influence, and the signs of the
zodiac.

What was left? Nothing more than the "constellation," the
position of the planets in the firmament at a given time. "Observe this: if today two planets stand at 89 degrees from one another, nothing new will happen in the air. But tomorrow, when
the full 90 degrees is reached, a thunderstorm will suddenly arise.
The effect, therefore, does not come from a single star, but from
the angle, from the harmonious segment of the circle."

Here was, truly, the most improbable sort of influence anyone
could imagine. Astrologers would consult the ephemerides to
reckon out the angles of the planets with pedantic care, but only
in order to estimate the mutual influence of their rays and the
influence of planetary radiation upon the houses; whereas Kepler
held that the angle quite by itself was of significance. This
sounded foolish. And yet he was able to offer sound reasons for
it. His only premise was that the rays of the planets exerted some
mysterious effect upon human beings. All the rest he left to the
geometrical principle, the reflection of God's spirit.

In the past he had tried to fit the five regular solids in between
the spheres of the planets. Now he pointed out that the regular
polygons which could be constructed within a circle yielded the
astrologically important planetary angles: conjunction, opposition, quadrature, sextile aspect, etc. Kepler demonstrated, moreover, that these angles were related to the total number of degrees
in a circle in the proportions of $1:2$, $2:3$, $3:4$, $4:5$, $5:6$, $3:5$, $5:8$.

And if he now straightened out his circle into a violin string, the astrological angles corresponded to the differing lengths of string which yielded harmonics.

Everyone feels the logic of the harmonic tones—proof that human beings are affected by the underlying geometrical proportions. Why should they not also be affected by the geometrical principles underlying the radiations of the planets?

Kepler could truly assert that he was free of superstition when he ascribed to the human soul "sympathy with the heavens." The soul, he argued, received at birth emanations of the planetary constellation because it bore within itself the underlying harmonies, because it reacted instinctively to geometrical proportions. Throughout its life it continued unconsciously to respond to this constellation. In rather grandiose metaphysical terms he put it thus: "The music God made during the Creation, He also taught Nature to play; indeed, she repeats what He played to her."

Here, indeed, was a unique justification for the ancient, ineradicable belief in the mystic link between man and the stars. But out of the whole of astrology Kepler left only the planets, only the radiations of the nearest heavenly bodies, whose influences united in musical harmonies.

This reformed astrology constituted only the ground floor of a larger structure, the "harmony of the world," which was nothing less than an attempt to show the Copernican system as a divine cosmos displaying perfect order. Kepler's scheme was a late-born child of the Greek spirit, which ever since Pythagoras had held it the highest goal of science to reveal harmony. It is curious that Kepler considered the fulfillment of this ancient dream his true lifework.

He had determined to justify mathematically all the peculiarities in the orbits of the planets. With infinite labor he figured out that their maximal and minimal velocities also corresponded to the musical harmonics, and that their mean velocities produced a scale. He even detected major and minor in the irregular movements, and was ultimately able to compose a highly involved polyphony of the solar system, a wonder of mathematical subtle-

ties—although he never succeeded in reproducing the observed motions of the planets. Compared to Kepler's system, the Pythagorean music of the spheres was like a lyre as against an orchestra.

He also discovered a reason for the small deviations of his cosmography from the actual distances of the planets. Evidently God's geometrical ideas had to be reconciled with the harmonies of velocity, and that was impossible without small discrepancies. But that both these divine tendencies were at work in the creation, Kepler was convinced. And this mystical astronomer proved it by demonstrating a mathematical relationship between the distances of the planets and their velocities.

PLANET	RELATIVE DISTANCE FROM SUN	PERIOD IN YEARS	SQUARE OF THE PERIOD	CUBE OF THE DISTANCE
Mercury	0.387	0.241	0.058	0.058
Venus	0.723	0.615	0.378	0.378
Earth	1	1	1	1
Mars	1.524	1.881	3.538	3.540
Jupiter	5.203	11.862	140.707	140.851
Saturn	9.539	29.458	867.774	867.977

No one else would have hit upon anything so strange: the cubes of the mean distances of any two planets from the Sun are to each other as the squares of their periodic times of revolution. Kepler had discovered this unexpected proportion by mere trial and error. The above table indicates how apt it was.

This was the famous third law of Kepler, from which Newton derived the law of universal gravitation. Thus one of the most solid and important pieces of astronomical knowledge sprang from rash and apparently crotchety mystical speculations, from the religious impulses of a man who stood between two eras.

"I have touched mountains. It is tremendous, what smoke they belch forth."

GALILEO THE PATHFINDER

Experiments

PROFESSOR OF MATHEMATICS Galileo Galilei of the University of Padua excited the envy of his colleagues because he lectured in the Auditorium Maximum. Besides his flock of ordinary students he had young noblemen from all over Europe sitting at his feet— among them the crown prince of Sweden, Gustavus Adolphus. From this master they learned bridge building, harbor planning, fortification, construction of artillery. He drew for them a fort of the future whose polygonal design permitted the entire terrain to be covered, a fort without perilous blind spots. Two generations later a Frenchman named Vauban won fame by employing the same system.

His colleagues resented Galilei; they said he behaved like a charlatan or a juggler; he possessed not a trace of academic dignity. And in fact his classes were somewhat like a magician's booth at a fair. He whistled to an organ pipe, and it answered him on the same note. "Resonance," Galileo called this. He had pistols fired on a mountain, and counted the seconds between the flash and the report. Thus his students learned that sound traveled at measurable speeds. He constructed calculating devices that enabled his students to spare themselves half the labor of arithmetic. Later, as architects and engineers, they saved material by hollow-pipe construction, the strength of which he had demonstrated to them by the example of animal bones.

For the students the most unusual aspect of his teaching was that they saw things with their own eyes, instead of merely hearing about them. The rest of their studies at the university were pure book learning, theorizing for or against Aristotle. Galileo made fun of this pedantry, of the belief that truth could be found by poring over old manuscripts. His method was to seek truth in nature.

Galileo's mind had been nurtured in a far more brilliant atmosphere than Kepler's, in the city that before 1600 was the heart of European culture: Florence. His father, who was one of the originators of opera, introduced him to the Medici Academy where all the higher interests of man were cultivated: literature, art, science, music, philosophy—a scintillating show in which the young man promptly displayed his own talents. He took part in the fashionable dispute over the merits of Tasso and Ariosto by producing an intensive comparison of their rhymes, images, and ideas. He also calculated precisely the dimensions of the various circles of Dante's inferno from Dante's own data.

His impulse to grasp reality clearly destined him for deeds as great as those of Copernicus. Copernicus had toppled Ptolemy from his throne; Galileo challenged Aristotle, the even mightier Greek. Nor did he confine himself to one particular; he attacked all Aristotelian science.

Among his other achievements, Galileo was the first to free the human mind from the prejudice inherent in the pairs of opposites, hot and cold, heavy and light. We now take it for granted that heat and cold are merely variations of the same phenomenon, their only real difference being degrees of heat. Galileo was the first to point out that we ought not to speak of heat and cold, but invent a new word for the amount of heat—"temperature." Everything would then have a specific temperature, just as everything has a specific age or size. If only there were some way of measuring temperature.

Here was presumption: how could something people feel be measured? Nature herself was supposed to be insensitive to cold or heat. But Galileo discovered that, on the contrary, Nature was

extremely sensitive to "temperature," that a drop of water in a tube would expand if he warmed the tube in his hand. He had invented the principle of the thermometer.

Far more important was his demonstration that "heavy and light" are only human prejudices. Aristotle had drawn a sharp distinction; according to him, heavy bodies had an impulse to go down, light bodies to go up. Air, for example, mounted. Galileo's idea that air had weight was a revolutionary revision of common sense and appearances. For he hit upon the mad idea of weighing the invisible gas of life which could not even be felt unless the wind blew.

His experiment was both simple and ingenious. He balanced a pig's bladder full of air against a vessel of water. Then he punctured the bladder, letting out the air. The scale of the balance sank—and the loss of weight was measurable. Air proved to be 1/800 as heavy as water.

This demonstration must have seemed like a revolution to his students. It marked the beginning of experimental physics.

Patient observation led Galileo to another remarkable insight. In the cathedral at Pisa a new chandelier was hung. It swayed back and forth on its long rope for a good while. As the swings shortened, Galileo was struck by the fact that they seemed to go neither slower nor faster. He began to count, counted until the chandelier at last came to a standstill—and discovered something that neither Aristotle nor Archimedes had known: a pendulum swings with complete regularity, no matter how wide its swing. It was the finest imaginable clock. A pity that its oscillation stopped so soon.

All his life Galileo took steps to prevent this cessation of motion, but he did not succeed. For all that he was so unique an experimenter, he was too impatient to work out subtle mechanical devices. Consequently, the glory of making the first precise chronometer went to someone else. Nevertheless, he recommended to his medical colleagues that they count the pulse of their patients by the oscillations of a pendulum.

While making all sorts of experiments with pendulums, he came across the one of his discoveries which proved to be fraught

with the deepest consequences. A ball of lead and a ball of cork of the same size, hung on threads of equal length, swayed at the same speed. This was strange, for after all the oscillation of a pendulum was a type of falling, and heavy bodies ought to fall faster than light bodies. Galileo began to suspect that this obvious fact might not be true. His doubts led him to the famous climb up the Leaning Tower, from which he dropped balls of all sorts. They struck on the pavement below almost simultaneously. A musket bullet arrived at the same time as a heavy cannon ball, or almost at the same time, although according to Aristotle the ball should have struck the ground while the bullet was hovering near the balustrade.

Galileo quickly perceived the reason for the small deviation from simultaneity: the resistance of the air. Once again he proved his point by clever experiments: he dropped bodies of different weights into water. The rate of fall differed greatly here, for the water offered far more resistance to them than the air. From these experiments he drew the conclusion that in a vacuum a feather would drop as quickly as lead. For the time being this statement had to stand without proof, for it was "well known" that Nature had a *horror vacui,* that she would not tolerate emptiness. It remained for his pupil Torricelli to dispose of this Aristotelian prejudice.

Galileo's technique must have seemed to his contemporaries a form of witchcraft. He used ingenious trickery to prove facts that at the time were undemonstrable: setting up a series of experiments whose results all pointed in the same direction, and indicating what the final step in the series would be. He could not actually carry out the final step, but he approached closely enough to it so that everyone who followed his line of argument had to join him on the road into the unknown.

In this same ingenious manner he conceived of the law of gravity, by setting up his famous experiment with an inclined plane. The movement of a rolling ball along an inclined plane obeyed the same law as an object freely falling, he argued boldly; free fall was merely the limiting case of a fall along his inclined plane. Thus, by simple means, but by the exercise of a great deal

of preliminary reasoning, he established the first principles of
dynamics. The man who was the first of all systematic experi-
menters was also the most ingenious of physicists.

Most of his results appeared paradoxical. They were in
thorough opposition to common sense. Aristotle had summed up
in a host of dogmatic statements the conclusions the ordinary
person would arrive at out of his everyday experience: that some
things are hot, some cold, some light, some heavy; that heavy
weights fall faster than light weights. And as it turned out, all
these common-sense ideas were wrong; there are only degrees of
heat; all things are "heavy"; all things fall with constant acceleration. Galileo proved these novel and surprising facts because he
asked questions instead of pronouncing dogmas.

Appearances are deceptive in both astronomy and physics.
Human beings are not naturally equipped to guess the secrets of
nature. It is certainly as humiliating to recognize this as to realize
that man's abode is not the center of the universe. The conclusion
that the laws of nature are not obvious, cannot be fathomed by
mere reasoning, was at least as fraught with consequences as the
Copernican revolution. Once it was accepted, the old way of
philosophizing was discredited. Once it was accepted, Western
man began his investigation and conquest of nature.

The Sky in the Telescope

The rumors sounded like a fable: a Dutch spectacle-maker was
said to have invented a pipe through which he could see the
sailors clambering up the masts on a sailing vessel far out at sea.
A spectacle-maker? Spectacles magnify or reduce objects, according to the way they are ground. Why should they not magnify
distant objects also? Undoubtedly, the secret of this magic pipe
must be a matter of lenses. A pipe has two ends; therefore the
Dutch spectacle-maker must have combined two lenses.

Within a short time Galileo had reproduced the invention. A
convex lens at the front of the pipe, a concave lens at the back—

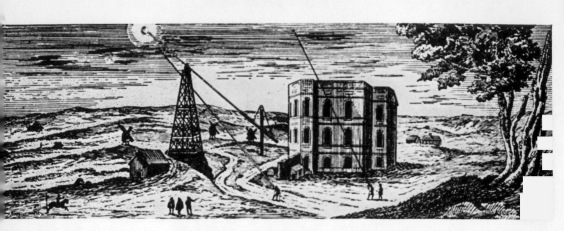

Paris Observatory at the time of Louis XIV. Lens tower of aerial telescope at left center.

Greenwich Observatory around 1680. The observer at right is using a telescope mounted on a sawhorse and ladder. At left, a quadrant.

PLATE I

Olaus Roemer at his meridian circle, 1689. Roemer was the first to measure the speed of light.

PLATE II

PLATE III

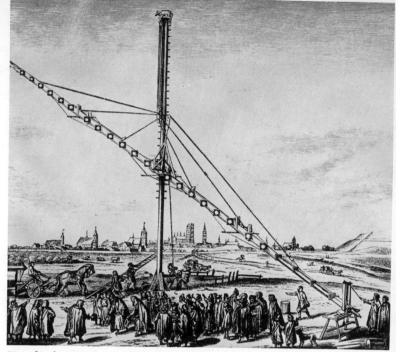

Hevelius's 130-foot telescope, Danzig, 1650. From an engraving in Hevelius's *Machina Coelestis*.

Herschel's 40-foot reflecting telescope, 1789. The mirror of this instrument was 48 inches in diameter.

The 36-inch refracting telescope at Lick Observatory, Cali-

One of Lassell's reflecting telescopes, 1865. He discovered the

PLATE IV

The 100-inch Hooker reflecting telescope at Mount Wilson. Installed in 1917, this instrument opened up the new universe of extragalactic nebulae.

PLATE V

The 48-inch Schmidt telescope at Mount Palomar. A hybrid of reflecting and refracting telescope, the Schmidt combines the advantages of both.

PLATE VI

The 200-inch Hale telescope at Mount Palomar, showing observer in prime-focus cage and reflecting surface of the mirror in background.

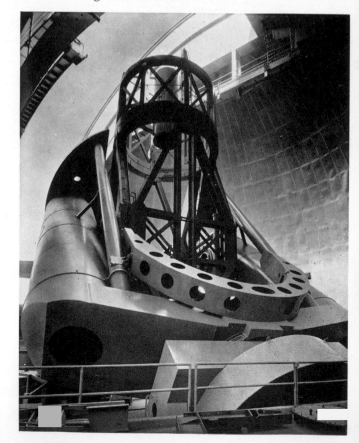

The Hale telescope pointing to zenith.

PLATE VII

The new radio telescope at Jodrell Bank, England, completed in 1957. Radio waves from space are reflected from the concave surface and focused on the aerial in the bowl's center. The bowl is 250 feet in diameter and weighs 750 tons, but a precision mechanism

PLATE VIII

PLATE IX

Zodiacal light, photographed above the Yerkes Observatory dome. The streaks are star trails caused by the motion of the Earth during the exposure.

The great aurora of August 19–20, 1950, photographed by a camera that takes a 140-degree picture of the sky.

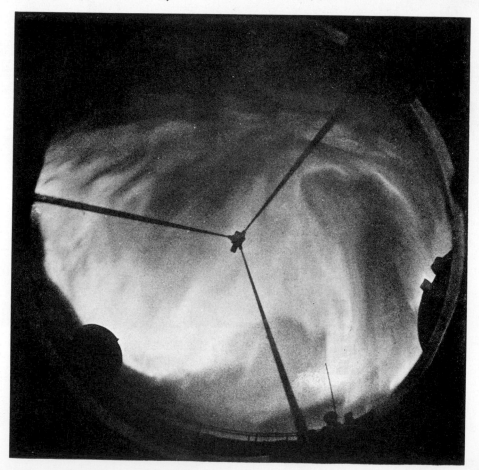

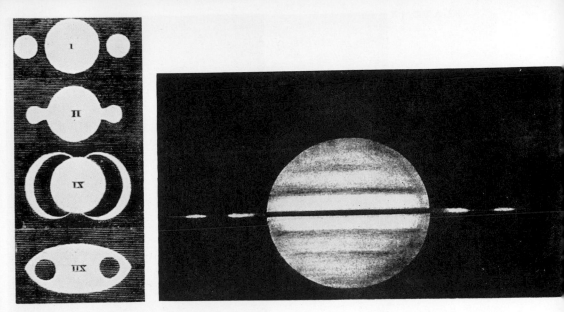

How Galileo and his seventeenth-century contemporaries visualized Saturn (LEFT). At RIGHT, an edge-on view of Saturn, from a drawing by Barnard.

Saturn and its ring system; 100-inch photograph. The rings are composed of many small bodies in rapid motion.

PLATE X

Jupiter and one of its satellites (white spot at right); 200-inch photograph. The black dot on the planet is the shadow of the satellite.

Head of Halley's comet, May 8, 1910; 60-inch photograph.

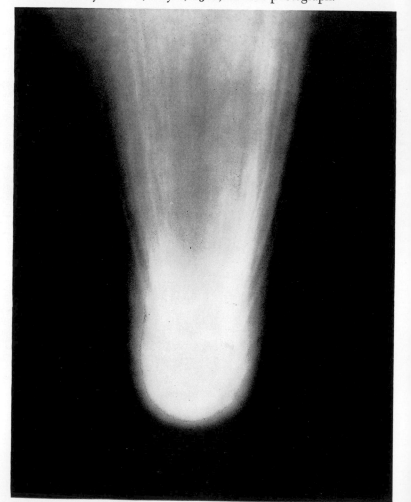

PLATE XI

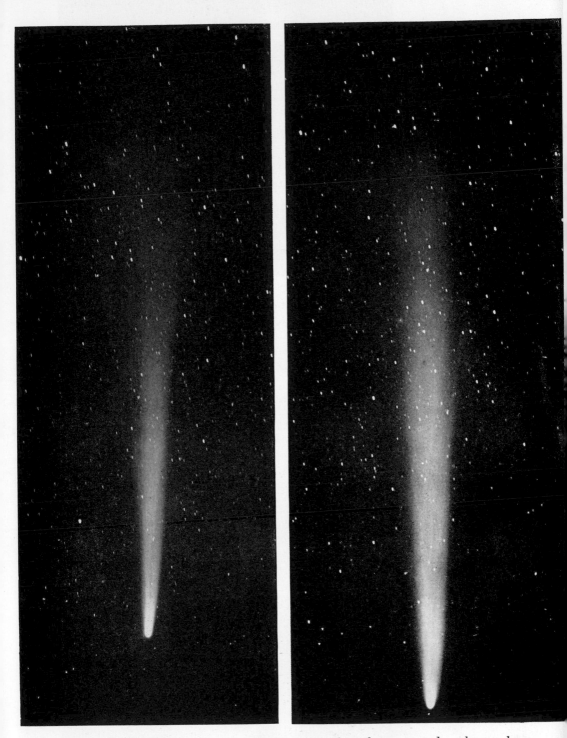

Halley's comet on May 12 (LEFT) and 15, 1910. The tails are 30 and 40 degrees long. Photographed from Honolulu with a ten-inch lens.

PLATE XII

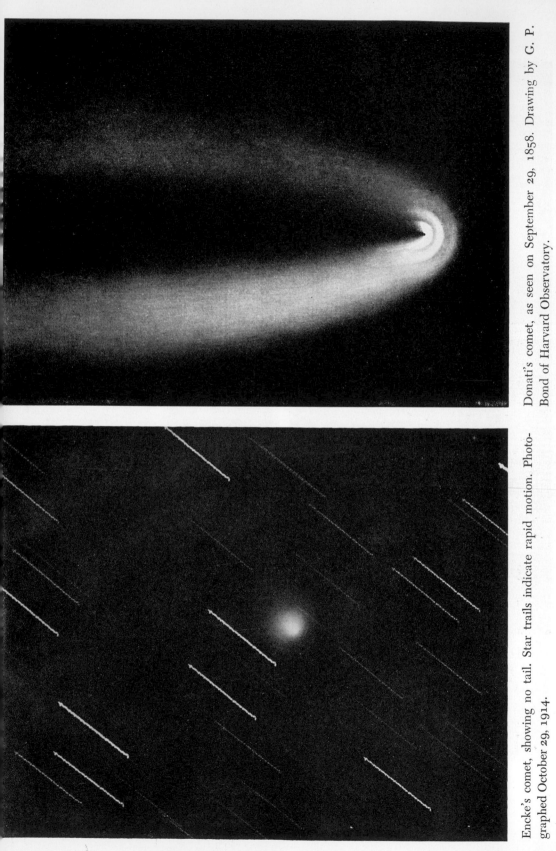

Donati's comet, as seen on September 29, 1858. Drawing by G. P. Bond of Harvard Observatory.

Encke's comet, showing no tail. Star trails indicate rapid motion. Photographed October 29, 1914.

PLATE XIII

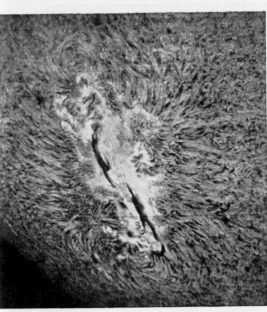

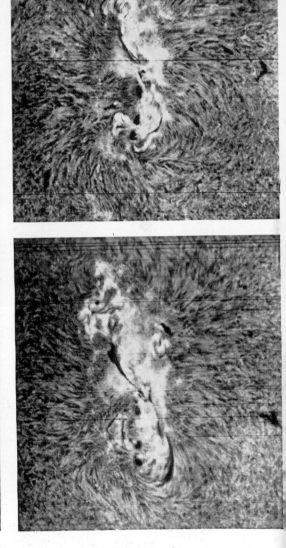

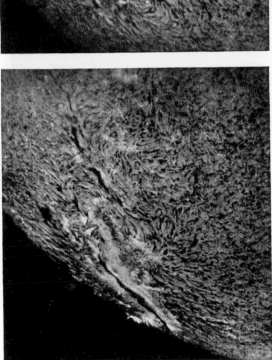

Hydrogen spectroheliograms (made by monochromatic light) of the Sun, taken on August 3, 5, 7, and 9, 1915. Photos show association of hydrogen clouds with sunspot groups. Sequence indicates Sun's rotation.

PLATE XIV

PLATE XV

Solar corona photographed at the total eclipse of June 8, 1918, at Green River, Wyoming.

A large, active solar protuberance, 140,000 miles high.

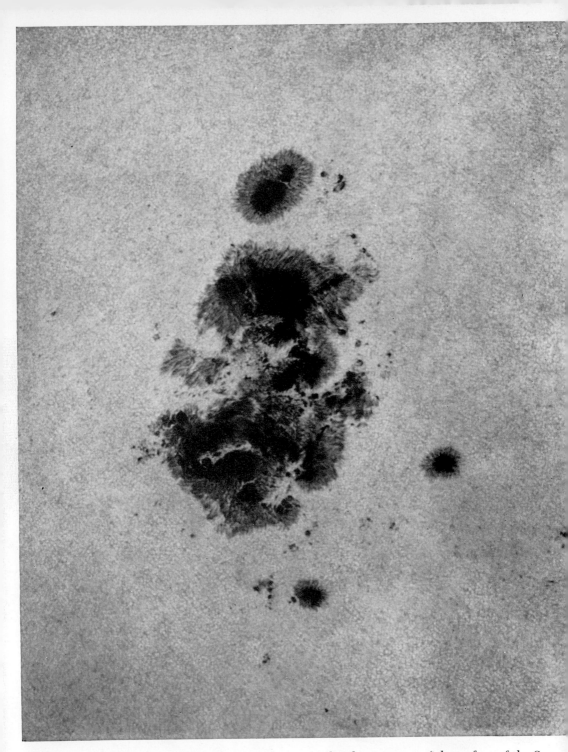

The large sunspot group of May 17, 1951. Note granulated appearance of the surface of the Sun.

PLATE XVI

and when he directed his pipe at the nearest church tower, it seemed close enough for him to touch it. Galileo experimented with lenses of different powers, made his tubes longer and longer. At a magnification of thirty he stopped because everything quivered and flickered and the church tower kept jumping out of his field of vision. Then he fastened his tube to a column and pointed it at the Moon.

At first glance he saw that the Moon was not the smooth sphere the philosophers held it to be. He saw mountains and valleys, great dark areas that looked like seas, and round, walled craters; he saw shadows cast by the Sun, and lofty peaks brightly lit while their bases were still wrapped in shadows. From the length of the shadows he was able to calculate that the mountains on the Moon compared in height with those of the Earth.

Galileo was thus the first man to see a heavenly body as it really was. Why had the Hollander, who had had his telescope for a full year before Galileo, never directed it at the Moon? The urge to get to the bottom of everything, which characterizes most of the human race nowadays, at that time burned in only a few individuals. Galileo's colleagues, for example, refused to look through his godless magic tube. They mustered sufficient logic to refute his tale of what he had seen on the Moon, even as the University of Salamanca had refuted Columbus's dream of a voyage to the West Indies.

The stars, Galileo discovered, were not enlarged by his instrument, but innumerable new ones became visible. Instead of six Pleiades he counted fifty. The Milky Way appeared as myriad tiny dots. "I know now what the silver girdle around the celestial sphere is; I am filled with amazement and offer unending thanks to God that it has pleased Him to reveal through me such great wonders, unknown to all the centuries before our time."

All the planets appeared as small round discs. But the greatest wonder of all was the discovery of four new moons. Close to Jupiter Galileo saw three bright little stars, two to the left and one to the right of the planet, and in a relatively straight line. The next week he could scarcely believe his eyes; all three had gathered together on the right side of the planet. Two nights

later there were only two in evidence, both on the left. The third could only have been hidden by the shadow of Jupiter, for that same night it suddenly reappeared. In other words, these tiny stars were racing around Jupiter at an extraordinary speed. Soon he discovered a fourth satellite farther away from the planet. Jupiter represented a solar system in small.

THE FIRST FOUR SATELLITES OF JUPITER WERE DISCOVERED BY GALILEO ON JANUARY 8, 15, 17, AND 20, 1610, IN THESE CHANGING POSITIONS. IN THE FIRST THREE DIAGRAMS, ONE OR MORE ARE ECLIPSED.

One day he noticed that a small piece seemed to be missing from the disc of Venus. After a few months, Venus appeared as a crescent—in other words, it had the same phases as the Moon. Planets therefore were dark spheres illuminated by the Sun on one side; we alternately see them fullface, in profile, and from the back, so to speak. Planets had day and night like our Earth.

The greatest surprise was provided by Saturn. It was a disc like the others, but one day handles appeared on either side; these increased in size until they looked like two giant ears. After three months they receded, finally vanishing again. Galileo was completely baffled; he lamented that his mind was too weak to

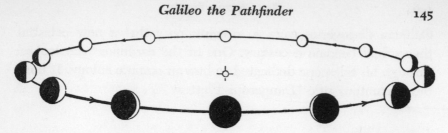

PHASES OF VENUS, DISCOVERED BY GALILEO. VENUS APPEARS AS A CRESCENT AS IT APPROACHES AND RECEDES FROM THE EARTH DURING ITS CIRCUIT OF THE SUN.

comprehend the phenomenon. Actually, his telescope was too weak; a better telescope would have showed the ears as rings. But even Galileo's successors were a long time recognizing this. (See Plate XA.)

When he looked at the Sun through his glass, he was blinded for a week, and his eyesight remained permanently affected. The result was that someone else discovered that the Sun's complexion was not all it should be. The Jesuit Christoph Scheiner first chose cloudy days for observing the Sun; then he made lenses of dark bottle-glass, and finally conceived the simple notion of holding a sooted sheet of glass between his telescope and the Sun. But Galileo again had a superior idea; he darkened the room, placed his telescope at an opening in the window shutter, and caught the image of the Sun on a sheet of paper: the first projection apparatus. He was then able to follow the path of the sunspots with a pencil. In the course of a few days these moved across the disc of the Sun, vanished around its left edge, and reappeared on the right. Plainly, the Sun was rotating on an axis just like the Earth.

All these discoveries were made within a few years. Never again was an astronomer in a position to announce so many new facts as was Galileo in the little book to which he gave the title *Herald of the Stars with Great, Wonderful Novelties, unto This Day Unknown to Mankind*. It made his name as famous as that of Columbus. The Grand Duke of Florence appointed him to the Academy, with an annual salary of a thousand florins. The Pope invited him to Rome; the University of Rome gave a banquet for him; and the astronomer of the Jesuit College announced that the

Galilean discoveries were so revolutionary that a new celestial theory had become necessary. One of the cardinals who looked through his telescope dedicated to him an ecstatic eulogy. It bore the portentous title "Dangerous Flattery."

"But It Does Move"

At the Florentine Academy Galileo lectured to scholars, clerics, and princes on the basic meaning of all his discoveries: that they provided splendid substantiations of the Copernican doctrine. The Moon was a globe like the Earth, with seas and mountains; the planets were globes like the Earth, having day and night; Jupiter was a solar system in small—how could it still be doubted that the Earth circled about the Sun like one of the planets?

When someone cited Aristotle in objection, he replied sharply that human authority proved nothing in science, and that Nature mocked at dogmas. Aristotle, he pointed out, was a man with eyes and ears whereas he, Galileo, was a man with eyes, ears, and a telescope. Because he could not see very far, Aristotle had thought the Earth the center of the universe—whereas the telescope showed everyone that the Earth moved around the Sun.

Galileo's own authority was so great that the cavilers were silenced. But one day the Grand Duchess sent for him. She was uneasy because her confessor had told her that the teachings of Copernicus were contrary to the Bible. The scientist was prepared for this charge. In substance he replied:

"The statement that Joshua made the Sun stand still, and not the Earth, must not be taken as a revelation concerning Nature. The Bible contains no astronomy, not even the names of the planets. Of course Holy Writ cannot err, but some interpreters of it can. For example, it would be blasphemy to take literally the passages concerning God's wrath, hatred, and repentance; this everyone admits. Similarly, those Scriptural passages that do not agree with the findings of science are not to be taken literally. For the laws of nature operate with absolute inevitability, and these laws are the creation of God."

The great lady was convinced, and so was her confessor. But soon afterwards a monk began ranting from the pulpit against Galileo's heresies. The Dominican Order took an interest in the matter and brought it to the attention of the Roman Inquisition. Indignant, Galileo invoked the Grand Duke's aid. Out of pure malice toward himself, Galileo protested, the attempt was now being made to proclaim Copernicus a heretic. Copernicus's book had been tolerated for sixty years; this belated effort to ban it could only spring from enmity toward Galileo himself.

The Grand Duke advised him to go to Rome in person and enlist his many friends there in his cause. Galileo, by now fifty, threw himself energetically into the struggle. He called upon abbots, bishops, and cardinals, disputed in a different place every evening with brilliance and wit, and was rewarded with nothing more than well-intentioned warnings to think what he liked, but to give up trying to convert others, for such conduct could only bring him grief. To these recommendations he replied that the honor of the Church was at stake; for that reason he could not consider his own ease. And he demanded that his proofs of the doctrine that the Earth moved be examined before Copernicus was placed on the Index.

The Pope requested the Jesuit College to send him an advisory memorandum. The result was negative; the Jesuits decided that Galileo's discoveries had not proved the Copernican theory. Therefore, Copernicus's book was temporarily banned until it could be amended by the statement that what was therein was only an unproved hypothesis. The Inquisition commissioned Cardinal Bellarmine to break the news gently to Galileo that henceforth he must not defend the theory of the moving Earth, either in writing or orally. The bitter pill was sweetened by the comment that he had made the best of impressions upon the Holy Office, and that the Pope personally would shield him against further attacks.

But Galileo had not been concerned about his own comfort. He had acted out of his pride as an Italian and a Catholic. The truth that had been discovered by a Catholic canon must not triumph only in Germany and through the efforts of Protestant sci-

entists like Kepler. On the contrary, it must be proclaimed to the world by Italian science, and for the good of the Church, even though all the Church resisted. The world must learn that Rome still cherished the accomplishments of the mind, and could still lay claim to being the heart and brain of Christendom.

This was why Galileo could not accept his defeat. If he did indeed utter that famous cry, "But it does move!" it must have been after he had been strictly forbidden to speak out. Galileo had not the slightest intention of submitting forever. He was merely waiting for the opportunity to violate the armistice that had been imposed upon him. But the opportunity did not come for nearly ten years—years of suffering for a man of his impetuous temperament. By nature this great scientist and scholar was bellicose, passionate, spiteful, ruthlessly determined, and unscrupulous in his choice of methods. His former colleagues had trembled before his cruel tongue; at one time he had been ordered by a court to hold his peace. Now that he was truly silenced, he fretted in his cage, could not go on with his observations and experiments, could think of nothing but the outlawed truth of the Earth's motion. In several of his polemics written during those years the tremendous tension can be felt; it was discharged in outbursts that were argumentatively overwhelming, linguistically charming, and factually incorrect. These writings won him enemies, but also an audience for his next book, one of the most influential books ever written by a scientist.

He was sixty years old when a new Pope was elected, Urban VIII, who as Cardinal Barberini had dedicated to him the eulogy entitled "Dangerous Flattery." Here was Galileo's chance. He went to Rome. Six times he was received in audience —six audiences, each lasting more than an hour. No ambassador to the Holy See could boast of such a privilege.

Galileo demanded recognition of the Copernican system. Within a short time, he argued, it would be accepted in all the Protestant countries, and then Catholic science would be despised and the Church decried as anti-intellectual.

The Pope pointed out to him that the Copernican doctrine had

not been declared heretical, that he and the Church did not consider it heretical, but only too bold and beyond proof. Galileo promptly produced his newest proof: the phenomenon of the tides. Just as water in a bowl slaps back and forth when the bowl is shaken, so the seas rise and fall because the Earth is moving, he declared.

This argument did not impress the Pope as conclusive—and certainly he was right not to accept it. Galileo himself should have realized that the motion of the Earth alone could not produce the tides, that an external force was needed. He should have seen that the only proof of the Earth's motion existing at the time was the Copernican explanation of the planetary loops. But he hardly raised this issue; he seems to have felt that the average person was not able to think through such a phenomenon and would prefer to be convinced by half-truths, figures of speech and images, rather than by strict reasoning.

Urban VIII was no ordinary person. In the sixth audience he closed the fruitless conference with the statement: "You will admit, beloved son, that the Almighty could also command the seas to sway back and forth without any motion of the sea-bottom, even though the human intellect might not comprehend this."

The aging scientist bowed, kissed the Holy Father's shoe, and returned home.

Still he did not give up. For five years he worked stubbornly away at his *Dialogue on the Two Chief Systems of the World*. He hoped to be able to force the Church to ally herself with science, in spite of her reluctance. Smitten by his arguments, she would have to admit that the Earth moved. He thought he would make it easy for the Church; in his foreword he would declare Copernicus's doctrine an unproved hypothesis, as required by the Church; and he would close by paraphrasing the sentence with which Urban had dismissed him.

The result was the first book of popular science written by the foremost scientist of the age in the form of a lively, dramatic dialogue; it was stimulating throughout, full of excitement, irresistibly leading the layman to join in the processes of thinking,

discovering, and understanding what the genius had thought, discovered, and understood. So vividly did Galileo describe his experiments that his readers could not help but take them on faith.

For example, he answered the eternal objection that the motion of the Earth must influence the movement of the clouds, the flight of birds, the direction of cannon shots, and the falling of stones, with the following example: "I invite you to enter with me the cabin of a large ship. In it are gnats, ball players, and a bowl of goldfish into which drops of water are falling from above. Whether the ship lies at anchor or moves uniformly through the water, the gnats will fly with the same ease from wall to wall; the balls will be hit with the same force in all directions; the fish will swim undisturbed; the drops fall vertically upon the same spot. No one can guess, by observing these processes, whether the vessel is at rest or moving—no more than we can say this about the Earth."

Here was the notion of relativity formulated in embryo. With this book, moreover, Galileo made himself an Italian classic, for he was the first scientist of his time to abandon Latin and write in his mother tongue, of which he had a sovereign command. In his youth he had written poems and comedies, corrected Tasso, improvised songs and composed accompaniments to them on the lute. And by virtue of his poetic fervor, he succeeded in the task at which Kepler had failed: bringing about the triumph of the Copernican theory. The next generation grew up with Galileo's version of the new cosmology. It learned to laugh at objections before these had been finally refuted. It no longer asked for perfect proofs because it was intoxicated by Galileo's masterpiece; and when the proofs were subsequently provided, no one was interested any longer.

The old wizard accomplished this transformation in men's minds with arguments that were often dubious, that were plausible rather than convincing. Yet he brought about the true dawn of modern times because he incidentally implanted a new mode of thinking, a trust in experimentation rather than authority. Galileo's *Dialogue* nurtured the spirit of modern science.

Inquisition

To be printed, his book required papal approval. Urban's secretary thought the dialogue a brilliant piece of work, and obtained the imprimatur of the Master of the Palace on condition
that the bishop of Florence supervise the printing and check carefully to be sure that the motion of the Earth was consistently represented as a mere hypothesis.

After the book was published, it received general approbation.
The Jesuits at the University of Rome found much good in it.
The astronomer of Perugia announced that he had become converted to the Copernican theory. Galileo's friends were wild with
enthusiasm. Then, suddenly, the remainder of the edition was
confiscated and an investigation ordered. The Pope spoke angrily
to the Florentine ambassador about Galileo's behavior, saying
that between Galileo, his Master of the Palace, and his secretary,
he had been tricked. However, he was entrusting the investigation to a special commission, not to the dread Holy Office.

Galileo and his Florentine friends breathed easier. But the
special commission decided that the book in fact advocated the
theory of the Earth's motion. Galileo had directly violated Cardinal Bellarmine's order not to defend this theory.

This order had been issued so long ago that it had been completely forgotten. Now that it was brought up, the Master of the
Palace and the Pope's secretary no longer had any defense. The
Master of the Palace was fortunate, and was only suspended from
his office, but the secretary was sent into exile. With these sup-
porters of Galileo out of the way, the Pope ordered an Inquisition
trial. In vain Galileo, now in his seventies, pleaded the weakness
of age. Testimonials from doctors did not help him; he had to
face the tribunal. In the Palace of the Inquisition he was treated
with great courtesy, assigned a splendid suite of rooms, and permitted to keep his own servant. But he was nonetheless interro-
gated rigorously. The Inquisition appeared to be solely interested
in his conversation with Cardinal Bellarmine seventeen years before. What had been the course of that conversation? *

* The following dialogue is condensed and summarized from the records of
Galileo's trial.

thought then and thought now that the Ptolemaic theory was indisputable.

Yet he had maintained a different opinion in his book, his inquisitors pointed out.

Once again he vowed that his book merely showed that no convincing proofs existed for either theory, and that the decision therefore had to be left to a higher authority. Although threatened with torture, he stubbornly repeated this equivocation.

Since nothing more could be had from him, he was dismissed. The following day he heard the verdict. It was an enormous relief to him. The judges ordained that he had placed himself strongly under suspicion of heresy, and was therefore subject to all the penalties for that crime. Nevertheless he might recant, in which case the gravest penalties would not be imposed. His book would remain under ban, however, and he himself sentenced to lifelong incarceration in the prison of the Inquisition, with the reservation that this last might be modified or waived.

On his knees, Bible in hand, he read out the formula: "I adjure, condemn, and abhor my errors and heresies. I swear henceforth never to maintain any similar doctrines, either by word or in writing. If I encounter any heretic, I will denounce him to the Holy Office. So help me God."

Thus the famous Inquisition trial turned out tragically not for Galileo, but for the Church and for science. A great scientist had given twenty-five years of his life to the goal of uniting the two. He failed. At its very beginnings science was condemned by the clergy, and the unnecessary, senseless rift persisted too long.

The entire decision hung by a thread. With a little luck, Galileo could have brought forward a visible, irrefutable proof—if only he had observed, while watching the suspended chandelier in the cathedral at Pisa, not only the equal oscillations, but the alternating direction of the oscillations. For in the course of a day a long pendulum moves in a circle because the Earth turns under it. But it was not until the middle of the nineteenth century that Foucault demonstrated this by suspending a pendulum from the dome of the Panthéon in Paris.

The Inquisition undoubtedly proceeded with extraordinary leniency in Galileo's case. But if the Church was spared the crime of burning another genius after Giordano Bruno, this was due only to Galileo's steadfast refusal to admit the truth. He did not make himself a martyr to science, did not cry out: *"Eppur si muove!"* And we can only consider it a blessing that he did not. His life was too precious to be sacrificed to any gallant act of heroism.

It was only after his terrible experience, after his abjuration of the truth, that the old man fulfilled his mission—perhaps the most glorious mission ever imposed upon a scientist.

Wordless Thoughts

Galileo was not sent to prison, but placed under a form of house-arrest in his own country house near Florence, not far from the convent in which his two daughters lived. He was allowed to receive visitors. Descartes and Milton, among many others, made pilgrimages to see him. Two pupils took down his dictation. He lived for another eight years, during the last of which his sight failed him. But his mind rose to heights where he no longer needed his eyes.

The Church had, in fact, done a great service for science by forbidding Galileo to continue his campaign for Copernicus. Now he turned back to his proper profession. From the paradoxical results of his earlier experiments he developed the *nuova scienza* upon which all of physics is based, the new science of dynamics.

Dynamics is the theory of motion. For Western man, motion is the source and the beginning of all things; his character demands a dynamic rather than a static point of view. Galileo showed how motion could be dealt with mathematically. He developed a hitherto unknown type of thinking, free from the ambiguities of language, a thinking in formulas rather than words. Today all physicists, engineers, and astronomers employ that basic

approach to any complex task. As soon as a question is asked, they formulate it as an equation; from then on, all reasoning continues in the abstract realm of mathematics. The details of calculation are often left to machines; the most difficult computations are nowadays performed by computers. But the computer does not do the most important work: the setting up of the equation, the translation of the problem from words to formulas.

This art was invented by Galileo while he was studying the processes of falling. He did not arrive at his concept of gravity by his experiments; the experiments came later. He reasoned it out, taking detours about which we know no more than that they led him astray for many years. But his ultimate line of reasoning became the model for all future reasoning in physics, technology, and astronomy, the model of what we nowadays call "theory," and which also might be called the specifically Occidental manner of reasoning.

There was, above all, the graph. Everywhere nowadays we find Galilean curves representing some development—the increase in production, the rise in prices, the gain in population, and so on. Time is taken as the abscissa (base line), and no one today considers this strange. Yet what boldness, what an inhuman feeling for abstraction is required to draw a geometric figure containing time! Galileo was the first to represent movement in falling by graphical means. Here, too, was unparalleled boldness; he did not draw a picture of the path of a falling stone, but merely an ascending line which symbolically depicted the increase in velocity.

From the figure he derived formulas; from them, purely mathematically, without "thinking" of anything concrete, he developed a brand-new concept basic to physics and astronomy: that of acceleration. Galileo defined it without words more exactly than language can ever define it. When the concept was expressed as a formula one saw at a glance the connection of acceleration with time and distance; the falling stone could be held fast at any desired moment; its movement could be defined throughout its course.

"The book of nature is written in the language of mathematics,"

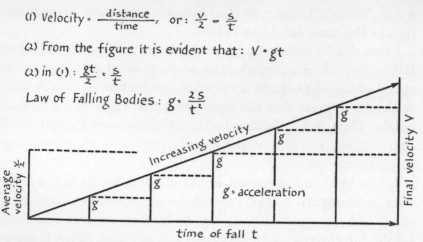

(1) Velocity = $\dfrac{distance}{time}$, or: $\dfrac{V}{2} = \dfrac{s}{t}$

(2) From the figure it is evident that: $V = gt$

(2) in (1): $\dfrac{gt}{2} = \dfrac{s}{t}$

Law of Falling Bodies: $g = \dfrac{2s}{t^2}$

Increasing velocity

Average velocity $\frac{V}{2}$

Final velocity V

$g =$ acceleration

time of fall t

HOW GALILEO DISCOVERED THE LAW OF FALLING BODIES BY GRAPHIC REPRESENTATION.

Galileo proclaimed jubilantly. And yet he realized quite clearly that mathematics had not played too important a part in his own work. He even, at times, spoke contemptuously of it: "I have devoted fewer months to mathematics than years to philosophy." His achievement seemed to him a philosophical one, and he was right; but his was a new style of philosophy, infinitely superior to all the older types of thinking in bondage to the tyranny of words.

Galileo developed the concept of acceleration into a theory of motion. From his law of acceleration of a falling body he derived the new science of dynamics like a magician pulling streamers out of an egg.

He recognized the motion of the pendulum as a type of falling in a necessarily curved track. The falling movement of the pendulum had, moreover, the special quality that the falling body used the energy of its motion to climb to the same height on the other side. And unless slowed down by an external force, Galileo said to himself, it must always be the same height, no matter how steep he made the climb by shortening the arc. He performed this experiment very simply by catching the oscillating string with

a nail; the arc became shorter, but the pendulum nevertheless rose to the same height as before.

From this he deduced a general rule for all types of fall—free fall, or the fall of a pendulum on a string, or of a ball on an inclined plane: the velocity attained at the bottom of the descent is always so great that the body must rise again to its original height. Then, in his brilliant fashion, Galileo went a single small step further, and this step suddenly produced an astonishing, revolutionary paradox.

It was only an experiment in the mind. After its fall, a body rises to its original height. Let it do so on an inclined path. Next time, make the path flatter; the body then rises to the same height, but traverses a longer distance in so doing. What happens if the path is made horizontal? The body will continue to move on horizontally until it has reached its original height. But since it will never attain this height, it must go on forever.

Could there be any deduction more paradoxical and at the

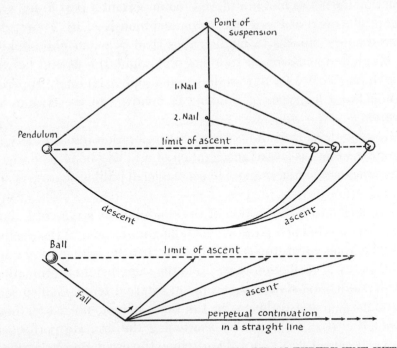

GALILEO ARRIVED AT THE LAW OF INERTIA BY AN EXPERIMENT WITH A PENDULUM.

same time more compelling? No one could gainsay the logic of it. Reasoning a known fact out to its limiting case results in a consequence that appears to be contrary to reason: endless movement produced by a single impulse, without an addition of force after that single impulse.

Thus Galileo arrived at his famous law of inertia: a body does not only remain at rest when no force affects it; if it happens to be in motion, it continues to move. Movement is a primal condition, a quality which need be given things only once in order to remain with them forever.

Aristotle could never have accepted such an idea. For us, however, it is an inescapable part of our thinking, a consequence of our inborn concept of force, which Galileo brought out of our unconscious minds into consciousness when he investigated the laws of motion. Why do stones fall faster and faster? Not because they have a mysterious urge to plunge downward, but because the Earth attracts them, Galileo said. The unchanging attraction of the Earth continually applies fresh force to the stone, constantly increases its velocity. In short, force produces accelerated movement. Therefore force can be measured by acceleration; the formula for acceleration contains the formula for force.

Motion itself, however, uniform, unaccelerated motion, no more needs force than does a state of rest. This insight marks the beginning of the dynamic concept of nature. The old man who presented it to the modern world also recognized the motion of projectiles as a type of falling in which two forces operate simultaneously: the Earth attracts the projectile, while the first impulse given to it has the tendency to send it forever ahead in a straight line. To the horizontal uniform velocity is added a component of vertical acceleration which results in a curved path, the parabola of a projectile.

This analysis also provided an explanation of celestial motion. A planet had once received an impulse that sent it straight ahead into the universe at eternally uniform velocity. But the Sun attracted it as the Earth does a projectile; it fell toward the Sun, but did not reach it because both motions added together formed a curved path, Kepler's elliptical path. What Kepler had longed

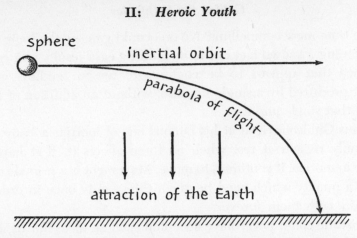

GALILEO ANALYZED THE MOTION OF PROJECTILES AND THEREBY UN-
WITTINGLY FORESHADOWED THE GRAVITATIONAL LAWS GOVERNING
THE ORBITS OF THE PLANETS.

for, an explanation of the planetary orbits, was provided by Galileo's physical dynamics. An initial impulse and then the constant
attraction of the Sun were the motive forces of the Copernican
system.

But the great Italian was not destined to arrive at this insight
as a crown to his work. The task of uniting the accomplishments
of these two men of genius, and so creating dynamic astronomy,
was reserved for another. And Isaac Newton first saw the light
of the world in the very year that the prisoner of the Inquisition
closed his blind eyes forever.

Book Three

THE MATURING
COSMOLOGY

THE SUN KING'S REPUBLIC
OF SCHOLARS

An Observatory Fire in Danzig

MOST ILLUSTRIOUS *and mightiest King, most beneficent Lord: Your high Favour and incomparable Mercy have ever spurred me to scatter with diligence the Seeds of my Gratitude and to sow them in the Bosom of Urania, so that I have set in the Heavens nigh to seven hundred Stars which were not there aforetimes, and have named some of these after Your Majesty, as may be seen upon Page 616 of my* Machina Coelestis, *altho not all be as yet listed there. In the Work which is to follow the Aforesaid their Positions will be published with Exactness.*

But alas, will this Fruit of the Labours of mine Age ever see the Light of Day? For no man knoweth what the Dark of Even bringeth. Woe and alas, how multitudinous the Misfortunes that embroil the Life of Man. All my worldly Goods and Hopes have been overturned in the Space of scarce an Hour.

Rumour of the dread Conflagration which hath destroyed my astronomical Tower hath no doubt already sped upon rapid Feet to Paris. Now I come myself hasting to Your Majesty as Herald of this great Woe, clad in Sackcloth and Ashes, deep distressed by this Visitation from Him Who judgeth all Things.

On that unhappy Evening I felt sorely troubled by unwonted Fears in my Soul. To restore my Spirits I persuaded my young Spouse, the faithful Aide of my nocturnal Observations, to spend the Night in our rural Retreat outside the Walls of the City. I sent the Coachman back to warn the Maidservants to keep careful

watch over the Hearth Fire. Indeed I delivered up to a Judas my Treasures, the Sweat of Tens of Years, the Salt of incessant Endeavours toward the Increase and Glory of our Divine Science. The Murderer of my Hopes has taken Flight; I would not have him pursued, since how would it help me to chastise the Instrument whom the Lord of Hosts has employed in His inscrutable Counsel for this Visitation upon me?

May the Windows of the Human Soul never again look upon such a Conflagration as devoured my three Houses with all their precious Paintings, Chests of Linen, Wool and Silk, copper and tin Vessels, silver Candlesticks, and Ornaments of Gold and Gems, so that it is now impossible to find any Trace of these things among the Ruins. I cannot describe how eighty Rolls of paper, intended for the Printing of my new Book, flew flaming through the Air, carried off by the Wind. And if God had not commanded the Wind to turn in its Course, all of the Old City of Danzig would surely have burned to the Ground.

When my Study was seized by the Flames, the People who had come posthaste to offer aid threw Multitudes of Books through the Window, but many were stolen by godless Thieves. Saved by God's Mercy were my Manuscripts, including Kepler's immortal Works, which I purchased from his Son, my Catalogue of the Stars, my New and Improved celestial Globe, and the thirteen Volumes of my Correspondence with learned Men and the Crowned Heads of all Lands.

But the cruel Flames have consumed all the Machines and Instruments conceived by long Study and constructed, alas, at such great Cost. Consumed also the Printing Press with Letters and delicately engraved Copperplates for the Illumination of the Books; consumed the stock of printed Copies; consumed, finally, my Fortune and the Means which God's Mercy had granted me to serve the Royal Science.

If such Damage should crush me to the Ground, I whose Locks are Hoary and who am not far from my Appointed End, could any reasonable Man cast Blame upon me therefor? Yet with the Aid of my many Friends I hope that I may restore my Specula observa-

toria, and implore you, Most Illustrious Monarch who have so often manifested Royal Munificence toward me, to breathe by some further Token of your Generosity new Life into the Work which may still lie before me. Then will I no longer bewail my cruel Misfortune, and yours, Noble Majesty, will be eternal Fame for all Posterity.

The Sun King, Louis XIV, received the above missive from a man named Hevelius (originally Hewel), a beer brewer of Danzig. The letter is a remarkable example of the moral force inherent in baroque pompousness and pathos. Those gentlemen in their powdered wigs not only knew how to bear the blows of fate, but how to enjoy them. Nowadays we think we are remarkably clever to have discovered that misfortune gives secret pleasure. Men of the seventeenth century may not have been up to such psychological refinements, but they profited by misfortune, glorified their particular cases, converted a cry for help into a proud expression of their personalities.

The Baroque was the age of dignity. It was interested in mathematical problems almost as much as in questions of etiquette, and called astronomy the queen of sciences because it provided a noble foil to life's endless festivities, because it intensified the century's feeling for personality by opening up a prospect of the infinite universe.

Astronomy was accorded such honor precisely because it no longer served utilitarian ends. It had at last freed itself for good from astrology; no one would any longer dare to ask an astronomer for a horoscope. That sort of thing was for pettier spirits; an astronomer belonged to upper-class society. He personified the power of thought—which the Baroque Age respected above all else.

The brief dream of the humanists of 1500 became a reality around 1650, in the lasting form of an international republic of learned men who enjoyed extraordinary freedoms under the most absolutistic regime in history. The most imperious monarch of the age, the Sun King, assembled around himself a college of great

savants, the French Academy of Sciences. To it he called members of a great variety of nations, and paid sizable sums to the foreign academicians without imposing any obligations upon them.

One of these was the beer brewer Hevelius of the Hanse city of Danzig. He kept his subsidies from Paris such a secret that his daughter unwittingly perjured herself after his death: "My father never stooped to accepting money from the archfoe of Germans, Louis." But he had done so nevertheless "for the greater glory of the Almighty and the deeper knowledge of His Works."

Hevelius was a very rich man in his own right. He devoted vast sums to an observatory that extended over the roofs of four houses and was equipped with the most beautifully decorated astronomical instruments ever made.

"I would not be boastful," he wrote, "but indeed I am much exercised not to neglect my Brewery, to fulfill my Duties as Magistrate, Overseer of the Orphanage, Chief of the Fire Guard, Member of seven Guilds, and to continue my Inquiries into the Heavens. For my astronomical Work I employ a dozen Carpenters, Smiths, Box-makers, Painters, Mechanicians, moreover six Printers, and a Dutch Type-cutter. A Mathematician from Leyden performs Calculations for me, and reads the Proofs of my Works." He goes on to complain of the enormous cost and the time he must expend to directing all these activities. His crew spent all winter laying the foundations for the 130-foot telescope. "But now it turns in all Directions more lightly than a Weathervane. I know not of anyone who hath made anything like unto it."

Therefore we can well imagine the blow it must have been to have this observatory go up in flames. He rebuilt it, but he was by now seventy, and the effort taxed his strength severely. His hope of saying the final word in all fields of astronomy by assembling his own observations of everything proved to be utopian, a dilettante's idea. Nevertheless he succeeded in making the miracles of the heavens tangible to everyone. Hevelius understood his century's love of pomp and circumstance. Among his other achievements, he presented his age with more than a hundred prints of the Moon, which he himself had both designed and engraved on the copper plates. The Baroque Age treasured these

JOHANNES HEVELIUS AND HIS WIFE OBSERVING THE HEAVENS. FROM HEVELIUS'S *Machina Coelestis*.

engravings as triumphs of man over nature in the same way that our fathers hailed the zeppelin and the airplane. Hevelius's contemporaries assured him that his fame would endure as long as the Moon itself.

Instruments

At the time the observatory in Danzig burned down, a fine new one had already risen in the city of Paris. It was a baroque palace which also served as the meeting place for the Academy of Sciences. When it had been only half finished, its future director, Giovanni Domenico Cassini of Bologna, viewed it, and instantly requested an audience with the King. He tried to convince Louis that all the money spent on the building would be wasted unless the top floor, at least, were redesigned. The building as planned would be utterly useless for observations, he maintained.

The architect was sent for; the minister of finance joined the discussion; and there followed a sharp debate in which the emotional Italian violated etiquette by his forceful expressions and sweeping gesticulations. In his zeal for the cause he did not notice the eclipse passing over the Sun of France; he was barely saved from eternal disfavor by the finance minister's whispering: *"Sire, ce baragouineur là ne sait ce qu'il dit*—Sire, this blabbermouth doesn't know what he is talking about." In baroque architecture functionalism was of small account. A building was a feast for the eyes; that was what mattered.

Cassini set up his instruments in the open air outside the observatory. That proved in the end to be the only possible solution, for they grew to such proportions that a dome the size of St. Peter's in Rome would have been necessary to house them.

The Baroque Age employed gigantic telescopes, 100, 125, and 150 feet long. They would have looked like tilted factory smokestacks—if they had had tubes. These they did not have, however; guiding poles or a girdered tower served for a tube. The path of

the light rays was not shielded from surrounding illumination.

These curious, cranelike monsters were called "air telescopes." The lenses were suspended in air; Cassini's largest lens hung from a tower that reared far up above the "observatory" proper. It must have been amusing to watch the dignified gentlemen at their observations; they trotted around in wide circles in the grass, like circus horses on a lead rope, constantly taking aim at their elusive targets. For the stars glided like snowflakes out of the field of vision, bobbing and trembling at the same time. The astronomer could not stand still for a moment; these high academicians performed a nocturnal ring dance on the lawn.

The awkward apparatus had been devised out of a desire to achieve the greatest possible magnification. For this purpose a long focal length was necessary, a large distance between objective and eyepiece. The eyepiece had recently been greatly improved; it was now made of two lenses. But the objective still gave trouble: colored fringes, tremendous distortion, rings around the stars; in practice, good seeing was to be had only in a tiny central field. If we remember also how unsteady the tower frameworks were, and that the observer had to keep moving about, we feel a greater measure of respect for those bewigged gentlemen.

For there is no denying that they made a remarkable number of discoveries with their air telescopes. The finest of these were made by a Dutchman, young Huygens, who observed the equatorial bulge of Jupiter, and the first moon of Saturn, discerned that Saturn was not a pot with handles, but had a ring; he also observed the white polar caps of Mars, detecting the extensive changes that took place in them. He noted also a cradle-shaped object that enabled him to estimate the rotation of Mars at about twenty-four hours, about the same as the Earth's.

Cassini rectified this estimate by forty minutes. He also saw that Saturn's rings were divided by a fine black line, observed the dark streak on Jupiter's equator, determined Jupiter's rotation period and discovered a second, third, fourth, and fifth moon of Saturn.

With these achievements, the potentialities of the air telescope were about exhausted. For generations thereafter no more surprises were discovered in the skies. The entire following century

contributed little that was new. The first period of discovery, which had begun with an Italian, Galileo, came to an end with another Italian, Cassini, working on the lawn of an observatory that was no more than an impressive monument.

After their brief era of glory, the monster telescopes vanished like dinosaurs. The public missed them, but the astronomers wanted no more of their excessive magnifications and dancing images. They had found another use for the telescope—as a measuring instrument—and for a while considered that to be its prime function.

It was a wonder that they had not thought of it before: the optical axis of a telescope provided the most precise sighting line an astronomer or a navigator could desire. If cross hairs were inserted, stars could be shot like clay pigeons—provided the gun were given a firm foundation.

This innovation was the work of a Danish astronomer, Olaus Roemer. He attached a telescope rigidly to a wheel whose axis was supported by two solid piers. Now the telescope was set for good in the north-south direction. With this "meridian circle" he could determine the longitude and altitude of any star, planet, and comet he chose. Altitude was measured by the number of degrees the wheel turned, longitude by the time required for the rotation of the Earth to bring the object into the field of vision. There was no longer any need for the astronomer to chase the stars; they came before his telescope of their own accord.

For determination of longitude one thing more was needed: a perfect clock. That, too, promptly appeared on the scene. Huygens, the ingenious Dutchman, constructed one by making use of Galileo's idea of the pendulum to impose an undeviating rhythm upon a gear. Thus he created the first really efficient chronometer. Astronomical precision was increased tenfold.

For the meridian circle quite modest telescopes with small lenses could be employed; in these, the distortions of the lenses were scarcely noticeable. With such devices for careful measurement, astronomy emerged from the adolescent years of joyous discovery to the maturer age of quiet, sober work.

Circumference of the Earth, Distance of the Sun, Speed of Light

The greatest achievements of the French academicians could be summed up in three measurements: the circumference of the Earth, the distance of the Sun from the Earth, and the speed of light. Each of these calculations was dependent upon the preceding one; each was achieved within the span of three years. Here was a sterling example of energy and consistency: each achievement served as a springboard for the next.

The interrelationships are easy to see. Once the circumference of the Earth is known, the distance of given points on the Earth's surface can be determined by astronomical means. The French thus measured the distance from Paris to Cayenne, and so obtained the base for the triangle Paris-Cayenne-Mars. From the distance to Mars thus obtained they easily calculated the distance of the Sun, that is, the radius of the Earth's orbit around the Sun. From the Earth's orbit they could deduce the speed of light.

The Greeks had come fairly close in their estimate of the circumference of the Earth; they had utterly failed in their attempt to calculate the distance of the Sun. The very idea of the speed of light went beyond the limits of their imaginations.

Each of the three new figures represented important pioneering. To determine the circumference of the Earth, the distance as the crow flies between two places had to be measured with great exactness. The principal method of geodetic surveying was utilized to accomplish this: triangulation, or measurement by means of a chain of triangles. By extremely careful measurement of one short base line and two angles of successive triangles culminating at a common distant point, the French succeeded in determining the length of a degree on the Earth's surface. One degree multiplied by 360 gave the circumference of the Earth. Their calculation of the distance of Mars was correct to within 6 per cent.

The distance to the Sun then turned out to be twenty times greater than Ptolemy had assumed. The academicians could gratify their King with the information that the sound of a cannon ball fired on the Sun years earlier would only now be reaching his ears.

Presumably Louis XIV was much edified by this; he might well take such magnitudes as symbolic of the distance of a Sun King from the ordinary rabble of humanity. In terms of cultural history, the figure for the Sun's distance was, as it were, a trophy of maturity. The struggle for the new spirit had been concluded; the last remnants of Ptolemaic data had been corrected. Astronomers were now making themselves at home in the Copernican system; what had been a purely theoretical construct was becoming observed reality.

The distance of the Sun from the Earth, 93 million miles, has become the fundamental measurement of astronomy, its standard yardstick, so to speak, for the solar system. For if a single distance is known accurately, the others can be simply calculated by means of Kepler's laws.

Naturally, these early French measurements have not ever been regarded as final. The Sun's distance from the Earth has been repeatedly checked by various methods ever since. This standard yardstick has been rectified with great precision, and has now been determined within a possible error of only a few Earth diameters.

The third vital figure, the speed of light, made less of an impression upon the Baroque Age. Indeed, contemporaries were somewhat disillusioned to learn that light was only 900,000 times as fast as sound, that the Sun's rays take a full eight minutes to reach us. For the general feeling was that a ray of sunlight should take no time at all. There was nothing tangible about light; hence it ought to be seen instantaneously at any point in the universe. When lightning flashed, was it not seen everywhere at the same moment? Upon this phenomenon Galileo had based his measurement of the speed of sound; he had counted the seconds between the flash and the thunder, between the flame from the mouth of a cannon and the report. Sound took time; light seemed to be quite timeless.

Galileo himself had not pursued this particular logic. Descartes, however, offered astronomical evidence that light was independent of the concept of time. An eclipse of the Moon, he argued, would not take place at the calculated moment, but sometime later, if rays of light possessed a measurable velocity.

Olaus Roemer, who was a member of the French Academy of Sciences, disproved this contention by measuring the eclipse of a far more distant object, the largest of Jupiter's satellite moons. This moon revolves around Jupiter in 42 hours, 27 minutes, and 33 seconds, and during each revolution disappears in Jupiter's shadow. The moment when it emerges from the shadow and shines again can be determined to the second. Since the Earth in its annual voyage around the Sun moves a considerable distance away from the planet Jupiter, there ought to be a measurable delay in the reappearance of the satellite if the light from its moon actually takes time to reach us.

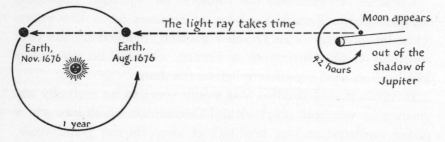

HOW OLAUS ROEMER MEASURED THE SPEED OF LIGHT: WHEN THE LIGHT FROM JUPITER'S MOON APPEARED OUT OF THE SHADOW OF JUPITER IT TOOK ABOUT TEN MINUTES LONGER TO REACH THE EARTH IN NOVEMBER THAN IN AUGUST. THE ADDITIONAL DISTANCE TRAVELED BY THE LIGHT DIVIDED BY THE ADDITIONAL TIME GIVES THE SPEED OF LIGHT.

Delay there was: the time the light of Jupiter's moon took to reach the Earth differed between August and November 1676 by ten minutes—minutes, not seconds. And during the next half year, when the Earth was moving closer to Jupiter, the lag correspondingly diminished. Once again a philosopher's fancies had been overturned by observations. Light actually had a measurable speed of approximately 186,000 miles per second. In deter-

mining this figure Olaus Roemer provided astronomers with a unit of measurement for the entire universe: the distance traversed by light in a year. This distance is, obviously:

$$60 \times 60 \times 24 \times 365 \times 186,000 \text{ miles},$$

or about 6 trillion miles. This "light-year" is so utterly inconceivable that we are no more stirred at hearing that a spiral nebula is a million light-years away than we would be at hearing it was a thousand light-years away. But with such a unit astronomers find their way about the universe as handily as we do in our own yard.

Mynheer Huygens's Compelling Logic

Christian Huygens was the youngest but the most important member of the French Academy of Sciences for a few years. Then he returned to his Dutch homeland, repelled by the persecutions of the Huguenots in France, although he personally had been assured complete religious freedom.

Huygens united abilities that would seem to be mutually exclusive: he was both observer and theoretican, simultaneously a clever mechanic and an architect of ideas on the grand scale. His improvement of the telescope by introduction of a two-lensed eyepiece was one of the finest inventions of his generation. In meeting an urgent need of astronomy by devising a pendulum clock, he also fulfilled modern man's need to stimulate and govern his short life every hour and minute by means of a little ticking machine. The discovery might have brought him untold wealth; instead he revealed the secret of perfect clocks in a small book that proved to be a veritable cornucopia of ideas. In addition to the theory of the pendulum it developed the theories of cycloids, evolutes, and other complex curves, also the long-sought solution to the problem of the center of mass—an invaluable contribution to physics—and finally the theorem of centrifugal force

in circular motion which helped Newton to formulate his law of gravitation.

Galileo had recognized the attraction of the Earth as a force accelerating a falling object, and had defined the rate of the acceleration by a formula. Huygens adapted this formula to the oscillations of the pendulum, and suddenly realized that the acceleration of gravity could be calculated with great precision from these oscillations. He found it to be approximately 32 feet, or more precisely 32.17 feet per second per second for the latitude of Paris.

How amazed Aristotle would have been to see his vague conception of an impulse in heavy bodies to seek the Earth transformed into a numeral exact to several decimal places. He would have shuddered at men's daring to probe so intimately into the mysteries of the Creation. But Huygens was beyond any such timorousness. There was no element of medieval anxiety in his language, nor did he have anything of Kepler's or Galileo's struggle to grasp concepts like that of force. In Huygens' thinking and attitude we can already discern the clear, transparent air of modern science.

That attitude became most evident when his pendulum clock revealed an unexpected defect. A French academician took such a clock with him to tropical Cayenne, to be used for astronomical observations. It there developed that the clock ran a full two minutes and a half slow every day. There was nothing to do but shorten the pendulum. When he returned home, the corrected clock ran two minutes fast in Paris. He confronted the inventor with this curious problem.

Huygens solved it at once: at the equator the centrifugal force of the rotating globe would be greater than it was at the latitude of Paris, and this centrifugal force to some extent counteracted the force with which gravity attracted the pendulum, therefore making it run slower.

Centrifugal force was Huygens's own discovery. Everyone knew that a sling exerted a powerful tug on the arm, but Huygens was the first to derive from this commonplace a law govern-

ing all rotary motion, and to express this law in a mathematical formula. The Galilean achievement of rethinking ideas until they could be expressed in numbers had already become second nature to scientists.

What was more, Huygens was clearly and consciously aware of the difference between the functioning scientist and the natural philosophers of earlier days.

"The ancients," he wrote, "derived their principles from inviolate basic premises. My theories find confirmation only in their results. In this way, however, it is possible to attain to a degree of probability every whit as valid as strictly logical proof. That becomes so when the results harmonize with reality, and especially when numerous phenomena may be explained by a single theory and when previously unknown phenomena may be predicted and afterwards corroborated."

In this statement Huygens set up the criterion of truth which modern science recognizes as the supreme, in fact the only criterion: corroboration by reality. At the same time Huygens differentiated between degrees of truth, a vital distinction. For we see in everything a process of becoming; we no longer recognize absolute truth, but only different degrees of probability.

Huygens provided an example of this fruitful mode of thinking in his development of the concept of centrifugal force. He demonstrated it with various types of rotating mechanisms which are now common in science and in the household under the name of "centrifuges." For example, he set a soft sphere of clay whirling; it flattened out. By some such process, he maintained, the heavenly bodies flattened out at the poles. He had observed such flattening in Jupiter; hence Jupiter must rotate unusually fast. His friend Cassini (of the astronomer dynasty in charge of the Paris Observatory for over a century) then produced evidence that Jupiter rotated in ten hours, which meant, since the planet is so much larger than the Earth, that its speed of rotation was many times that of the Earth.

When, however, Huygens assumed that the Earth must be soft as a ball of clay in its interior, and therefore must also be slightly flattened at the poles because of its centrifugal force, neither

Cassini nor any of the other academicians was willing to go along with him. But Mynheer Huygens's probabilities were inexorable, and fifty years later the French Academy of Sciences decided to test them against reality. It sent out two expeditions, one to the equator and the other to Lapland, as far north as it was possible to go. And the expeditions discovered an actual difference, though a tiny one, in the curvature of the Earth. Its diameter at the equator was to the diameter at the poles as 300 to 299. Theory had forecast a proportion of 289:288.

The most exciting of Huygens's assumptions was his development of the wave theory of light. The theory sounded like something dreamed up by a mystic, utterly strange, defying all traditional experience, contradicting logic and outraging common sense. But Huygens had to show that similar phenomena existed in nature, though they had hitherto not been properly understood.

A wave of water glides under a boat. The boat rises and falls, but does not move from its place. The water does not flow; rather, a vibratory action spreads out over its surface; one molecule of water imparts its oscillating motion to the next. Similarly, when a violin sounds, nothing concrete reaches the ear; there is only a trembling in the air which is propagated by vibrating strings and eventually transmitted to the eardrum. And so, according to Huygens, light consists of nothing but an oscillation of the ether that fills all space, and that oscillation is detected by the human eye.

How far Huygens had come becomes apparent when we compare his proposition with Descartes's conception. Descartes considered the ether the basic substance of the universe, the medium that contained all forces. But as for light in the ether, he could only say: "It does not move; it merely strives toward movement." This was true Aristotelian philosophizing. Huygens replaced this hypothesis by his description of a "wave" in which nothing material was propagated, only the movement itself, a vibration and oscillation. His suggestion proved to be one of physics' most fertile principles; ultimately it provided the explanation for a great many strange phenomena, including X rays, radio, and radioac-

tivity. Like the concept of force, it linked mechanics, sound, light, heat, and electricity—for waves are everywhere in the universe.

When Huygens applied the wave concept to light, he divested the Sun of its circle of rays; instead he showed it as a sphere surrounded by an endless succession of spherical emanations of light expanding at incredible speed, each flanked by other spherical emanations from every point on the Sun, all crossing one another. To derive from that image the laws of optics, the angles of reflection and refraction, bordered on magic.

LIGHT WAVES FORM SPHERICAL EMANATIONS THAT INTERCROSS LIKE WATER WAVES.

The prerequisite for the entire theory, the ether, was a nothingness, an impossibility, sheer madness. It had to be so elastic that it would transmit light waves to infinity; yet it must also offer no resistance to any solid body. Huygens found an analogy for it in a row of billiard balls packed tightly together; if the first one is struck, the last one rolls. The particles of the ether must, he believed, be packed just as tightly and must be just as solid—and yet the heavenly bodies must pass through this substance.

These were impossibilities, and yet physicists unanimously accepted them when, in the nineteenth century, they obtained experimental proof of something Huygens himself had considered madness: that light turns corners. A light wave spreads out to all

sides; therefore it must go around corners, just as sound does. And in spite of the apparent sharp edges of a ray of light, it proved possible to make light turn a corner if the corner were small enough.

Even today, when the "ether" has vanished from the physicists' view of the cosmos, and when we know that light is propagated in doses, in "quanta," the wave theory still has its place in science. Huygens's probabilities are still compelling.

One of his most astounding efforts was to define the concept of probability itself in mathematical formulas. By analyzing the possibility of different faces of dice turning up, he founded that truly modern speciality which we call the calculus of probabilities, and which has become indispensable for work in economics, genetics, atomic energy, and astronomy.

The last of his inspirations was an effort to drive wheels by the force of exploding gunpowder, utilizing a kind of cannon with pistons that would be pushed back and forth by the explosions. He hazily conceived the internal combustion engine two centuries before its birth.

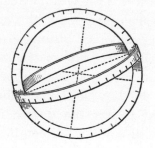

MONARCH NEWTON

The Many-Colored Sun

WHEN A BOY GOES out into a furious thunderstorm and jumps about like a billy goat, this may be put down as high spirits. But when he then stoops and begins measuring his footmarks with a string, while the wind blows his hat away, the neighbors are likely to tap their brows meaningfully.

"It was my first experiment in physics," Isaac Newton later averred. "I measured the force of the wind by the length of my jumps with and against it. That was the year Cromwell died."

This was how this man obsessed with the investigation of nature remembered contemporary history. A noteworthy event in the history of the world served him merely as a reminder of something he had tested or calculated at the time. Naturally, ordinary daily events passed by him altogether unnoticed. His absent-mindedness exceeded by far the degree usually permitted to scholars. The tale of his holding the egg in his hand and boiling the hourglass may be apocryphal, but it could have happened to him. For he often completely forgot to eat, came home empty-handed from shopping expeditions, turned up in church in his dressing gown unless some neighbor stopped him in time.

Even as a young man, these incongruities of his attracted attention. In the museum of his native town of Woolsthorpe, England, there is a drawing of Newton with the lady of his heart. He is tenderly holding her fingers in his hand and using them to stuff his pipe.

That lady was the only one in his life. He forgot her immediately after his entrance into the temple of science at Cambridge. This university suited his inclinations. There was nothing to disturb his meditations but the common midday meal. When the bell rang, he reluctantly set himself in motion; frequently he found himself unaccountably on the street and returned, shaking his head in bewilderment, to his cell-like room.

A friend came to call. Newton was not in; his supper stood on the table in covered platters. The guest decided to play a joke, ate everything on the table, and neatly covered the platters again. Newton came, was delighted to see his friend, and, begging his pardon, said he would sit down quickly and have his supper. "Strange," he said when he discovered the empty platters, "I thought I had not yet eaten. As I see, I was mistaken."

Such concentration on essentials enabled him to make rapid progress in science and mathematics. When he completed his doctoral examination, the professor under whom he had worked declared Newton more learned than himself, and drew the logical but unusual conclusion that he would retire and arrange for the young man to take the chair in his place. The name of this unique professor was Isaac Barrow.

The other Isaac did not lose much time over the job that had thus fallen into his lap. Only one lecture a week was required of him, and since he often forgot that, virtually nothing interfered with his tinkering and calculating.

The first tangible product of his genius was an entirely new type of telescope. Instead of a lens in front it had a mirror in back. A concave mirror converges light just as a convex lens does. Newton poured his mirror out of a metal alloy that he himself compounded, and polished it with loving patience. Since he could not very well hold his head in front of the telescope to see the mirror image, he placed a second tiny mirror in the center of the path of the rays from the concave mirror to reflect the light out through a hole in the side. This might seem somewhat strange, but it served the purpose. The reflecting telescope had been born.

Newton had gone to so much trouble because the curves and

NEWTON'S INVENTION, THE REFLECTING TELESCOPE.

distortions and the colored fringes of lens images disturbed him. A mirror eliminated these faults. Newton was pleased by the clear, sharp image; unfortunately, however, it was exceedingly faint because so much light was lost by the double reflection. This defect more and more spoiled his pleasure in his new apparatus. While others hailed his invention and declared that the lens telescope was already outmoded, Newton began considering how to produce faultless lens images, or at least to eliminate the colored fringes. He did not succeed, but in the course of his work he discovered the spectrum and solved one of the prime mysteries of science: the nature of color. Was color a quality of things which they preserved even in darkness, or was it a quality of the light which fell upon objects? The question was much discussed in his day. Newton approached the problem in the Galilean manner, by experiment.

Colored fringes were also seen when light passed through a wedge of glass. A prism was, after all, nothing but a section of a lens. Newton bored a hole in the window shutter of a darkened room so that a fine ray of light gleamed in the dancing motes of

dust and fell on the opposite wall, making a round white dot. Then he held a prism in front of the hole—and the colors appeared, a whole rainbow of colors, but far brighter and more glowing than any rainbow. The wonderful sight, never seen before except by a doctor in Prague named Marci von Kronland (1595–1667), so enraptured Newton that he wrote a glowing description of it in his treatise—an excursion into the realm of emotion which he never again permitted himself.

His enthusiasm was short-lived. Soon he discovered that his rainbow was the wrong shape; it was not round like the white spot, but oval, in fact five times as wide as it was high. It was as though the prism had pulled the ray of sunlight apart. Newton's mathematician's brain rebelled against the thought that a ray of light could suddenly grow thicker. It was a line, after all; it must have been split, the light torn apart.

Now he began a series of amazingly simple and intelligent experiments, a systematic examination of nature. The experiments led him to suppositions which he then tested. He began to wonder whether the light ray were not running in a curve after passing through the prism.

Mother Nature gave a negative answer to all his simple questions. Then he was ready to deliver an ultimatum to her, his historic *experimentum crucis*. Roger Bacon had first suggested the idea of a crucial experiment; Newton put it into practice.

In his treatise he did not, unfortunately, formulate his question; he merely described the order of his experiments, and their result. We must therefore attempt to reconstruct the train of thought that led to the *experimentum crucis*. His reasoning must have been something like this:

"After all my failures it is evident that the prism disperses a ray of sunlight into a fanlike shape. This could be only if sunlight is not single in nature, but is a kind of compound which is broken up by the prism. Broken up into what? Into colors, obviously. Therefore sunlight must actually be not white, but colored. Although this may sound mad, it becomes comprehensible if we reject an apparent reality, as Copernicus rejected the apparent

reality of the revolution of the heavens. I cannot see colored sunlight because all the colors are mixed. Only my prism shows me genuine sunlight, elemental colored light."

At this fantastic idea even the sober mathematician felt a certain shudder of awe. Were human eyes then looking upon true light for the first time? It was in such a mood of awe that Newton may have baptized his artificial rainbow the "spectrum"—the ghost of light. But he would have gone on thinking logically, objectively, and boldly:

"If I now take a ray of elemental light by itself, let us say a green ray, it would no longer be dispersed by a prism, and I would see a round green spot on the wall. That would be proof that I was dealing with pure, unmixed elemental light."

Such, approximately, must have been the considerations which led Newton to single out a green ray of the spectrum, and send

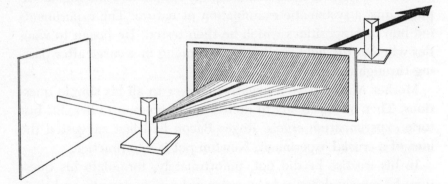

NEWTON'S *experimentum crucis*. SUNLIGHT ENTERING FROM THE SOURCE AT LEFT IS BROKEN UP BY THE PRISM (CENTER) INTO THE COLORS OF THE SPECTRUM. ONLY ONE OF THESE COLORS IS ALLOWED THROUGH BY THE FILTER. THIS COLOR IS NOT DISPERSED BY THE SECOND PRISM (RIGHT). THIS PROVES THAT LIGHT IN ITS PURE FORM IS COLORED LIGHT.

this green ray through a second prism. His demonstration worked perfectly: a round green dot appeared on the wall. The prism was unable to disperse the elemental light any further. There could no longer be any question about it: color was a basic property of light. In fact, only colored light existed; the white of sun-

light was a mixture that our eye was unable to dissect and therefore grasped as a whole and called "white."

The final test of this hypothesis was to reunite the spectrum. Nothing was simpler; Newton converged the separate colored rays by using another prism, reversed, and they united to form a white spot. The knowledge that today is the property of every schoolboy was then the revelation of a mystery of nature which the human mind had puzzled over since the days of the Greeks. Newton also made a color wheel revolve, and saw it as a dirty yellow. He had proved that the eye itself united colors; naturally, his color wheel could not yield pure white since he was unable to paint the color wheel with primary light. When he mixed colored powders, however, their colors also disappeared; they yielded gray or brown shades.

Color, therefore, was no quality of objects. There are no green leaves which are also green in the dark; the Sun alone makes them green; their green arises from the spectrum. This, too, Newton proved; in a dark room he let a spectrum fall upon a maple leaf. The leaf turned green only when it was held in the green part of the spectrum; otherwise it was black. He directed the green ray at materials of all colors; only the green parts showed; the other colors remained dark.

One after another Newton went through most of the experiments with the spectrum which are now part of elementary courses in physics, all of these logical consequences of the crucial experiment. Newton was very well aware that everything depended upon this alone. He pointed out that there no longer could be any doubt that colors were not qualities of things and that colors do not exist in the dark. Since colors were qualities of light, they could not be thought of as qualities of objects.

This declaration was a shot heard round the world. Half the scientists in England, France, Germany, and Italy felt challenged. This man was throwing overboard all the rules of decency. Hitherto experiments had been pretty illustrations of a theory; now this impertinent young man would have them be decisive arguments. Hitherto scientific disputes had been conducted in dignified philosophical fashion, by logical proofs. The

opponent presented counterarguments which were just as logical, only proceeded from other premises. Each was right from his point of view; therein lay the spice of the conflict. But this fellow Newton was a spoilsport of the worst sort. A young sprout barely thirty, he had the impudence to declare: "It's all over! I have the answer; there can no longer be any question about it."

How mistaken he was! Purehearted as he was, he imagined that the scientific world would be grateful to him for having solved one of its fundamental problems. Instead, the controversies raged more wildly than ever. In high dudgeon, Newton sharpened his pen and tried to explain to his numerous attackers that a new era had dawned. In effect he wrote: "My theory has not been proved by refutation of opposing hypotheses, not by logical deduction; it is correct because it has been demonstrated by positive, crucial experiments. Therefore all objections based upon hypotheses are pointless; the only answer would be to demonstrate errors in my experiments."

What a tone this was, what a set of new rules!

Some natural philosophers took up the challenge and answered with counterexperiments. But here, too, they came a cropper. Newton showed them that they had no inkling of the precision necessary for true experimental science. They worked constantly with mixtures of colors instead of with pure primary light—the same mistake that Goethe made one hundred forty years later.

The Falling Moon

In 1666 the concept of the mutual attraction of every body in the universe, the theory of universal gravitation, was born. Three fathers appeared simultaneously.

The first of them was Giovanni Borelli of Florence. In trying to fathom why the planets should revolve eternally around the Sun, he came to the conclusion that they must constantly strive to

move in two directions, toward the Sun, and straight out into space. He compared the movements of the planets with that of a sling, which tends constantly to fly off at a tangent, but which is held back by the leather strap and forced to swing in a circle. Analyzed thus, it sounds very simple, and yet not even a man like Galileo had seen that circular movement cannot be the most elemental type of motion, since it presupposes the contention of two forces, one outward and one inward.

The second man who claimed fatherhood was an Englishman, Robert Hooke. Characteristically, he made a visible demonstration: he suspended a sphere on a long string, drew it back, and then gave it a push to the right. Instead of swinging back and forth like a pendulum, it turned in a circle. In the same manner, he argued, the planets must once have received a push which sent them straight out into the universe. By Galileo's law of inertia they would have continued on in a straight line, but the Sun attracted them and forced them to wheel in a circle. In reality, of course, their movements are elliptical. This can be demonstrated by giving a stronger push to the sphere; it then flies around in an elliptical orbit.

This was all very ingenious and vivid, but it was only an image; it still had to be proved that the motions of the planets really followed the same principle. Independent of any knowledge of the others, Isaac Newton set about this task in the same year—he was at this time twenty-four years old! If the suspected attractive force of celestial bodies existed, he argued, it should be possible to define it in figures.

The Earth attracts the Moon as it attracts a stone, but because of the great distance the attraction is much weaker. How much weaker? The Moon is 60 Earth-radii distant from the Earth; therefore the attraction should be 1/60 of what it would be on the surface of the Earth. But from Kepler's third law—which states that the cubes of the mean distances of any two planets from the Sun are to each other as the squares of their periodic times of revolution—Newton deduced that the attractive force diminished inversely as the square of the distance; hence it

would be only 1/3,600. If he knew the attractive force on the surface of the Earth, he would be able to calculate the fall of the Moon toward the Earth.

At this point the time-honored tale of the apple springs to the fore. Let us take it as gospel truth: Newton sat under an apple tree reflecting on this matter of the Earth's attraction for the Moon, when an apple fell to the ground from a branch overhead. Distractedly, he toyed with the round object, and suddenly remembered that it fell with an acceleration of 32 feet per second every second. In the first second, therefore, it fell 16 feet. If the same force that attracted the apple to the ground also attracted the Moon, the moon would fall 1/3,600 of this distance in an equal time. Newton dropped the apple; out came his notebook, and he began scribbling figures. In one second the Moon should "fall" 16 feet divided by 3,600, or .053 inch.

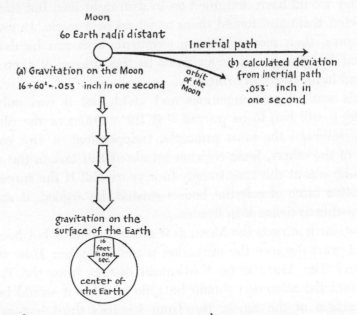

NEWTON'S CALCULATION OF THE EARTH'S GRAVITATIONAL EFFECT ON THE MOON.

There was a way to test this figure, to determine whether the Moon was attracted by the same force that made an apple fall. He needed merely to calculate how far the Moon in its orbit de-

parted from the straight line it would otherwise follow if there were no attraction. If the result were .053 inch, the principle of attraction between celestial bodies would be clearly established.

Unfortunately, fate played a trick on Newton at this point. His calculation did not work out correctly; the actual deviation of the Moon was a sixth smaller than it should have been. This so vexed the precise mathematician that he gave up his speculations on the subject for sixteen long years. Then he became acquainted with the results of the French measurement of the size of the Earth, and learned that the radius of the Earth was one sixth larger than had hitherto been assumed, precisely the apparent error in his calculations. Newton was in such a state of excitement that he could no longer multiply and divide; a friend had to do the simple arithmetic for him. And the calculations worked out neatly.

The rest of the work provided no further difficulties. It was now conclusively proved that celestial bodies mutually attracted one another, and that the attractive force depended upon their mass and their distance. The fundamental formula of astronomy was found:

$$\text{gravitation} = \frac{\text{product of the masses}}{\text{square of the distance}}$$

That formula has proved its validity for comets, meteors, binary stars, for every moving dot of light in the firmament. It has enabled astronomers to weigh stars, clouds of gas, remote nebulae as though they could be put on a scale. It has explained the tiny deviations in the orbits of the planets as resulting from the influence of other planets. It has successfully predicted the position, orbit, and mass of unknown bodies. Subtle measurements in the laboratory have further demonstrated that every mass possesses gravitation, and that Newton's formula is applicable to the tiniest particle of matter.

Kepler's dream of deriving the entire mechanism of the cosmos from a single universal force was fulfilled by Newton's law of gravitation.

Ocean of Truth

Having discovered this law, Newton now felt called upon to master numerically every possible motion in the skies and on Earth, to construct a universal and comprehensive theory of force. He spent five years doing so.

His findings appeared under the title *Mathematical Principles of Natural Philosophy*—the famous *Principia,* which became the lexicon of mechanics, the foundation of both astronomy and physics. It represented the culmination of one of the most significant intellectual processes in the entire history of our civilization, the struggle of such titans as Copernicus, Kepler, Galileo, Huygens, and Newton to reshape the modes of human thought.

Occasionally Newton himself saw his achievement in these terms, and was wont to say: "If I have seen further than others, it was because I stood upon the shoulders of giants." In his book, however, he wasted not a word on the historical evolution of his ideas; instead he presented a strict system of doctrine as the perfected truth. Ideas that Kepler jubilantly proclaimed as revelations and mystic insights, that Galileo arrived at by brilliant intuition or bold dialectic, Newton formulated in crystalline statements that have remained axioms of science to this day. He defined the fundamental concepts of force, motion, space, and time in the ways we now understand them. These ideas are taken for granted today, yet in their present sense they have existed only since Newton's *Principia.* Galileo's ideas were always to retain the marks of conflict with the older spirit. Newton wiped away these stains, perceived the true import of these ideas, grasped their permanent forms: acceleration as a measure of force; continuance of bodies in a state of uniform motion as well as rest; action and reaction; the parallelogram of forces.

The practical consequences of his work were immeasurable. He enabled astronomers to reckon precisely the workings-out of the Copernican system; he calculated the flattening of the Earth at the poles, explained the tides as the resultant of the joint attractive forces of Sun and Moon, pointed out that weight was a

variable quantity, differing with distance from the center of gravity, less on mountains than in valleys. His book was an ocean, an ocean of truths. His contemporaries were overwhelmed by it, swept along; Newton's propositions were beyond cavil, but they were not given precisely a stormy welcome. For Newton again offended his fellows' deepest feelings, upset one of their fundamental ideas about the world in denying the existence of Descartes's ether eddies.

René Descartes dominated the first half of the seventeenth century in his dual capacity of mathematician and philosopher. He had developed mathematical analysis, which wiped out the boundary between geometry and algebra, in which curves became functions. By comparison, Euclidean thinking seemed pedantic and limited. Then he attempted to explain the entire mechanism of the world by ether eddies. These supposedly transmitted light, and at the same time set the celestial bodies in motion. He succeeded in reducing all the phenomena of nature known at the time to this single cause, which transmitted its effect tangibly from one thing to another; thus everything was connected in a chain with everything else. Descartes's contemporaries hailed this triumph of reasoning which seemed to explain every detail of the entire Creation.

Then Newton came along with his mathematical proofs of gravitation, which could not be explained by ether eddies. Gravitation was a mystery working over great distances in some inconceivable manner. Such a thing was repugnant to Europeans, who wanted to see the interlocking of cause and effect with their own eyes. Newton's version of nature therefore seemed to be a descent from the heights attained by Descartes, retrogression to an outmoded stage of philosophy.

Worse still, in Newton's mighty system there was no room left for the ether. This also undermined the wave theory of light, which Huygens had recently presented to the world. Newton himself regretted this, for the wave theory was essential to his theory of color. There still remained the problem of explaining the spectrum: why were the rays of primary light arranged in the particular order of red, yellow, green, and violet? Why did

light consist of many colors; what were colors? According to Huygens they were simply waves of differing lengths, differing frequencies, just like different pitches. The spectrum represented a scale, a gamut of light.

This explanation seemed to emerge again from another of Newton's experiments. If light is passed through a lens pressed upon a plate of glass, a wreath of colored rings is produced. When monochromatic light is sent through such an apparatus, the rings of each color appear at different distances from one another. Newton measured the distances—and was in effect measuring the wave lengths of light. But he would not accept this explanation; light waves could not exist because there was no medium, no ether, to transmit them. So impossible, nonsensical a concept as that of the ether had no right to existence. Anything that did not follow from observations was a hypothesis, he maintained, and hypotheses had no place in experimental science.

Newton therefore concluded that light consisted of corpuscles passing through empty space. The differing distances of the colored rings proved only that the corpuscles were affected by their passage through the lens and the glass, that their character was affected in some way, to what degree depending on their color.

Only Newton, with his incredibly sane and all-embracing system, could have succeeded in putting across so absurd a conception. He won the battle completely. The wave theory vanished, and with it Descartes's ether eddies. The whole triumphant world-view of the Baroque Age had been shattered. In its place Newton offered the inexplicable, remote force of gravitation which was, admittedly, a mystery to himself. When he was asked what accounted for it, he flatly refused to venture any opinion: "I do not invent hypotheses."

This attitude of his became a model for future natural philosophers. Henceforth scientists considered it more important to recognize where the limits of science lay than to satisfy the urge for knowledge by unproved speculations, no matter how pretty they might be.

The incomprehensibility of gravitation Newton considered a divine dispensation. The Almighty had denied man ultimate in-

sight into the mystery of His Creation. A Christian must be able to reconcile himself to this fact—and Newton was a devout Christian. After the completion of his *Principia* he plunged head over heels into Biblical studies of a sort least to be expected from him. He believed he could identify the Son of Man in Daniel vii with the Word of God on the white horse in Revelations x. "For both are destined to rule the peoples with an iron rod."

These delvings into theology, in conjunction with his ascetic mode of life, brought Newton to a condition of extreme nervous irritability. Several acute misfortunes were contributing factors. He lost his mother; his best friends died; a fire in his room destroyed valuable manuscripts. He started to send out confused letters. Suddenly a rumor began to circulate that Newton had become insane. At last he confessed that for months he had scarcely been able to eat or sleep. Under care and a sensible regime, he slowly recovered.

Newton had fought through to the fundamental concepts of modern thought; he had discovered the formula that governed the motions of the universe—and everything had only become the more incomprehensible. Out of this terrible disillusionment arose his distaste for hypotheses. If he could not see the truth whole, he would no longer content himself with the cheap substitute of probabilities. His denial of the wave theory of light was not obstinacy, but proud and bitter renunciation, obedience to his rule of research, which might be summed up in these words: "In spite of opposing hypotheses, premises which are deduced from phenomena must be considered true or very close to true until other phenomena contradict them."

Yet at bottom this rule was nothing but Huygens's insight that ultimately only probabilities exist, no absolute truths. To Huygens this insight was liberating and positive; to Newton it was an abdication. Huygens by nature took pleasure in development, in eternal seeking; Newton's whole desire was to come to conclusions, to fathom the deepest causes of things. It is sad indeed to hear this man who had plumbed immensity confess: "I remind myself of a boy playing by the seashore and rejoicing because now and then he finds a smoother pebble or a prettier shell than

his comrades—while the great ocean of truth lies before him, un-examined."

Sir Isaac's Parliament

In his mid-fifties there came a radical change in Newton's way of life. He was appointed master of the Royal Mint, an office equivalent to what would now be governor of the Bank of England. He exchanged his modest lodgings at Cambridge for a palace in London, entered society, kept horses, carriages, and servants. His income shot abruptly from sixty to five hundred pounds a year, besides various perquisites; he was able to indulge his taste for philanthropy. He was knighted, and became an influential personage at court. Most important of all, he became president of the Royal Society.

This celebrated association of scientists was about the same age as Newton himself. At the time he was given his professorship, the society became "royal," and was provided with special privileges, robes of state, a mace, and a seal bearing the motto: "Let no one's word be law." But the motto went by the board once Newton was elected with absolute regularity to the presidency. His word was sacred. An excellent model for a cannon was unanimously rejected because Newton declared: "This diabolic instrument will only multiply mass killing." In London the Royal Society was generally known as Sir Isaac's Parliament.

This parliament became the platform for Newton's world fame. But it also embittered the closing days of his life by its frenetic partisanship, in connection with his fourth great contribution, the calculus of fluxions, which has become the core of modern mathematics. This time, however, Newton was not the sole discoverer of the method. It was simultaneously developed, under the name of the differential calculus, by the German philosopher Leibnitz.

Leibnitz was a highly versatile personality. No cloistered scholar, he was a man of the world who was sent on diplomatic missions—on one such occasion he proposed to the King of

France that he conquer Egypt instead of contesting with Germany for Alsace and the Palatinate. He attempted to reconcile Catholics and Protestants. He founded an academy of the sciences and conducted a correspondence that extended as far as China. Historical research, even if it concerned only the genealogy of a prince, was as important to him as mathematics, the problem of a universal language and universal script as intriguing as the profoundest questions of philosophy.

Most of the technical terminology of modern mathematics derives from Leibnitz. All of Europe learned the differential calculus from his textbook. He described the new art of reckoning in such lucid terms that a veritable race began among mathematicians, each trying to outdo the other in elegant solutions of hitherto unsolved problems. Mathematicians posed each other riddles, and sent each other the results in code to be sure that no one copied. The period immediately after Leibnitz was an exciting and glorious era in the history of mathematics. And all the newest discoveries were made by means of Leibnitzian differential quotients. No one had ever heard of Newton's counterpart, his fluxions. Newton had created the method for his own private use, and hesitated to publish it because it was so difficult to grasp. For his *Principia* he therefore invented a less difficult, more geometrical method of proof. But that he was as capable as the Leibnitzians he proved when he took part in the problem competitions. On one occasion he solved a problem in a single night, sent the answer in anonymously, and received by return post the compliment: "Naturally we instantly recognized the lion by his claws."

Newton thought his rival pretty much of a lion himself. To Leibnitz and to Leibnitz alone, he gave extensive credit in his great work. He wrote: "In correspondence with Leibnitz I mentioned that I had a method for determining the maxima and minima of curves, for drawing tangents and carrying out similar operations. That famous man replied that he had likewise devised such a method, and informed me of it. It differs only slightly from mine in the mode of writing and of generating magnitudes."

Newton, therefore, proved himself generously ready to share the glory for the greatest mathematical discovery of the century with a foreigner. But Sir Isaac's parliamentarians were not so large-minded. It vexed them that mathematicians were employing differential quotients instead of fluxions, and still more that the Leibnitzian method was so easy to use, while they had to struggle to learn their master's technique and apply it practically. And so they began, in their various papers, to make unpleasant insinuations directed at the German. Finally one of them said flatly that Leibnitz had plagiarized Newton's ideas, only changing the terminology.

This was a declaration of war, and mathematicians throughout Europe threw themselves into the fray. It was waged with documents and accusations, with problems hurled at the adversary to prove his incompetence, with strategic retreats and savage charges, dignified gestures and ugly insults. The war lasted thirteen years, until the death of Newton.

At first the old master held back, but his party gradually drew him into the dispute, and finally decided to settle the matter with a grand flourish. The Newtonians insisted that the evidence be submitted to an international conference of scholars, diplomats, and statesmen, who were to decide whether Newton or Leibnitz had invented the new art of reckoning. Incredible though it seems, the conference actually convened: so seriously were learned quarrels taken even by crowned heads in those days, so powerful was the influence of a scientist upon the world.

The outcome was inevitable. The high judges examined the books and the multitude of documents, shook their majestic wigs, and finally recommended that the two chief participants come to an understanding on this world-shaking priority question by personal correspondence.

Newton had not aimed at anything of the sort. Vainly he protested that no good would come of it; not until the King himself requested it did he decide to make the offer of peace. The result was that the two elderly scientists now became irreconcilable personal enemies. Even after Leibnitz's death the struggle went on; the Newtonians were gradually driven on the defensive,

and their leader remained obsessed with the affair until his dying day.

The most remarkable aspect of the whole barren struggle was this: no participant doubted for a moment that Newton had already developed his method of fluxions when Leibnitz began work on the differential calculus. Yet there was no proof, only Newton's word. He had published nothing but a calculation of a tangent, and the note: "This is only a special case of a general method whereby I can calculate curves and determine maxima, minima, and centers of gravity." How this was done he explained to a pupil a full twenty years later, when Leibnitz's textbooks were widely circulated. His own manuscripts came to light only after his death, and then they could no longer be dated.

Though Newton's priority was not provable, it was taken for granted, while Leibnitz was always asked to prove that he had not plagiarized—a charge as humiliating as it was absurd. This grotesque situation demonstrates most vividly the authority Newton enjoyed everywhere. He was truly the monarch of all he surveyed, a unique phenomenon. To Western science he occupied the same place that had been held in classical antiquity by Pythagoras—whose disciples were wont to crush all opponents with the words: "Pythagoras himself has said so."

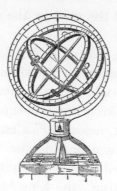

THREE GENERATIONS
AT GREENWICH

An Observatory to Solve a Navigation Problem

THE DUCHESS OF PORTSMOUTH was giving a reception. No one was particularly eager to attend that Frenchwoman's parties, but Charles II took offense if members of society declined. After dinner the conversation turned to the astonishing inventiveness of the human intellect, which was already beginning to create a perfect world.

"I fancy there is still some room for ingenuity," an old sea-dog commented. "For example, no one has yet made a clock that keeps good time aboard ship. Pendulum clocks don't like rough seas, you know."

"Cannot seamen read the time by the stars, Admiral?" one of the ladies inquired.

"Only their own time, ma'am. If they knew London time, they would be able to determine their position on all the seven seas. I'd warrant England would pay a fortune to the inventor of a ship's clock that would keep accurate time in any gale."

"May I count on that, *monsieur?*" a countryman of the Duchess asked smilingly. "I can provide you with a clock without a pendulum which will tell time as precisely as you wish."

"If what you say is true," the King himself intervened in the conversation, "I myself stand warrant that you will be royally rewarded."

"Even though the clock was created by God, not man, Sire?"

"No matter. Anyone who should perform so notable a service

for England has a claim upon England's gratitude. Tell us your secret, Monsieur de Saint-Pierre."

"Your wish is my command, Sire. The only clock that runs true anywhere upon Earth is to be found in the heavens above. Its hand is the Moon, its face the stars that it covers as it traverses its orbit. The moment a star vanishes behind the Moon's rim can be determined to the second. We need only have tables calculated beforehand, indicating the precise times when different stars are thus eclipsed."

The King was excited enough about the idea to promise Monsieur de Saint-Pierre that his astronomers would provide the tables; let him explain to the Royal Navy how these could be used for navigation. With that, the matter was dropped for the time being. Monsieur de Saint-Pierre bowed low, his smile somewhat forced, for he was none too certain of his ground.

The King promptly sent a request to the Royal Society for an opinion. The reply of these learned men was somewhat dashing. It seemed that the idea of navigating by observation of the Moon had been proposed to Cardinal Richelieu thirty years before, and had proved to be a snare and delusion. For the idea to be practicable the positions of the Moon and the stars had to be known precisely to within half a minute of error, but Tycho Brahe's stellar tables were at best correct only within two minutes because he had made his observations without benefit of a telescope. Lunar tables showed an average error of 15–20 minutes. Monsieur de Saint-Pierre, the report concluded, might have found this out from his countryman Morin, to whose book the Royal Society respectfully referred him.

This recommendation was somewhat embarrassing, since Morin's book happened to be the source of Monsieur de Saint-Pierre's intelligence. Saint-Pierre was not heard of again. But the King responded with indignation. Why, he demanded, had not his astronomers made better tables for his seamen?

It was not so simple a matter, the Royal Society informed him. Tycho Brahe, with the finest observatory in the world, had spent his whole life on the task and produced only the erroneous tables already mentioned.

But the King persisted. There were telescopes nowadays, he pointed out. And he vowed to set up an observatory to satisfy the needs of England's navy and merchant marine. The author of the Royal Society's little discourse seemed the obvious choice for director of the new observatory.

Thus John Flamsteed became Astronomer Royal, and the Royal Observatory of Greenwich was established to solve navigation problems. The foundation stone was laid on August 10, 1675, and the newly appointed Astronomer Royal amused himself by casting the building's horoscope, upon which he inscribed the motto: "Laugh not, Friends." For horoscopes by now were mere parlor games among astronomers.

The motto, however, might well have been carved above the entrance to the observatory, for it was not made for observing. It was a typical baroque building, with a magnificent façade and no provision for its technical functions.

John Flamsteed found a rich patron and obtained funds enough for a 120-foot air telescope that became one of the sights of London for the next few years. For the next four years, to be precise, for then the heirs of the aforesaid patron appropriated the splendid equipment and the Astronomer Royal found himself once again staring at bare walls. On one of these walls he painted a quadrant, suspended a homemade telescope from a hook in the wall, so that it would turn along the quadrant, and began observing. He knew nothing about Jean Picard's meridian circle (which allowed accurate measurement of a degree of meridian), and worked all his life with his own primitive instrument. After a small inheritance came his way, he gradually equipped the observatory with a variety of other instruments, although these, too, were distinctly modest. His best telescope was tied to a ladder and was pushed a few rungs higher or lower as need dictated.

Considering the circumstances, Flamsteed's accomplishments were fantastic. He drew the face for Monsieur de Saint-Pierre's Moon clock, fixing the positions of 2,866 stars—four times as many as Tycho Brahe had measured with a troop of assistants. Flamsteed had only one assistant, and even this one came only in the

last years of his life when rheumatism had so crippled the Astronomer Royal that he could barely hobble from one instrument to the next.

His successor, Edmund Halley, took office at the age of sixty-four. He resolved to follow the capricious movements of the Moon for eighteen years and 219 days—the cycle, already known by the Babylonians, in which most of the motions of the Moon repeat themselves. In this way he hoped to set the lunar clock going. But it was asking too much of Providence to permit him to continue observations until his eighty-second year. A stroke made him incapable of continuing the work.

The third Astronomer Royal, James Bradley, discovered that the Earth wobbles, and that the stars wobble also. Flamsteed's whole life work had to be revised, and the dial of the clock marked out anew if a sailor were to navigate by it.

Thus three generations passed without a solution to the problem for which the Royal Observatory of Greenwich had been founded. Parliament decided that the thing was taking too long, and posted a prize of 20,000 pounds for a method of determining position on the high seas. To the surprise of all the experts, two applicants promptly came forward with two different solutions, neither of whom had any connection with the Greenwich Observatory. The Astronomer Royal could do nothing but test the methods on sea voyages. He declared each one of them useful, and decided that the prize should be divided. Half of the prize went abroad, to the widow of a German professor named Johann Mayer.

On the basis of Halley's lunar observations, Professor Mayer of Göttingen University had drawn up formulas permitting the orbit of the Moon to be calculated each year with sufficient accuracy for occultations (eclipses of other heavenly bodies) to be timed. The Moon, it should be noted, is the most refractory heavenly body; its movements are so complex and its irregularities so many, that even Newton's mathematics had failed to cope with it. Professor Mayer had employed new methods devised by the Swiss mathematician Leonhard Euler, and had applied these methods with typical German patience and thoroughness.

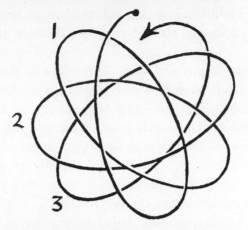

THREE IRREGULAR ORBITS OF THE MOON.

Meanwhile, however, a Yorkshire carpenter had spent twenty years putting together another kind of clock, of the sort the old admiral had wished—an altogether terrestrial clock that ran without a pendulum, but was nevertheless so reliable that with it Greenwich time could be transported across all the oceans, through all climates; unaffected by tempests and monsoons, it kept time correct to the minute over periods of months, therefore making it possible to compute distance by the difference between Greenwich time and sidereal time.

This clock received the honorific name of chronometer, and the carpenter who had made it, John Harrison, was awarded the other half of the £20,000 prize.

In strict justice, the prize should have been divided in thirds. For the use of both the lunar clock and the chronometer presupposed that the time at any given position of a vessel could be determined precisely by the stars or by the Sun. In effect this required the ship's navigator to make observations with astronomical precision without an observatory, on a rolling and pitching deck. How could sailors be expected to perform such a feat? Neither Monsieur de Saint-Pierre nor his critics had given this thought; none of the Astronomers Royal concerned themselves about it at all. A third outsider had to invent the small, handy instrument that has become the symbol of navigation, the sextant.

This outsider, John Hadley, was an English landowner who developed his instrument around 1730.

The solution of the problem of navigation had taken almost a century, about as long a span as had been required for the development of the Copernican system from Brahe to Newton. Thus, a minor practical application had involved almost as much effort as the creation of a science. However, pure science also profited enormously from this utilitarian invention.

The Gentleman Astronomer

Edmund Halley was the very model of a gentleman of the seventeenth century. A high brow, an aquiline nose, thin, faintly mocking lips, large eyes, now probing, now sensitive, he was a man of intellect, a gallant, and a man of the world. In his person he united all the most commendable traits of his age: self-assurance, courtesy, good manners, generosity, enterprise, loyalty to friends, sense of honor, and high ethical principles.

Halley was Newton's best apprentice; it was he who persuaded Newton to publish his *Principia,* and he who printed the book at his own expense. His generosity becomes all the more extraordinary when we consider that Halley himself had discovered part of the law of gravitation. When he came to Newton to discuss the matter, he found that Newton had already produced a complete solution of the problem—and was delighted.

At the age of twenty it occurred to this aristocratic gentleman that half the celestial sphere still remained for the explorer: the Southern Cross and all the stars of the southern hemisphere on the other side of the globe had not yet been measured. Promptly, he dropped the doctoral thesis on which he was engaged at Oxford and pleaded with his well-to-do father to send him off to St. Helena for a vacation. He spent eighteen months below the equator. Lonelier than Napoleon was to be afterwards, he stayed on the island and in spite of the everlasting clouds brought home with him a catalogue giving the positions of 341 stars.

On the long sea-voyage to St. Helena, Halley observed that the compass needle did not point precisely north, that the magnetic pole was not identical with the North Pole. In seafaring England the importance of this observation was promptly realized, and Halley was provided with a special ship in which he sailed halfway around the globe. This voyage resulted in the production of those marine charts with curves of magnetic declination which are as indispensable for navigation as the sextant.

After these expeditions, he settled down to less ranging but equally adventurous explorations in old books. It had not occurred to anyone before him to compare the dreadfully inaccurate stellar data of antiquity with modern catalogues. Halley proved that such comparison was worthwhile; he found that Sirius, Aldebaran, and Arcturus had unquestionably changed position since the days of Hipparchus. This meant that the fixed firmament, the symbol of immutability and eternity, did not at all possess those divine attributes. The stars, too, were subject to the primal urge toward motion.

That the stars should be in motion was only a logical postulate from the law of gravitation. If the force of mutual attraction were actually a property of all bodies, nothing could be at rest, for if there were no motion the universe would long ago have coagulated

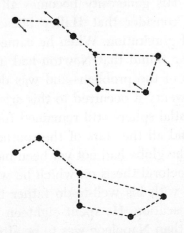

THE STARS ARE IN MOTION: THE DIPPER IN THE GREAT BEAR AS IT APPEARS NOW (TOP), AND AS IT WILL APPEAR IN 40,000 YEARS (BOTTOM).

into a single lump. Only motion can prevent a star from falling into the next nearest star. After Newton, therefore, it was evident that the host of lights in the celestial sphere were not placed there by the will of the Creator from the beginning to the end of all things; rather they were in pulsating motion like an ant heap, all appearance to the contrary. Halley was able to prove the reality of this premise in only a few cases, but these cases sufficed. The spell was broken, and a new revolutionary discovery had been made, a discovery that accorded with the modern need for a dynamic rather than a static concept of the universe.

Halley had come to this conclusion by careful and intelligent recalculation of old data. In the same manner he became aware of a fact that then seemed utterly incredible: that the Moon was moving faster than it had moved at the time of Christ. So bold an assertion shocked even Newton. But Halley was able to substantiate it by comparing lunar eclipses, whose day and hour had always been noted with care, with the values he had calculated for them.

Using the same method he immortalized himself by prophesying the return of the comet that bears his name, although he himself was never to see it again. His original intention had been to cal-

THE APPEARANCE OF WHAT WAS PROBABLY HALLEY'S COMET BEFORE THE BATTLE OF HASTINGS IN A.D. 1066. IT WAS REGARDED AS AN OMEN OF EVIL. ILLUSTRATION FROM THE BAYEUX TAPESTRY; THE LEGEND READS: "HERE THEY MARVEL AT A STAR."

culate the shape of a comet's orbit by the law of gravitation. For this purpose he gathered all earlier data on those long-tailed "harbingers of misfortune," but found that he did not have enough information to determine the form of their orbits. Nevertheless, he was able to deduce, as a corollary to his work, that the three comets of 1531, 1607, and 1682 were in all probability one and the same body.

This, too, was a revolutionary idea. Comets had always been considered special messengers out of the depths of space which swung once in a great loop around the Sun, and disappeared forever. Halley averred that there was at least one regular visitor which came streaking into our ken every seventy-six years, following a typical Keplerian ellipse, its orbit being at most three times the distance of Saturn, then the outermost planet. Halley also reckoned backward to still earlier visits, and decided that his might well be the comet which had stood above the battlefield at Hastings in 1066, and had perhaps looked down upon the destruction of Jerusalem by Titus. And he predicted that in 1757, or at the latest in 1758, long after he himself had been gathered to his fathers, a brilliant comet would be seen.

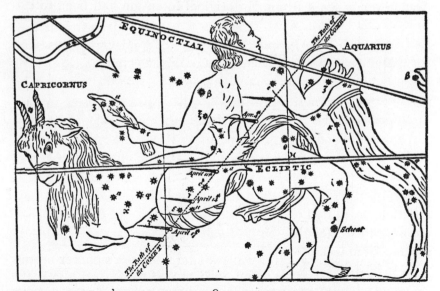

PATH OF HALLEY'S COMET OF 1758, FROM A CONTEMPORARY ENGRAVING.

Sure enough, in 1758 Halley's comet reappeared in all its magnificence.

Wobbly Earth, Wobbly Stars

Once a science has outgrown its infancy, someone must come along to teach it methodology and correct its childish errors. In astronomy this was done by the third Astronomer Royal at Greenwich, James Bradley, a former clergyman. He taught contemporary and future astronomers that observation is not merely a matter of reading off the figures. The principal work comes afterward; every figure must be corrected for refraction, precession, nutation, and aberration.

Two of these subtle rectifications were already known, and Bradley merely had to refine them; the other two were his gifts to astronomical science.

Every observation is affected by the four types of error. The first is the refraction of light rays by the atmosphere. Light is bent when it passes through dense layers of air. We still see the Sun on the horizon when in reality it has already set. This fact had long been known, and Tycho Brahe had calculated the error for different altitudes. But the amount of refraction changes with the temperature and pressure of the air; therefore thermometers and barometers had also to be consulted. Bradley drew up the appropriate tables to facilitate the complicated calculations.

The second error is precession, the shifting of the Earth's poles. Although this shift takes place with extreme slowness, it has a notable effect over the years. Bradley discovered that the Earth's pole is also subject to a third error, a wobbling motion, nutation, and that the period of this motion is only 18.6 years. Under these circumstances, the altered positions of the stars had to be calculated from week to week.

In regard to the fourth error, aberration, Bradley set hard assignments for future observers by demonstrating that even the stars wobble to a considerable extent, and each one differently

from the others. Some sway back and forth, others weave in and out, and a third group perform a round dance, all in the course of a year. We can see the endless computations that must be done before the true position of the star is determined at last.

This wobbling of the stars is not due to the intrinsic motion of the stars themselves. The annual periodicity would signalize that it must be connected with the Earth's voyage around the Sun. But how?

A flag on a moving boat streams backward in a direction opposite to that of the motion. But if there is any wind, the flag will not stream straight back, but in a direction that is a compound of the force of the wind and the force of the motion. Starlight, then, may be imagined as similar to the flag. It moves toward the Earth at a speed of 186,000 miles per second. But the Earth is moving on its orbit at a speed of 18 miles per second. Consequently, the direction of the light is slightly changed; we see the star in a position slightly different from its real position. In the course of the year these positions change constantly as the Earth races around its orbit.

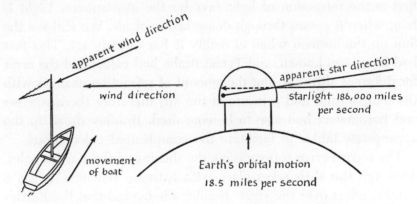

BRADLEY'S EXPLANATION OF THE APPARENT DISPLACEMENT OF STARS. THE DIRECTION OF THE FLAG ON THE BOAT IS A COMPOUND OF THE FORCE OF THE WIND AND THE FORCE OF THE BOAT'S MOTION. STARLIGHT IS SIMILARLY AFFECTED BY THE EARTH'S ORBITAL MOTION.

This notable insight resulted in a table of corrections for observers, and in other highly fruitful consequences: for the first time it proved beyond question that the Earth did journey around

the Sun; it permitted a better estimate of the speed of light; it demonstrated that the stars were at considerably greater distances than had been hitherto assumed—at least 200,000 times more distant than the Sun.

With Bradley, proverbial astronomical precision really began. His observations yielded the first truly correct figures, positions that can still be used today. To appreciate his feat, we must picture Greenwich as it was then: an ordinary building on a hill, where two ill-paid men spent the few clear nights eternally repeating measurements with the most rudimentary of instruments, and sat all day long over dull calculation of endless tables. In addition to Greenwich there was only one other observatory, the Sun King's impractical, palatial structure at Paris, where the astronomers toiled under similar difficulties.

When we keep these facts in mind, we realize how little equipment it took to create our present picture of the world: a few telescopes with crude lenses and cruder frameworks. All the essential work was performed by pure intellect, and sprang from the minds of about two dozen men.

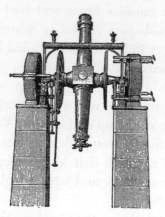

PERSPECTIVE, PROSPECT, RETROSPECT

The Galactic Island

A<small>T FIRST</small> it was a sailor's yarn. Then a saddler's son made a comprehensive world-view out of it, and a onetime tailor's apprentice conferred upon it the hallowed quality of a cult. Contemporaries who lived through this development must have felt like the sultan of the Arabian Nights when he looked out the window in the morning and saw Aladdin's magic palace standing before him. For the familiar firmament had been shattered. In its place was a lens-shaped crystal in which man's Earth was enclosed like an insect in amber, surrounded by the innumerable glowworms of the heavens.

The sailor who rubbed the magic lamp was named Thomas Wright. Like other sailors, he was well acquainted with the stars. Like other sailors, he stared up at the Milky Way during his night watches. But he differed from other sailors in his craving for knowledge; he read so much that he gave up the seafaring life, becoming first a private tutor and later a highly respected maker of precision instruments.

Undoubtedly, Wright knew the Greek myth of the origin of the Milky Way—that scandalous story of the goddess Hera who, upon awakening, found a strange infant sucking at her breast, and angrily pulled it away so that her milk spurted over the sky; forever after she was to persecute the unlucky infant, Hercules, because he was a bastard son of her divine spouse.

The Milky Way has captured the imagination of all ages. That prime mystery of the Creation had been resolved into stars by Galileo's telescope, but it was for the first time seen for what it truly was by Thomas Wright around 1740. Wright looked at the same firmament that had been scanned from time immemorial by sailors and astronomers, but he viewed it differently.

He looked up at the celestial sphere, embroidered with stars and girdled by a belt where the tiny dots of light seemed extraordinarily thicker. This was what all men had seen before him, but Wright for the first time asked the question: Was there really a greater density of stars in the Milky Way? And he concluded that the appearance of density was an optical illusion. In reality the points of light must be just as far from one another as elsewhere in the heavens, but along this one belt more layers of them could be seen, so many layers that the eye could not distinguish among them and their massed light merged into a milky glow. Our stellar system, Wright decided, is not spherical in shape; rather, we ourselves are in the heart of a lens-shaped system of stars. If we look at the lens broadside, we see relatively few, isolated stars; if we look toward the rim of the lens, however, more and more of them are visible, so that we cannot see out to the boundary of the lens, cannot discern the farthest stars separately. Instead we see a pale band of light which we call the Milky Way.

For the first time the appearance of the entire firmament was explained; for the first time someone had envisioned the stellar system as a whole, simply by synthesizing the elements of a familiar experience. There could scarcely be a better example of how difficult it is to see what lies before our eyes. How many thousands of years had men studied the various constellations, attributed to them mystic influences upon human destinies, marked them in horoscopes, worn images of them as luck charms around their necks, determined the times of their rising and setting with great precision; how many astronomers had mapped the stellar hosts, fixed the position of every dot of light on celestial globes, by dint of the greatest patience measured the latitude and longitude of stars with instruments—and yet it had not oc-

curred to anyone to picture to himself what the whole looked like.

Thomas Wright's vision was revolutionary. Alongside the solar system he presented humanity with the stellar system. He showed us the star-filled spaces in their true depth and form: not as a sphere, but rather as a lens the edge of which was drawn out into the silvery band of the Milky Way. The picture was obvious and incontestable to anyone who once looked at the sky in the way Wright saw it.

The saddler's son who built a philosophy out of Wright's vision was Immanuel Kant. Before he set about his lifework of writing critiques of man's capacity to know, he examined Wright's discovery with his peculiar critical techniques, and came to two remarkable conclusions.

The first of these was that the stellar system has a form similar to that of the solar system. Both are flat discs. All the planets travel in the plane of the zodiac. It would not be inconceivable that the flat stellar system also rotates. Halley had demonstrated that the stars moved. Kant conjectured that they revolved in elliptical orbits around an unknown center. The "Galaxy," henceforth conceived of as the totality of all stars, would then be a kind of wheel turning in a tremendous ellipse.

His second conclusion was this: there is no reason to believe that the galactic system represents the entire universe. There might well be countless other such wheels in space. In fact, Kant thought some of these had already been seen. For the finest telescopes had detected among the stars "nebulous spots" of irregular shapes, but largely oval. These might be distant galaxies, so far away that the combined light of all their stars merged into a tiny cloud.

What an extension of man's horizon this was! What a magnificent picture of creation: an ocean in which floating island universes revolved around their own axes. Our Milky Way, our Galaxy, would be only one such island, just as the Sun was only one among countless stars, as our Earth was only one of the planets. Solar system, stellar system, and nebular system—three nested universes, each of the higher order than the one before. And the

supreme cosmos was not something finite and rigid, but a shoreless ocean in which galaxies whirled and intersected, vast firewheels in the heavens.

This cosmology constituted an ideal toward which European astronomy had striven since the Renaissance. In the eighteenth century it was at last perfected. And at the same time it found a herald who employed his singular eloquence to spread word of it in ladies' drawing rooms and at royal tables: the former tailor's apprentice, Johann Heinrich Lambert, self-taught surveyor, mathematician, physicist, and philosopher. He was also the inventor of the hygrometer, pyrometer, and photometer—in other words, he made it possible for science to measure moisture, the heat of a flame, and the brightness of a light.

Heinrich Lambert also sketched in a further vista for the new cosmology, a more sublime horizon. The universe of milky ways need not be *the* universe, he suggested. A further universe was conceivable, in which the totality of all nebulae need represent only a drop in the ocean of a still vaster cosmos. And this concept might be extended ad infinitum. No matter how many systems man might, in the remote future, see with telescopes of incredible power, his mind might conceive another system of a still higher order.

This proposition of Lambert's presented the idea of "infinity," to which the spirit of Western man so naturally subscribes, in its purest and most mature form. At this point science culminated in philosophy, and philosophy in religion.

However, objections to his principle of infinity arose during the nineteenth century. If, it was argued, the material of the universe extended on indefinitely, there should not be a single spot in the sky where there was not some star showing. The twentieth century added another argument: that if there were infinitely numerous centers of gravitation, the sum of their effects would be felt everywhere, and a closed planetary system with exact orbits, like ours, would be impossible. But in 1922 C. V. L. Charlier, a Swedish scientist, proved mathematically that neither light nor gravitation from any higher system necessarily need affect the lower system nested within it.

Future of the Solar System

At Christmas 1758, after an interval of seventy-six years, Halley's comet reappeared just in time to make good Halley's prophecy; the astronomers had already begun to fear that the theory of elliptical orbits for comets was false. Most pleased of all was a mathematician, Alexis Clairaut, for he himself had recalculated the orbit and predicted that Halley's comet would reappear almost a year later than expected, while his own calculation would be correct to within two weeks.

Clairaut was a veritable prodigy. He wrote his first mathematical treatise while still a schoolboy; by the time he was a student at the university, he was also a member of the Académie des Sciences. That Halley's comet was late was due to the interference of Jupiter, whose gravitational attraction slowed the comet in its orbit this time. To divine such perturbations, as they were called, was the particular ambition of a group of five mathematicians belonging to Frederick the Great's circle at Sans Souci: Euler, Clairaut, d'Alembert, Lagrange, and Laplace. Each of these men vied with the others, and each pushed the cart a little farther along. What emerged from their efforts was an apotheosis of the law of gravitation, a cosmic philosophy in figures, a reconstruction of God's most secret thoughts about His creation. Their ideas went far beyond Kepler's "harmony of the universe," and often contradicted it.

Scientifically, the great scheme these five mathematicians worked out bore the modest name of perturbation theory. The planets, it follows from the law of gravitation, are not only attracted by the Sun, but also attract one another. These counter-influences were extraordinarily difficult to calculate. Clairaut and d'Alembert debated fruitlessly with one another for years over the simplest of the problems, the mutual effects of the gravitational attraction of three bodies upon one another. Lagrange succeeded in solving this three-body problem for certain special cases, but to this day these remain the only ones that have been solved.

EIGHTEENTH-CENTURY ORRERY. THIS FORERUNNER OF THE MODERN PLANETARIUM ILLUSTRATED THE RELATIVE POSITIONS AND MOTIONS OF BODIES IN THE SOLAR SYSTEM BY ROTATION AND REVOLUTION OF BALLS MOVED BY WHEELWORK.

One such case became of practical interest when, during the nineteenth century, a whole family of minor planets was discovered. A group of these tiny members of the solar system, designated by Trojan names—Hector, Paris, etc.—took a path across the orbit of Jupiter which perturbation theory would have ruled impossible until Lagrange demonstrated that a small body could revolve in an orbit in such a way that its distances from the Sun and Jupiter equal the distance of Jupiter from the Sun. In other words, the three form an equilateral triangle.

On the other hand, another and negative characteristic of gravitation was revealed by an American astronomer, Daniel Kirkwood, in 1866, and this one put an end to Kepler's music of the spheres. The workings of this characteristic rule out orbits whose periods bear to the period of Jupiter the simple fractional ratios, 1/2, 1/3, 2/5, etc. The minor planets in the solar system are forced to limit themselves to incommensurable orbits. This rule serves to explain the striking split in Saturn's rings; the split lies at a harmonious distance between Saturn and its next moon, within which no matter may move; the ring has been cleared by the gravitational forces. The swarm of minor planets between Jupiter and Mars illustrates the same principle; they shun the forbidden zone.

It should be noted that this theory has not been conclusively demonstrated mathematically, and that there are exceptions to it. Jupiter permits the asteroid Hilda to revolve in the 2/3 zone. Moreover, the major planets Saturn and Jupiter revolve obstinately in an entirely commensurable 2/5 relationship, which results in no catastrophic perturbation, only in an oscillation that balances out every 930 years.

Euler, who took the lead in the theory of perturbation, found that Kepler's ellipses were extremely fickle. The mutual attractions of the planets resulted in constant variations in their orbits, including that of the Earth. In addition to the well-known perturbations in the motion of our globe, the wobbling and nodding known as precession and nutation, there were at least three other perturbations: the Earth's orbit turns, changes its inclination, and changes its diameter, with the result that the length of the year changes. All this takes place over thousands of years, and therefore does not produce noticeable effects. But ultimately the Earth might elongate its orbit so far that the Sun's warmth would no longer suffice for the preservation of life.

In the eighteenth century, humanity was not yet hardened to the fate of distant posterity. Men were seriously concerned about God's plans for His image; they wanted to know whether He had indeed created so transitory a world.

On the whole it turned out that the initial anxiety for the solar

system was greatly exaggerated. Everywhere there are balancing forces; almost all perturbations so far discovered are periodic and are readjusted by the alternating interplay of gravitational forces. This fact was demonstrated by the last of the great five, Pierre Simon de Laplace.

Laplace brought in the harvest. In his *Mécanique Céleste* Newton's law was elevated into the true formula for the universe, by which every minute influence could be analyzed, and the remotest future of the solar system could be calculated. In its very complexity the Copernican system now appeared a miracle of creation, far more harmonious than Kepler could ever have dreamed.

Only a single troublesome question remained: the acceleration of the Moon, which Halley had demonstrated upon the basis of old records. Laplace concluded that it was one of those periodic perturbations produced by the Earth's gravitation, and he worked out a theoretical value which agreed with Halley's figures. Unfortunately, this reassurance was destined to last only a short time. A nineteenth-century mathematician showed that a remainder of five seconds still had not been eliminated. In other words, the Moon ran five seconds ahead every hundred years. Theory could not account for this; a reason had to be found. Someone recalled a paper Kant had written as a student, bearing the alarming title "Does the Earth Undergo Changes in its Rotation?" Kant thought that the friction of the tides might cause a braking of the Earth's rotation and therefore an apparent acceleration of the Moon.

This possibility was now worked out mathematically. To all appearances, changes in the Earth's rotation actually do take place. Modern perturbation theory even poses the probability that our day is constantly increasing, that the Moon is steadily accelerating and at the same time fleeing from us—so that after millions of years the month and the day will be equal. Kepler's dreadful picture of the Moon's plight would then be fulfilled on the Earth: we would experience fifty days of fiery, burning sunlight—then an equally long, continuous bitter-cold night.

Evolution of the Planets

Suddenly, around 1750, the idea of evolution in its largest sense crept in some unexplained manner into the consciousness of European humanity. It was our culture's profoundest idea, and one inseparable from its character. We see ourselves as part of an eternal process of growth, growth of nations and of the mind, of nature, the Earth, and the heavens. Only knowledge of how a thing became what it is gives us a feeling of really understanding it. We are not satisfied with insight into the character of things; we must fathom their origins before we feel that we have begun to reach the ultimate truth about them. Ancient thinkers sought the common beginning and end of things; we interpose between beginning and end the protracted process of "evolution."

Even such superior minds as those of Descartes, Huygens, Newton, and Leibnitz still considered the cosmos immutable. The French mathematicians of the middle eighteenth century recognized that extremely minute changes took place in the secular rhythm, but since they considered these to be only long-term oscillations, the sum of such movements nevertheless constituted a static picture. It remained for Immanuel Kant to conceive the universe as actually the result of a process of growth, and as undergoing perpetual change.

It is significant that Kant also considered biological evolution three generations before Darwin, but quickly rejected it on philosophical grounds. Here we are concerned only with Kant's importance for the science of astronomy. He will be remembered for having ventured to outline the first Western cosmogony.

Natural History of the Heavens, Kant called it, by the very name sharply distinguishing it from Greek cosmogony. His aim was not a mythology, but a realistic mechanics of nature. Kant realized, quite as clearly as had Kepler, that he was thereby leaving to the Creator only the prime impulse, the first day—the other six days of creation were then to be governed by the "forces" the Deity had set free.

Kant was also fully aware of the offense his undertaking would

give to many persons. "I have chosen a subject that in addition to internal difficulties is subject to grave criticisms on religious grounds. To derive the origin of the universe from its primal state by mechanical laws would seem to be far beyond the faculties of man. And the Church threatens solemn condemnation if anyone attempts to make nature responsible for the works that dogma has assigned to the hand of the Supreme Being. Well do I see these obstacles, but I shall not lose courage. On slender conjecture I have set forth upon a perilous journey, and already I see the promontory of new lands."

The idea of evolution was suggested to him when he saw Wright's stellar system multiplied in distant universes, the nebulae. At that point he hit on the idea which to this day lies at the root of all attempted cosmogonies: that the beginning of all heavenly bodies was a nebula.

"This condition of nature seems to me the simplest that can succeed the Void," he wrote.

In this striking sentence he represented the instinctive approach of the Western mind to the problem of the beginning of all things. In considering the primal state of the universe we must look for the simplest condition that experience has shown us to exist. The Kantian primal nebula was accepted by virtually all astronomers as the beginning of the universe. To deduce everything purely mechanically from that primordial state, to interpret the history of the universe as the development of natural forces, is the sole aim of scientific cosmogony.

Kant could only suggest the approach. He did not plunge deep enough into empirical evidence to arrive at actual demonstrations. He assumed nothing but a primal nebula with its molecules in random motion. As the result of collisions, he believed, small cores of mass would arise, and these would attract other molecules. Thus the matter of the universe would condense of its own accord into great spheres of gas, stars. The successive impacts from collisions would have started these rotating. Several smaller masses would be prevented by collisions from fusing with the great ball of gas, and these would then revolve around it as planets.

All this was formulated vaguely, dubiously, unsatisfactorily. Kant was in truth seeing only the promontory of the new lands. Laplace pushed his way into them.

Laplace's theory remained for over a century the last word in cosmogony, the crowning achievement of astronomy. For he provided a picture comprehensible and convincing to everyone of the origin of our planetary system, including the Earth. Yet he advanced it in a footnote to his five-volume *Mécanique Céleste*, putting it forward almost with a guilty conscience, and at any rate "with that uncertainty which attaches to everything that is not the result of observation and calculation." Nevertheless, this theory brought him more fame than all the rest of his work—and justly so. For he had founded it upon extremely in-

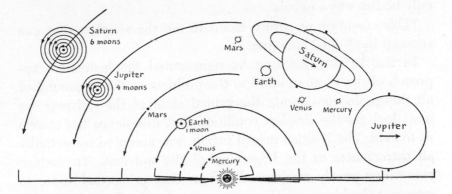

LAPLACE'S FOUR MIRACLES: (1) ALL PLANETS AND MOONS REVOLVE IN THE SAME DIRECTION; (2) THE PLANETS (AS FAR AS THEN KNOWN) ROTATE IN THE SAME DIRECTION; (3) THE PLANETS ALL MOVE IN THE SAME PLANE, WITH ONLY MINOR DEVIATIONS; (4) THE PLANETS AND THE MOONS DESCRIBE ALMOST CIRCULAR ELLIPSES.

teresting facts which had been obvious for centuries, but which had spurred no one before him to reflection. Apparently no one had hitherto considered them significant. There were four such facts:

1. The planets and their moons all revolve in the same direction. All the thirty planetary bodies and satellites known to Laplace revolved from east to west. Was this not strange?

2. The planets, as far as was then known, also rotate without exception in the same east-west direction. Could this be chance?

3. The planets all move in the zodiac, that is to say, within the same plane, with only small deviations. How could that be explained?

4. The planets and the moons describe ellipses of very low eccentricity—in other words almost circular ellipses—while the comets have extremely elongated orbits. Whence this tendency toward circularity among the moons and planets?

Laplace explained these four striking peculiarities of our solar system by a single hypothesis: that the system had arisen out of a rotating nebular sphere. He pictured the process in the following manner:

When the nebula slowly cooled off in the cold of space, and therefore contracted, its rotational velocity increased. Centrifugal force would then stretch it out; from a sphere it became an ellipsoid and a disc. At a certain point centrifugal force in this flattened disc became more powerful than gravitation. Consequently, a nebular ring broke free, something like the ring of Saturn. This ring naturally continued to participate in the rotary motion and went on cooling. Eventually, a center of mass arose in the cloud, which attracted to itself the rest of the cloud; this became a spherical planet. It rotated of its own accord because, true to Kepler's law, it revolved more slowly on the exterior than on the interior.

Such was Laplace's world-famous account of the birth of the planets. The same process needed only to be repeated to yield several planets and their satellites. The smaller these were, the more quickly they condensed into solid bodies; consequently, great Jupiter and Saturn were still spheres of gas. And, exceptionally, one moon of Saturn condensed so evenly that it remained in its original ring shape.

With this wonderfully consistent, crystal-clear, and supremely orderly version of evolution, Laplace capped the summit of astronomy's two-hundred-year ascent.

Book Four

THE ADVENTUROUS
AMATEURS

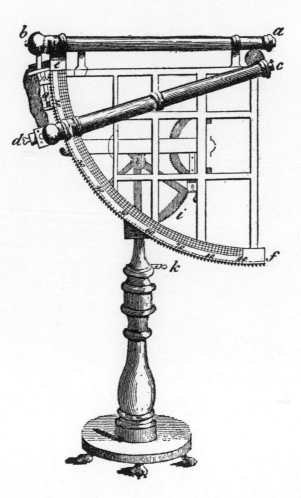

HERSCHEL'S PLUNGE INTO SPACE

The Seventh Planet

SINCE THE DAYS of Galileo, no telescopic find had created a greater sensation than Uranus. "We see," said the President of the Royal Society as he presented its discoverer, William Herschel, with the Copley Medal, "that the treasures of the heavens are inexhaustible. If more unknown planets exist, we may look forward to new surprises on the part of Science."

Only a little while before, no one had been counting on any surprises, especially not from astronomers. They had become bureaucrats, reliable timekeepers for the universe. No doubt they would be making their calculations a little more precise, measuring the positions of a few more stars, but there seemed small likelihood that they would do anything exciting.

European astronomy had apparently reached its goal. Everywhere, it had corroborated Newton's universal law, even forcing the fractious Moon to obedience; everywhere it had replaced the Greek harmony of the spheres with the modern concept of infinity; it had fitted the stars into galaxies, the galaxies into universes; it had described the evolution of the planets from the primal nebula. No greater accomplishments could be imagined. Frederick the Great was only expressing the convictions of his generation when he declared that everything essential had already been done in science and technology.

In the light of contemporary knowledge such a statement appears comical, for at that very time Watt was making his steam

engine, Hargreaves, Arkwright, and Jacquard were introducing machine technology, and Leblanc founding the chemical industry. Lavoisier and Davy were making chemistry a science; Galvani and Volta were becoming acquainted with one of the most powerful and mysterious forces of nature. And William Herschel was setting entirely new goals for astronomy.

Before Herschel became world famous as the discoverer of the planet Uranus, he was almost completely unknown in professional circles. The *Gazette Littéraire* referred to him as Mersthel, the Astronomer Royal of Greenwich did not know whether to spell the name Herthel or Herrschel. He was, in fact, a musician, a *Kapellmeister* who had only been engaging in astronomy as a hobby for a very short time. But how he went about this hobby!

In the first place, he employed a completely new type of telescope, so unusually wide that a man could put his head into the tube. The metallic mirror at the lower end was twice the size of all known telescopes. Why this abnormal width when the magnification depended only on the length of a telescope? To gather light, Herschel explained when his instrument was tested at Greenwich. He wanted to see objects whose light was feeble, stars and nebulae smaller and more distant than any that had been seen before. For these, the brightness and not the magnification was what mattered. This, he explained, was how he had found the hitherto unknown planet.

It was not the instrument alone that had enabled him to find it. His method of searching, what he called sweeping, was also an important factor in his great discovery. Every night he took a strip of sky of about two degrees. He went through it twice in order not to miss anything. Herschel regarded the firmament as his private hunting ground. He did not sit at the telescope in order to make measurements, but only to search for new bodies. His kind of observation was a perpetual exciting journey into unexplored territories. Five times he swept the entire celestial sphere, and each time it was a new adventure, for each time he worked with a larger, wider telescope of his own making, which showed ten times as many objects as the preceding instrument.

Thus this outsider broke through the rigidity that had over-

taken astronomy by the seventeen eighties. For the next three generations, the progress of astronomy was almost exclusively the work of amateurs. Each one of these established himself in some corner and looked around until he had discovered something special, to the utter amazement of the professionals. Never since has anything similar taken place in the sciences.

Herschel, however, surpassed them all. He was a true Titan. In his day he was the pioneer of a new type of astronomy; he remains still the most brilliant, successful, and fruitful representative of his science. During forty years of constant activity he published some sixty-four papers far superior to anything produced by other astronomers of his time. In all fields he outstripped his colleagues. If some German found a few dozen binary stars, Herschel discovered several hundred. If a Frenchman listed sixty nebulae, Herschel soon afterwards published a catalogue of a thousand. There was no special branch of the science in which he did not take the lead.

Even contemporary astronomy is still feeding on some of Herschel's ideas. Of modern astronomy's three principal methods of approach, Herschel was the father of the most original: stellar statistics. Hitherto, he pointed out, astronomers had conceived of the starry firmament as the inner surface of a hollow sphere. He chose to see it as extended three-dimensional space. In the future, he avowed, astronomers would peer into the universe as if it were a landscape of many vistas and strata, and would explore and measure it like geographers.

Finally, Herschel had formulated for his colleagues the supreme imperative of the scientist with a clarity unsurpassed since Kepler: that a scientist must be prepared to revise his entire doctrine in the light of a single new fact. In his old age he often retracted his most ambitious hypotheses because he chanced to discover some nebula that did not accord with them. Observation must always take precedence over theory, he held; therefore he did not care that his current views might stand in direct contradiction to his earlier ideas.

He knew that he was not a perfecter, but a forerunner; and, indeed, one had to wait for the twentieth century to complete

the work he had begun. By then many of his unique ideas had already been so entirely forgotten that two astronomers, Seeliger and Kapteyn, won fame when they took up once again Herschel's technique of stellar statistics.

Curiously enough, this Titan, this super-astronomer, did not develop his hobby until he was nearly forty.

Double Stars, Star Clusters, and Nebulae

When George III of England first gave audience to the discoverer of Uranus, he indulged the whimsey of handing Herschel a pardon. For Herschel had been a deserter twenty years before; he had taken French leave from a Hanoverian regiment of guards, and fled to England, never thinking that the House of Hanover was also the ruling house of England.

In England he was not molested, however, and made his way as a musician—Herschel sprang from an unusually cultivated and gifted German-Jewish family. In an organists' competition Herschel won the prize for his expressive playing and extremely powerful chords; he placed lead weights on some of the keys, thus intensifying the basses. It might be said that his "fondness for excessive magnification" showed early in life.

At the age of thirty-six he became the music master at Bath. There he conducted Handel's oratorios with a hundred-man orchestra and large chorus, played the organ in the biggest church and first violin in the theater, gave private recitals, had a host of pupils, and won esteem as a composer. After his fourteen-hour working day as a musician, he sat up half the night reading enthralling books on the calculus of fluxions, theoretical optics, and mathematical astronomy. Soon he bought a small telescope and began sweeping the sky with it. By and by he built a telescope of his own, and this was followed by a second and a third.

His house became part music studio, part observatory, part forge, and part optical works. To this cozy home he brought, from Hanover, his brother Alexander and his favorite sister, Caro-

line, then eighteen. She learned successively English, house-keeping, singing, and polishing optical mirrors. She wrote out orchestrations and copied astronomical tables. In this family sleeping and eating were considered concessions to the weak-nesses of human nature, and were reduced to the absolute mini-mum.

Everything that Herschel undertook he pursued on the same grand scale. Since the height of the mountains of the Moon in-terested him, he measured more than one hundred lunar craters, making each measurement by three different methods. When his third telescope revealed to him that certain stars were actually double, he set about tracking down such binaries, and located three hundred of them. With the passing of years and the im-provement of his instruments, he raised this number to eight hun-dred. Every third fixed star in the relative vicinity of our Sun turned out to be paired.

The question was whether there were really binaries, or whether they happened to be in the same line of sight, with the one actually a thousand times more distant from us than the other. Herschel concluded that a genuine pair must revolve around one another; otherwise, if they were really close to-gether, their mutual attraction must have brought them to a col-lision long before.

Herschel demonstrated the orbital motion of many double stars. If in one observation a partner appeared to the right of the other, an observation the following year would show it below its companion. He was even able to estimate the periods of rev-olution. These differed widely, varying from 2 to 700 years. Usu-ally the members of a pair remain at a considerable distance from one another, minimally as far apart as Mars from our Sun.

It might be pleasant to occupy a planet in such a system: when one sun set, the other would rise. Possibly there would be no nights at all, and for many hours at a time two suns would illu-minate the heavens. Objects would cast two shadows. What brightness, warmth, and growth there might be on such a green-house planet!

There are further possibilities, for in addition to binary sys-

tems, there are groups of four, six, and eight stars. If the Earth circled Zeta in Cancer, we would have two yellow suns, and one orange sun with a darker companion beaming down upon us. Once a year they would cluster close together, glowing like so many colored spotlights.

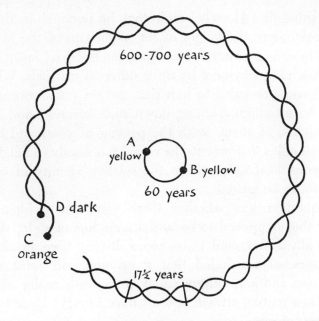

FOUR-STAR SYSTEM IN CANCER. THE BINARY CD CIRCLES THE BINARY AB.

Since the orbits of binary stars are governed by the law of gravitation, their masses can be calculated. They are thus of enormous value to astronomers, and this is one of the reasons why they have been favorite subjects of study since Herschel. From their behavior, the characteristics of a whole host of other stars can be deduced. Today some thirty thousand of them are known, but there are innumerable others too far away for the best telescope to resolve. Herschel's estimate that a third of all stars are binaries remains valid.

During Herschel's first exploration, he unwittingly came across the new planet Uranus, which gave him a flattering but troublesome spell of glory: the audience with the King, honors by the

Royal Society, invitations to London society. He lost a whole three months of observation. It was all very well, he wrote to his sister Caroline, but he wanted to finish polishing his new mirror. And he complained that being a social lion verged perilously on the role of court jester.

His new mirror was a foot in diameter. For pouring it, Herschel had a smelting furnace built in his conservatory; it evolved such fierce heat that the stone floor split apart. For the mold, baskets of horse manure had to be pulverized and sifted—a pleasant little chore for Caroline. The framework for the twenty-foot tube was still unfinished when Herschel climbed up in the darkness one evening, to test his marvelous new mirror. The whole structure collapsed; Herschel was lucky to escape with nothing worse than several sprains. He met Caroline's upbraidings by appointing her his assistant—so that from then on she spent her nights delicately turning micrometer screws, or stooping over the Flamsteed celestial atlas, registering their discoveries. In winter her work took up ten to twelve hours of the night, while the day was devoted to running the household.

Herschel's fourth sweep of the sky was an affair of four years. This time he specialized in hitherto almost unknown bodies: star clusters and nebulae.

The Pleiades are the most striking example of a star cluster: six dots of light close together. Nearsighted persons cannot distinguish them, but even a pair of weak binoculars will show them to be a collection of about fifty stars. Herschel discovered clusters containing many thousands of stars, clusters of every imaginable type, from those that looked like widely scattered clouds of powder to those that resembled closely packed balls of shot. This last type contains so many stars that in the center of the cluster even the best telescopes cannot resolve them. In some spherical clusters Herschel estimated the number of stars at twenty-five to forty thousand.

It was not tenable that so many stars were close to one another only in appearance. These must be real clusters, Herschel reasoned, tremendous demonstrations of gravitational attraction. Apparently there were stars that had been unable to resist the

attraction of their neighbors, stars having little or no proper motion of their own. Consequently, Herschel thought, they rushed toward one another, forming still more powerful gravitational centers and drawing everything that approached them into bigger and ever-denser packs.

Globular clusters of this sort are not too numerous, however; even today, only some hundred of them have been counted. On the other hand, the nebulae are extremely common. Herschel sometimes discovered from four to six of them in a single night, and was firmly convinced that they existed in multitudes beyond imagination. Most of them were oval, some spindle-shaped, some round; some were quite ragged and irregular in shape. Like Kant, Herschel considered them remote island universes, gigantic stellar systems at enormous distances. But he went beyond Kant in ascribing an evolution to them. The variety of forms impelled him to consider them as stages of successive development. This was, he believed, a process of constant condensation under the influence of gravitation. In the beginning was the irregular primal nebula; this rounded out, became oval because of rotation, and so evolved into a stellar system like our Galaxy. But that would not be the end. Gradually their motion was slowed and the stars were drawn closer to one another, condensing further into globular clusters.

Thus Herschel was the first who ventured to predict the doom of universes. He pictured the single stars uniting irresistibly, pressing closer and closer together, until at last only a few gigantic clusters floated about in a fearfully empty universe. In one of these clusters would be the Earth, imprisoned among countless onrushing stars, a molten, lifeless planet.

The Sun's Orbit

While Herschel played with such visions, he was polishing one metallic mirror after another, not for his own use, but for sale. He had become a telescope manufacturer.

The reason for this was the King's benevolence in liberating him from his work as a professional musician by assigning him a pension approximately equivalent to the salary of the Astronomer Royal at Greenwich. This was all very well, but George III had no conception of the expenses of Herschel's hobby, or of how much he had earned by his various musical activities. Caroline wept with chagrin when she learned the amount of the pension. "Never has a king purchased such an honor so cheaply," she exclaimed.

Herschel found a solution; he decided to take orders for telescopes. Caroline was appointed a new chore: to feed morsels of food into his mouth while he bent for ten hours at a stretch over the grindstone. The result was tangible: within a few years the Brothers Herschel produced 200 four-inchers, 150 six-inchers, and 80 nine-inchers. These were sent as far as Madrid, and brought in fabulous sums.

Naturally, his nocturnal forays among the stars suffered no pause from this casual subsidiary occupation. He was, however, much troubled by the King's demands upon his time. The King insisted that Herschel move to the vicinity of Windsor and keep him informed of all astronomical novelties. Unfortunately, this could be done only at night. What was more, the meetings of the Royal Society, at which Herschel had to lecture, also took place at night. He made a point of sacrificing only full Moon nights, when he could not observe decently anyhow, to these activities. After his sessions with the King or his lectures, he would take the night stage home.

With him away, his sister was unable to sleep; he therefore proposed that Caroline spend her wakeful hours hunting comets. He did not much care for the pursuit of such tiny celestial objects; finding them was purely a matter of luck. When Caroline had grown accustomed to spending "every starry night on wet or hoarfrost-covered grass, without a human being within call," she did honor to the name of Herschel, and to herself as the first woman astronomer, by discovering eight comets. She worked on the lawn because it never occurred to Herschel to build an observatory.

At the age of forty-five Herschel married a rich widow. There-after, his financial troubles were over. The manufacture of tele-scopes was abandoned. Twice more in his life Herschel moved; each time he spent the last night at his old home at his twelve-inch mirror, and took care that the towering scaffolding stood on the lawn at his new house ready for use on the very first night.

After he had settled down finally in Slough he gratified his heart's desire, a mammoth telescope such as the world had never seen before. The construction of it required three tries and five years. The first metal disc was too thin; the second cracked in pouring; the third was ground and polished for six months, then proved still inadequate, and had to go back to the workshop. The new mirror had a diameter of nearly 48 inches, almost four times the size of the last one. At his first glance through it, Her-schel discovered two new moons of Saturn.

The tube for the telescope was forty feet long, and mounted on a turntable. After scrambling up a ladder, the observer stood in a wooden cage suspended from the tube, and looked down into it; he was raised and lowered with the tube, and turned in a cir-cle along with the entire apparatus—not the most charming sen-sation on a pitch-dark night, especially when the wind made the scaffolding groan and shiver. Sprains and broken bones were fairly common among the attendants; luckily for the ladies, hoop skirts went out of fashion, else they would never have been able to experience the thrill of gazing into the first great "eye" of mod-ern astronomy.

The telescope was enough of a sensation to bring a constant stream of the curious to Slough. In the end Herschel found that he had taken on still another profession: he now played the part of cicerone to astronomy. In this role, too, he displayed talent. If princesses chanced to turn up on a cloudy evening, he would show them how the huge telescope turned, explain in detail how binary stars were measured with a micrometer, and finally an-nounce: "Since, unfortunately, we cannot see anything in the sky tonight, I shall bring the most beautiful of celestial bodies out of the clouds for you." And suddenly Saturn would glow among the trees in the garden "so natural in appearance that

the best of astronomers might have been deceived." Herschel had made a papier-mâché Saturn and illuminated it with a shaded lantern.

"A delightful man," one lady reported, "extremely modest, for all his vast knowledge; candid as a child, delicately tactful and considerate. He responds with boyish gravity to all of one's questions, makes everything very clear, gives explanations which require little reflection on the part of the listener, and never loses patience. He puts forward his own ideas with indescribable charm. He knows the history of all the heavenly bodies to the farthermost boundaries of the Galaxy, and is more than willing to communicate to others all his wisdom. So confident is he of future discoveries that life seems a perfect joy to him. There is no happier man in all England."

His happiness was not dependent on his possessing the most powerful telescope in the world. Even without it he would have been a great astronomer, one of the greatest scientists who ever lived. For Herschel's creative imagination had as little need of instruments as the minds of Kant, Lambert, and Laplace. This emerges from his discoveries concerning the Sun.

Like every astronomer, Herschel saw the Sun's disc covered with spots for years at a time, then remain virtually unspotted for years. But he alone drew the conclusion that this phenomenon must cause variation in the Sun's radiation which would affect our Earth and would show up at least in the growth of plants. Consequently he studied the prices of grain for the past several decades, and detected a cycle. Many persons thought it a bad joke that sunspots should make bread dearer, but today it is known that the annual rings in trees reflect the sunspot cycles.

For the purpose of observing the Sun, Herschel devised combinations of colored glasses. He became interested in the fact that a combination which absorbed virtually all light permitted the Sun's heat to pass through unhindered. Other combinations screened out the heat and transmitted the light. Herschel concluded that light and heat were not inseparable, as had been thought, and cleverly checked this novel theory by allowing the light from a spectrum to fall upon a thermometer. Not bright

yellow, but the darkest red light, proved to have the greatest heat. In fact, to his surprise, the temperature registered still higher beyond the spectrum. He had discovered invisible heat rays, the infrared light with which so many "miracles" are performed nowadays.

His greatest achievement, however, was his application of the Copernican revolution to the Sun. He not only displaced the Sun from the center of the universe, but sent it off on a voyage through the Galaxy.

The astronomers of Greenwich had recently demonstrated and measured the movements of thirty-six stars, but remained unaware of the momentous conclusion that could be drawn from their work. The motions pointed in various directions, as if the stars were a flock of hens frightened by a carriage and fluttering off in all directions. But Herschel continued to recognize a common feature of the movement, and explained it as motion of the Sun, together with all his planets. By calculations that would have done honor to Newton, he determined the direction of the voyage: toward the star Lambda in Hercules.

Since Herschel's time we have to think of ourselves as being in motion in three major ways: (1) the daily rotation of the Earth around its axis at a surface speed of approximately .3 miles per second at the equator; (2) the annual revolution around the Sun at about sixty times that speed, 18.5 miles per second; (3) a similar speed in accompanying the solar system on its voyage toward Hercules. Another type of motion was discovered later, a revolution around the center of our Galaxy—in the Archer—at a speed of about 134 miles per second. It is this motion that is really responsible for Herschel's third motion, because the stars in the neighborhood of the Sun are also revolving around the center of the Galaxy, but in different orbits and with different speeds.

Of all this furious motion we notice nothing at all. Our tiny Copernican system of Sun, planets, and their flock of moons (ten circling Saturn alone) performs its own revolutions with fractional-second precision at the same time that it is being carried along in a mad rush at a tempo far in excess of our latest jet- and rocket-plane records. What more impressive demonstration could

there be of the sureness and smoothness imposed by the law of gravitation?

Sounding the Depths of Space

The most original of Herschel's inspirations were his three statistical methods: those dealing with standard fields, magnitude classes, and space-penetrating power.

If any science would seem predestined for statistical methods, it would be astronomy, with its millions upon millions of dots of light practically indistinguishable except for differences in brightness. To force this silent army of millions to yield secrets of the universe merely by counting heads was a task for which science was not yet prepared, would not be prepared for three generations.

The great astronomer was set on the track by the glorious sight provided him by his largest telescope. When he directed it at the Milky Way, he saw stars, nothing but stars. Galileo had detected a host of points of light in the silver streak across the sky, and had thereupon maintained that the Milky Way was nothing but an accumulation of stars. But while no one doubted his assertion, it remained at bottom a hypothesis. The vast mist was not truly dispelled until Herschel's great telescope penetrated it. The number of stars of all magnitudes to be seen therein astonished even Herschel. With his previous telescope he had been able to count no less than fifty thousand individual stars in an hour's time, but he estimated that there were, in the field he searched, at least twice that number, their light so feeble that he could detect only a vague gleam. With his new mammoth telescope even these remote stars showed distinctly; in an hour 140,-000 dots of light moved past him. He saw "myriads of worlds springing up like grass in the night." Herschel had a talent for dramatizing his observations, and he was not averse to flights of the imagination. "What would be the purpose of accumulating observations without making the attempt to draw conclusions

from them, and beyond that to develop theories, even if they should possess only a degree of probability? Our imagination desires to shape universes, and it may easily overstep the boundaries set by nature. I shall, however, endeavor to hold to the mean."

He already saw before him the wonderful prospect of drawing a map of the Galaxy, preferably to scale, as in a geographical atlas. Herschel hoped to transform Thomas Wright's intellectual construct into full-fledged reality. Wright had envisioned the totality of stars as a lens-shaped island universe, and interpreted the silver streak across the firmament as its remote edge. Herschel had succeeded in resolving this streak into countable points of light. The next step seemed obvious to him: to count stars systematically, and to derive from the differing densities of stars a true picture of our island universe.

For this purpose no complete count of the stars was needed; samples would suffice. Thus Herschel arrived at his method of "standard fields." He counted the stars in the visual field of his twelve-inch telescope, and repeated this count at selected spots distributed over the entire sky—some 3,400 spots altogether. His conclusion was that the myriads of stars form indeed a shallow disc with the Sun not quite in the center, but somewhat to one side. But there was no evidence for a lens-shaped galaxy; our island universe seemed to have irregular outlines, fiords and trailing arms, and moreover a deep split.

That this map of our stellar system was very rough, Herschel realized quite well. He was assuming uniform distribution of the

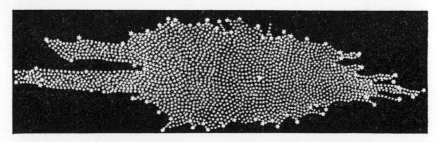

HERSCHEL'S MAP OF THE MILKY WAY (COMPARE DRAWING ON PAGE 347). OUR SUN IS THE BRIGHT SPOT IN RIGHT CENTER.

stars, for which there was no proof. Thoroughgoing as always, he determined to pursue the matter more deeply, and did so by further statistics.

Since ancient times the stars had been classified by orders of magnitude according to brightness. Herschel made an inventory of all stars visible to the naked eye, arranged according to six orders of magnitude.

Herschel's table led to some interesting deductions. It was a fair assumption, for instance, that the brightest stars would be the closest. Operating on this principle, Herschel boldly assumed that brightness provided a measure of distance. Six classes of magnitudes signified six shells of stars around the Sun, like successive layers of an onion. It should be possible to calculate theoretically how many stars each of these shells ought to contain, assuming uniform distribution.

Comparing the theoretical figures with those derived from observation, Herschel saw that theory and observation approximately agreed for the first three orders of magnitude. Thereafter, however, the actual figures far exceeded the calculated numbers. Regretfully, he abandoned his hypothesis of the uniform distribution of stars, and left it to future scientists to improve his map.

This they did after 1900, and their observations reversed his. The density of stars diminishes steadily, but only from the twelfth order of magnitude on. That is to say, our Galaxy forms eleven fairly evenly distributed layers around us. From the twelfth on, the layers thin out as light is increasingly absorbed by galactic dust. It is impossible to obtain reliable star counts beyond a distance of 6,000 light-years because of this obscuration.

In principle Herschel had attacked the problem correctly; he could not obtain correct results because he had no way of measuring the true brightness of the various orders of magnitude. He made strenuous efforts to obtain such data, but lacked the proper instrument. Two generations later measurement of brightness became one of astronomy's principal activities, Herschel having demonstrated that such measurements could carry man's vision beyond the bounds imposed by nature.

Herschel's third inspiration was the happiest of all. He resolved to determine the "space-penetrating power" of the eye and the telescope. When he announced this intention, a critic suggested that he was growing senile; boasts such as these should be left to the poets. But Herschel was able to attain this end and provide the first proper measurements of linear distances in space.

His measuring stick was the light-year, the distance traveled by light in the course of a year—approximately six trillion miles. Once we have accustomed ourselves to them, "astronomical" distances do not make us giddy; they simply derive from another world where a rather longer ruler is in order. Applying the ruler was the trick, and this trick we owe to Herschel.

If only we could know the distance of a single star, the distances of others might be reckoned from it, he reasoned. But as yet no one had ever succeeded with the initial measurement. From various vain attempts, however, Herschel concluded that the nearest stars, say Sirius, must be at least three light-years away. On the basis of this number he pursued his exploration of space.

By examination of various data, Herschel became convinced that each order of magnitude was half as bright as the preceeding one. Class 3 was one fourth the brightness of Class 1, therefore at twice the distance, for brightness diminishes as the square of the distance. Class 7—into which Herschel placed stars not visible to the naked eye—has 1/64 the brightness of Sirius, and is therefore eight times the distance of that star. Stars of the seventh magnitude are accordingly some twenty-four light-years distant from us. So Herschel reasoned.

Twenty-four light-years, in his calculation, is the eye's "space-penetrating power"; that was the extent of the "universe" before the invention of the telescope. Herschel was interested in determining the penetrating power of his various telescopes.

A telescope shows more stars not because it magnifies, but because it gathers in more light, concentrates feebler brightness magnitudes, as if it were an eye with a larger pupil. A telescope with a four-inch objective gathers four hundred times as much

light as the pupil of the eye, and therefore penetrates to 20 times the distance. But that is only an approximation, since a certain amount of light is lost when it is reflected by the mirror. Herschel investigated the loss of light with great care, and came to the conclusion that his twelve-inch mirror penetrated 75 times deeper into space than the eye, his forty-eight-inch mirror 200 times as far. Thus, the most distant stars of the Galaxy he was able to see with it were some 200 times beyond the range of the eye, approximately 4,000 light-years away. The diameter of the

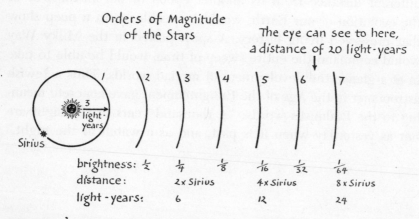

Orders of Magnitude of the Stars

The eye can see to here, a distance of 20 light-years

	1	2	3	4	5	6	7

3 light-years

Sirius

brightness:	½	¼		⅛		1/16	1/32	1/64
distance:		2x Sirius			4x Sirius			8x Sirius
light-years:		6			12			24

HERSCHEL'S GREAT ACHIEVEMENT: BY DETERMINING THE RANGE OF THE EYE AND OF TELESCOPES HE WAS ABLE TO MEASURE THE DISTANCES OF HEAVENLY BODIES. (HIS FIGURES ARE NOW CORRECTED, SEE DIAGRAM ON PAGE 284.)

Galaxy, he estimated, was twice as great, 8,000 light-years, and its thickness about 1,600 light-years. Herschel had measured our island universe.

Today these figures have been multiplied approximately by ten. But this correction does not detract from Herschel's glory in having been the first man to penetrate into infinity. He piloted the way into space—it hardly matters that one hundred and fifty years later we know our way about somewhat better than he. He even penetrated to structures that he considered to be other galaxies in various stages of development. Estimating 25,000 stars in one cluster, he calculated its distance as 600,000 light-years. For one nebula he estimated two million light-years. And

he was quick to see a further interesting conclusion: that if such a remote island universe had ceased to exist a million years ago, we would nevertheless continue to see it for another million years. Telescopes peer not only into infinite depths of space, but into infinite spans of time as well.

The implications of this unique insight carry characteristically modern overtones. If someone could look down upon our Earth from a star out toward the rim of the Galaxy, he would see not us, but, say, Homer's Greeks besieging Troy. From each star at a different distance from us another epoch of our history, or of the evolution of our Earth, would be visible, as in a peep show that preserved living history. A spirit posted in the Milky Way would command the entire sweep of time, would be able to take in at a glance the development of myriad worlds. Thus a Jewish astronomer in the Age of the Enlightenment gave concrete meaning to the Psalmist's words: "A thousand years in thy sight are but as yesterday when it is past, and as a watch in the night."

EXPLORATIONS IN THE SOLAR SYSTEM

Minor Planets Fill a Gap

ON ITS VERY FIRST DAY the nineteenth century proclaimed itself an era of lucky finds. For on New Year's Day of 1801 a Sicilian monk discovered a new kind of heavenly body within the solar system: the minor planet Ceres.

The monk's name was Giuseppi Piazzi. He had gone to England to study astronomy, and had broken a leg on Herschel's telescope tower. Employing the most expensive instrument-maker in London, he had a meridian circle, twice as large as the one used at Greenwich, built to his own design. The cost was borne by the Viceroy of Naples, whom Piazzi had so infected with his passion that he spoiled the lines of the beautiful Arab-Norman palace in Palermo by installing the most modern observatory of the age there.

Piazzi himself was unaware of the significance of his discovery of Ceres, and the true drama of the tiny planet was played out in Germany. The historic mission of Ceres was twofold: it put to shame a young philosopher, and it filled a gap in the world order.

The philosopher bore a name later to be famous: Georg Wilhelm Friedrich Hegel. Hegel then still subscribed to the ancient, long-forgotten mystical "science" of numerology. Since the days of the Babylonians the fivefold planets, which, with addition of Moon and Earth made seven wandering heavenly bodies, were held as the constants of the universe, and formed the basis for

the venerable game that mystics played with sacred numbers. Herschel's new planet, Uranus, upset the scheme; great obstinacy was needed to maintain that the number of seven planets (including the Earth) was something absolute and God-given, as Hegel then did. The paper by which he qualified for the position of *Privatdocent* at Jena University marshaled the strictest logic to prove that there could not be more than seven planets, and that it was therefore rationally impossible for any more planets to be discovered.

The paper came off the press just as news of the discovery of the first minor planet, Ceres, arrived from Palermo.

The Berlin professor of astronomy Johann Elert Bode had not long ago brought into notice a different sort of rationale for the planets, and one that would certainly have impressed Kepler. He found that all the distances of the planets from the Sun could be arranged in perfect geometrical succession, their ratios being those of the following table:

$$4: \quad (4+3):(4+6):(4+12):(4+24):(4+48):(4+96):(4+192)$$

Mercury Venus   Earth   Mars   ———   Jupiter   Saturn   Uranus

Evidently there is a gap between Mars and Jupiter—and this gap should not have been. Bode believed that a planet must once have traveled the orbit between Mars and Jupiter; then his series would be complete and order would once more be restored to the cosmos. It can easily be imagined how jubilant he was when news of Ceres' discovery reached him.

It was, however, somewhat more difficult to calculate Ceres' orbit exactly than it had been for Hegel to "prove" his theory. For Piazzi's new planet promptly disappeared, blotted out by the sunlight. Calculating an elliptical orbit for it from the few figures he had managed to garner was equivalent to constructing a complete ape man from a lower jawbone. Fortunately a mathematical genius was ready to attack this task. Karl Friedrich Gauss, then only twenty-four years old, had just invented his method of least squares, which enabled him to perform the feat of calculating an orbit from only three observations. The orbit, moreover, fulfilled Bode's exacting demands.

There was only one flaw. Ceres had so small a mass that she could scarcely be considered a planet. Her orbit certainly did not fill the gap between Mars and Jupiter in a satisfactory manner. Hence, there must be more such minor planets.

Sure enough, these were found. The following year Pallas was discovered, to be followed by Juno and then by Vesta. All of them followed orbits at approximately the distance from the Sun required by theory, and all of them were tiny, like Ceres. In short, they could be considered fragments of a former, much larger planet which presumably had exploded. Herschel was delighted when he heard this, and promptly came forth with the conjecture that some 30,000 more minor planets existed.

Modern astronomy is still inclined to accept his estimate, although the number of asteroids actually discovered so far is only about 2,000. Nowadays they are no longer found by chance; they are hunted by systematic photography of the sky at observatories that specialize in the subject, like the one at Heidelberg. The method is very simple; because of their motion they appear on photographic plates as tiny dashes. Year after year, the catalogue of them grows, and their size diminishes, since the larger ones have been discovered long ago.

The asteroids roam about the entire space between Mars and Jupiter; they revolve only in the plane of the zodiac; their orbits are at various angles to it, and some of these orbits are so long

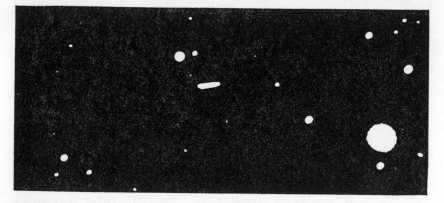

A MINOR PLANET APPEARS IN A STELLAR PHOTOGRAPH AS A DASH (CENTER) INDICATING MOTION.

that they extend beyond Saturn or as close to the Sun as Venus. Hermes veers toward the Earth to within the distance of our Moon, and it was recently feared that Eros would actually graze us.

But the hypothetical mother planet of these asteroids still seems to have been far too small, since the total mass of the known fragments amounts to only 1/800 of that of the Earth, and it does not seem likely that future discoveries will materially add to this figure.

There are now so many of these minor planets that astronomers have long since run out of the names of ancient gods and goddesses; all asteroids are now given simple numbers. The thousandth, however, was baptized Piazzia in 1923, in honor of the first discoverer of the tribe.

Encke's Comet and the Home of Comets

Johann Franz Encke consistently refused to forward his claim to the comet named after him. All his papers on the subject continued to speak of "Pons's comet of 1818." He had not discovered it, he maintained, only calculated its orbit; in fact, he pointed out, Pons had found it twice.

Jean Louis Pons of Marseilles was one of the most ambitious and successful comet-hunters in the history of astronomy. He found no less than thirty-seven comets, so that he may really be forgiven for having mistaken the same one for two different comets. After all, he was the first observer to have been favored with a return engagement of a comet. Usually comets remained on the stage too briefly for their orbits to be calculated with any exactitude.

Encke, primarily an observer at the University of Göttingen observatory, was forever tempted into calculations in his leisure time. He set to work on the orbit of Pons's comet, and arrived at a result that seemed utterly impossible. The orbit was an ellipse that barely extended beyond the path of Mars; the period

of revolution was slightly more than three years. Distraught, he searched for an error. When he could find none, he still felt so certain there must be one that he asked his teacher, Gauss, to correct his work. Gauss promptly had Encke's paper printed.

For Encke, this publicizing of his calculations meant three years of torment. If Pons's comet of 1818 did not reappear in 1822, he would be disgraced. In his anxiety, he went over the equations again and again, each time making them more difficult by including further possible complications. Would Jupiter's attraction divert the comet from its course? Would it come too close to Mars, Earth, or Venus, and be unduly affected by their gravitation? These considerations led him to formulas as involved as those dealing with the motions of the Moon.

The crucial day approached. As ill luck would have it, the comet would be seen, if it were visible at all, only in the Southern Hemisphere. At the observatory in Cape Town, South Africa, astronomers searched diligently. But the deadline passed, and they had still seen nothing of it. In despair Encke told the director of the Göttingen observatory that he was prepared to resign, that he was obviously incompetent as mathematician and astronomer. The director suggested that he wait until he had read a letter from Parramatta in New South Wales.

The letter was one of heartiest congratulations. At the Parramatta observatory the comet had been found, only two minutes of arc from the spot predicted by Encke.

Similar congratulations poured in from all over the world. At the same time astronomers were amazed at this new phenomenon of a comet which returned every three years. For although comets were no longer considered heralds of Heaven's wrath, they were thought to be heralds from outer space. Their orbits were mostly parabolas or hyperbolas, curves that run on to infinity. A comet, it had been thought, went flying straight through space until it was captured by the Sun and forced to curve around that body, then released to speed on in a changed direction back into the unknown. Normally, comets appeared once and never again. Halley's comet with its seventy-six year period was supposed to be a rare exception, apparently a chance captive whose para-

bolic course had been altered by the Sun's gravitation into an elongated ellipse.

The manner in which comets were captured was worked out by a French astronomer, Urbain Leverrier. From ancient annals he calculated that in A.D. 126, when Hadrian was building his wall in Britain to fend off the wild tribes to the north, a comet passed very close to Uranus. It whirled in one third of a circle around that planet, and started off into interstellar space, but the Sun's attraction forced it to turn once again. In so doing

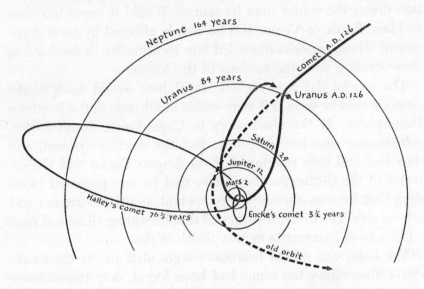

URANUS CAPTURED A COMET IN A.D. 126.

it lost impetus, and ever since has been revolving around the Sun and Uranus simultaneously in a constantly changing elliptical orbit.

Halley's comet must have met with a similar fate, except that it retained more of its impetus, its ellipse extending far beyond the orbit of Uranus.

Encke's comet, accordingly, was not a complete aberration; it was only an extreme case of capture and attachment on an unusually short gravitational chain. Perhaps it had passed too close to Mars as it came flying in from outer space, and was henceforth condemned to a relatively tiny ellipse and a brief period of revo-

lution. Afterwards, more comets of the same type were found.

The uniqueness of Encke's achievement was appreciated neither by himself nor anyone else at the time. It consisted in the new technique of calculating orbits devised by him out of fear of being disgraced: namely, the inclusion in his formulae of the gravitational effects of all the planets. A comet's orbit could not be reconstructed perfectly from its brief curve around the Sun; all possible perturbations by other members of our solar system had to be taken into account. Only then could the real orbit of a comet be determined.

This principle was not fully grasped until about 1900, when the Swedish astronomer Elis Strömgren realized that all former calculations ought to be revised. He undertook to compute the perturbations in Encke's manner for several hundred known orbits. This was an amusement that kept him busy for decades. It had the formidable result of overthrowing the existing theory of comets. The normal form of a comet's orbit was an ellipse! Parabolas occurred very rarely; there was not a single example of a hyperbolic orbit. In other words, the long-tailed heralds of the heavens were not interstellar vagrants, but respectable members of our solar system.

It has since been calculated that no comet can escape into infinity on a parabolic orbit. Its velocity as it moves away from the Sun constantly diminishes, and it shares in the general motion of our system toward the constellation of Hercules. There may be innumerable comets far, far out in space beyond the outermost planet, bodies we will never see in our telescopes. Nevertheless, they remain parts of the solar system.

The question remains: where have they come from? Strömgren fancied them by-products of the primal nebula from which Sun and planets were formed. But comets are transitory bodies; they can scarcely be as old as the Sun itself. It was therefore suggested that they might be splinters of the exploded planet that once revolved in an orbit between Mars and Jupiter, and left behind the horde of asteroids. Comets, then, would be fragments hurled in all directions, many beyond the verges of the solar system, but returning on elongated orbits to their place of origin.

They have lost the aura that hung over them when they were thought to be visitors from interstellar space. Moreover, in recent times only inconspicuous specimens have appeared, for the most part detectable only by telescopes. Since the First World War, until 1957, none of those mighty omens that were wont to make men tremble have appeared in the sky.

Death of Comets

In the past century every generation beheld at least one comet of overwhelming size and splendor, with a tail sometimes sweeping across half the firmament and occasionally visible in broad daylight. How is it possible for such tiny heavenly bodies to carry appendages millions of miles in length, stretching from the Earth to Venus and even farther?

The answer to this question was suggested by a German physician, Dr. Heinrich Wilhelm Olbers, who formulated the theory of flaming comets. Comets, he pointed out, are in themselves small and innocuous bodies. We see them only when they come close to the Sun, much closer than does any planet. Like moths they rush toward the great light, and catch fire. Their tails, Olbers held, were the smoke of this fire. Our Earth would probably suffer the same fate if it were to come too close to the Sun; it would flame up and burn, trailing a gigantic streamer of smoke behind it.

Olbers came to this conclusion from observation of Comet 1811 I. Comets had by then become such common phenomena that they were numbered like specimens in a laboratory. Most of them, however, were seen only in telescopes, and often their tails were lacking. This was because they were too far from the Sun, Olbers decided. "Only in the vicinity of the Sun do they blaze up. They catch fire like a sulphur match, and like a sulphur match, a bluish flame leaps forth. And just as from the flame of a sulphur match scorching exhaust gases are sent forth, so the tail is sent forth from the comet flame."

In this way the German doctor interpreted the three-layered

structure more or less distinctly exhibited by all comets. Comet 1811 I beautifully displayed this structure, for each layer was of another color. In the center was a red circular nucleus, like the glowing head of a match. All around it, especially on the side toward the Sun, was a blue-green mist: the flame. And surrounding the whole was a yellowish veil, the exhaust gases of the flame, glowing in the sunlight like particles of dust, and forming the tail.

As a rule, the tails of comets point away from the Sun. Could the Sun be blowing the tail away from the burning nucleus? Olbers maintained that it did, that the Sun somehow possessed a repulsive force, as others had already suspected. The only possible force opposing gravitation must be that of the Sun's radiation, he argued. After all, sunlight moved and had a measurable velocity; why should it not also possess force enough to push comet gases?

At the time this idea was daring indeed; not until the end of the nineteenth century could its validity be proved by the great Swedish scientist Svante August Arrhenius. Light does exert pressure, tiny in amount, but strong enough to push the molecules of gases and to scatter them across millions of miles of space. That fact was vividly demonstrated by Donati's comet of 1858. This comet passed unusually close to the Sun. Only 30,000 miles, approximately four times the diameter of the Earth, saved it from fiery extinction. But it wheeled past the Sun in some three hours, describing almost a semicircle in that brief span of time. And its two monstrous tails flew along with it, constantly keeping the direction of the Sun's outpouring radiation. If they had been fixed appendages, they would have to have curved, lagging behind during the rapid swing around the Sun. Instead they swept like searchlight beams across the sky, subject to the radiation pressure of the Sun.

Only in the tails of comets do light rays mark their path by pushing matter along with them. The flowing dust in a ray of sunlight passing through a dark room is not comparable, for the dust is dancing at random, and fills the entire room. The matter in a comet's tail, on the other hand, exists only within the

Sun's rays, and moves with them. Obviously, then, it must consist of much finer matter than dust, finer even than the matter of the comet's flame, for that is attracted by the Sun's gravitation. The tail consists of extremely tenuous gas, of isolated molecules of gas, the form of the tail depending on the size of the molecules. If they are large, they are braked by the Sun's gravitation; radiation pressure is opposed by gravitational force, the orbit curves, and the tail takes on the shape of a crescent. If the molecules are small enough, the radiation pressure alone affects them, producing sharp daggers or long needles. If molecules of various sizes are present, fan-shaped tails result; a degree of sorting out has taken place due to the opposing forces of radiation pressure and gravitation.

Olbers's theory of radiation pressure accounted completely for the direction taken by the tails of comets. In the last years of his life he was rewarded by the opportunity of observing such a tail from very close.

An Austrian army officer, Baron Wilhelm von Biela, had discovered a comet with the short orbital period of about six years. Olbers calculated that the Earth would pass through its tail in 1832. When this prediction was made public, however, it caused disproportionate excitement. Journalists drew dire pictures of the possible consequences of such a collision. At the very least, widespread gas-poisoning was expected, possibly tremendous conflagrations; all mankind might die of suffocation. In the general panic, opinion turned against Olbers, who had raised the threat. His colleagues attacked him as an irresponsible rumor monger while the director of the Paris Observatory took issue with his findings and let it be known that the tail would miss the Earth by a few miles. Little trust was placed in this reassurance, of course; the world waited in fear and trembling for the terrible moment.

Olbers was perplexed by all the uproar. What could possibly happen if the Earth passed through so tenuous a gas? At worst there might be a slight smell, possibly a glow in the atmosphere.

In fact, nothing happened, nothing at all. A comet's tail is in reality no more than a ray of sunlight laden with gases.

Nevertheless, Biela's comet was destined to show humanity the end of a world—not of the Earth, but of itself. Fourteen years later it floated into view once more, its nucleus distorted into the shape of a pear. A month later the dramatic event took place. A skeptical astronomer at Cambridge could scarcely believe his eyes: two comets had appeared. So improbable was this that, despite his excellent telescope, he retracted the report. But soon all observers had seen two comets. There could be no doubt that Biela's comet had broken apart before the eyes of watching hu-

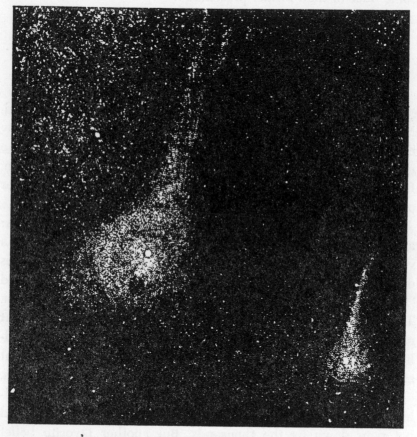

BIELA'S COMET, AS SEEN TO BREAK IN TWO IN 1846.

manity. More likely it had been torn apart, victim of the struggle between the gravitational forces of Jupiter and the Sun.

At the comet's next visit one of the parts was already lagging

far behind the other. That was the last that was ever seen of it. When the comet failed to reappear, astronomers concluded that it was scattered in space, annihilated. A heavenly body had vanished from the skies. Comets are transitory bodies; on each of their visits to the Sun, radiation pressure causes them to lose some of their material, which never again catches up with them. In addition, they are racked by tidal forces, the result of the Sun's enormous gravitation. Ultimately they are doomed to destruction. But they do not depart from the scene without leaving behind some trace of their former presence.

Meteor Swarms

On the night of November 12, 1833, the Earth was attacked. North America from Nova Scotia to Mexico was bombarded by cosmic shrapnel that apparently had its origin in the Lion. The entire sky was blazoned with sparks for nine hours in succession. It was afterwards estimated that a quarter of a million pieces of shot had fallen.

Fortunately, the bombardment was noiseless and innocuous: a rain of shooting stars, meteors. They came by the dozens, a veritable cloudburst of them, some stitching the sky with needles of fire, some bursting in a shower of sparks like shells. The word "fireworks" scarcely gives an adequate picture of the phenomenon. The effect was rather like that experienced by a man driving at night through a blizzard: the white flakes gleaming in the head-lights of the automobile no longer dance, but seem to leap straight at the driver, dashing at his face like a barrage of tiny sparks.

Those who beheld the shower lost, once and for all, their child-hood belief in stars falling from the sky. Stars, after all, could not pour down by the thousands. But another favorite belief that meteors were some sort of purely terrestrial combustion process in the atmosphere, was also put to flight. For the entire barrage in this shower of 1833 appeared to come from a single point in Leo.

The point was, in fact, an optical illusion, as a Yale University mathematician, Denison Olmsted, promptly demonstrated. In reality the 250,000 meteors had followed parallel tracks. Olmsted concluded that this blizzard of meteors had been shaken out of a swarm whose path crossed the Earth in the direction of Leo. If, moreover, the Earth passed through such a swarm on November 12 and 13, 1833, she would presumably do so every year. She might not necessarily run right through the heart of the swarm every time, yet a heavy meteor shower could be expected annually.

His prognostication was beautifully confirmed. Once astronomers' attention had been called to it, they were able to observe the annual meteor shower, although in subsequent years it was not nearly so impressive. They found other swarms whose date of reappearance was fixed. Apparently the solar system was sprinkled with such clouds of meteors. If the Earth on her annual orbit encountered dozens of them, how many must there be scattered throughout the solar system? Evidently, here was a new group to be added to the population of our system, and a group more numerous than any other. Olmsted assigned orbits to them, for the swarms of meteors must also be revolving in Keplerian ellipses around the Sun. For some of these swarms Olmsted was able to determine the points from which they appeared to diverge and converge, and the inclination and eccentricity of their orbits, just as if the swarms were planets.

These cosmic gnats must not be thought of as all alike. Ordinarily they are tiny, for they burn away to nothingness when ignited by friction with the Earth's atmosphere. But now and then one survives to fall to the ground, and is discovered as a stone with an iron core. Sometimes a great rain of meteors has descended, making a thunderous noise, and including fragments weighing many tons, as well as pieces as small as grains of wheat or motes of dust. In 1803 some three thousand meteorites of all sizes were picked up near a village in Normandy. In addition to iron they contained other metals and metallic compounds, mineral matter, and even carbon.

How many meteors bombard our planet was demonstrated by

a curious calculation. Simon Newcomb summed up the total light of the firmament, and was surprised to find how small the total was; it was insufficient to explain the measured brightness of the night sky. His conclusion was that the differential in light must be ascribed to the constant bombardment by shooting stars. Newcomb estimated that a hundred thousand tons of matter must fall upon the Earth annually in order to make our nights as bright as they actually are. The most modern estimates give a smaller figure, about 1,000 tons. This trivial amount increases the Earth's mass only imperceptibly.

In August 1866 a meteor shower occurred which rivaled Jupiter and Venus in brightness. A Milan astronomer Giovanni Schiaparelli set about calculating the orbit of this swarm, which was racing around the Sun at a pace faster than that of the Earth. He then wrote a letter to a friend, Father Pietro Secchi at the observatory in Rome. The pair were constantly exchanging letters, but this particular letter was soon circulating through all the world's observatories. For it contained the momentous news that the orbit of the August 1866 meteor swarm corresponded exactly with that of Tuttle's vanished comet.

Tuttle's comet, which, like Biela's comet, had been torn apart and had apparently vanished forever, had left its fragments behind. These were still flying through space, following the same old track, but now scattered so widely that they crossed the orbit of the Earth. They did so not only in 1866, but every August thereafter.

Showers of meteors, Schiaparelli concluded, were nothing less than annual fireworks commemorating some deceased comet.

His suggestion fired the imaginations of other astronomers. One calculated the path of the 1833 Leonides and determined that their ancestor had been a long-forgotten, vanished comet. Another showed the same origin for the April meteor shower, and so it went until Schiaparelli's theory had been confirmed by the history of some seventy swarms.

The huge isolated meteorites that occasionally fall to Earth are said to originate in outer space. On its voyage toward the constellation of Hercules, the Sun apparently carries us through

clouds in the Galaxy which release their cargo to burn holes in the Earth's crust. At times the holes are quite sizable. South Africa has a sixty-ton lump lying in the ground. In Arizona there is a crater three quarters of a mile in diameter. There, how long

DIGGING FOR A FALLEN METEORITE IN 1628, FROM A CONTEMPORARY WOODCUT. THE ARTILLERY OF THE HEAVENS CONTINUES TO BOMBARD THE EARTH.

ago no one knows, a giant meteorite crashed to the ground, plowing the earth into a wall around it, strewing lumps of iron over the vicinity and melting the sand into a glassy layer. In Labrador a lake more than two miles in diameter has been recognized as the shell hole left by some cosmic missile. This was exceeded in size by the meteorite that fell near the Tunguska River in Siberia in 1908, causing seismometers all over the world to jump violently. It carried with it a rain of huge boulders, flattened millions of trees, and apparently did no harm to any human being.

Yet it was only luck that made the monster fall in the taiga and not in the midst of a populous city. Should one ever do so, it would wreak damage beside which the immediate devastation

of a hydrogen bomb would seem minor. For the heavens are still the home of elemental forces, a fact modern man is apt to forget, both in the pride and the fear of his heart.

Life on Mars?

Schiaparelli was thirty-one years old when he discovered the origin of meteor swarms. Eleven years later he caused another sensation, the aftereffects of which persisted for years. The stir came about only because his colleagues knew so little Italian. Schiaparelli had observed several lines on Mars, apparent furrows or channels, for which he used the Italian word *canali*. Everywhere, this was translated "canals," and a popularizer who was editing an astronomical magazine reasoned: "If there are canals on Mars, the planet must be inhabited."

Schiaparelli initially considered the furrows natural formations that for unknown reasons ran curiously straight. Their width alone made the idea of "canals" untenable; he estimated the lines as at least twenty miles wide, with some more than one hundred. They usually linked those large, reddish areas on Mars which astronomers called seas, and frequently they widened out at their mouths. They were themselves the same reddish hue.

Several of them, however, extended as far as the white polar caps that are the most striking characteristic of Martian geography. These polar caps began shrinking in the spring, in the course of the summer diminishing to small dots, only to begin growing again in the autumn until they covered as much as a third of Mars at times. Like other astronomers, Schiaparelli thought these must be icecaps or snow at the poles, while the *canali* were outlets for the melting snow or ice, for they appeared to him darker and wider in spring than at other times.

He was well aware that this entire conception was a highly dubious one. The channels could only be made out after persistent observation; he himself had become convinced of their existence only after many years of devoted toil. They appeared

and vanished again. One day they were visible, the next gone. Often he rubbed his eyes, thinking that his vision was playing tricks; this was especially so when he saw individual *canali* as double. At intervals he would see along any one channel a distant parallel, as straight as if it had been drawn with a ruler. Another time the same parallel line would appear on the other side, and possibly at a still greater distance. He could not bring himself to believe they were real. How fallible was the eye, that essential part of an astronomer's equipment?

A further difficulty was that Mars could not be observed constantly. Only at opposition, when the Earth is on the same side of the Sun as Mars, is the fourth planet close enough for good observation. Favorable Mars years are extremely rare, and even then, the observing must be concentrated within a few weeks, with the planet viewed from a different angle and at a different distance each time. Consequently, the results of a whole decade have to be combined if any comprehensive view of the surface of Mars is to be obtained. Schiaparelli therefore combined a large number of observations, and was severely criticized for doing so. His colleagues protested that the geometrical network he had cast over the planet was "an inadmissible synthesis," that he had never actually seen anything of the sort. "It remains doubtful whether even a single one of his lines has any fixed place."

Thus matters stood until the eighteen nineties, when a French astronomer, Camille Flammarion, intervened, and wrote a weighty tome on Mars and its "canals." He contended that this astonishingly regular network of straight lines thousands of miles long could not possibly be a natural phenomenon; it proved the existence of rational beings on Mars, beings of remarkable abilities and an intelligence far superior to ours.

Now a veritable tumult began. Novels about Mars poured from the pens of imaginative writers. Telescopes were built for the special purpose of observing the next opposition. Mars observatories sprang up by the dozens. Amateurs detected light-signals from the inhabitants of Mars; Marconi heard mysterious wireless signals. Millionaires offered prizes for communication with the Martians. It was proposed that a drawing of the Pythagorean

theorem half the size of Europe be traced on the Sahara desert, that Martian astronomers might see it and realize that the creatures of Earth were also intelligent. Never had there been such wild popular enthusiasm for astronomy.

The Mars mania infected Schiaparelli himself. He decided that his channels were products of technology, and wrote an essay that he sent to Flammarion with the comment: "Fools' Day comes

MARS AND ITS "CANALS," FROM A DRAWING MADE BY SCHIAPARELLI IN 1888.

once a year." The essay set forth a detailed theory, which ran as follows:

Mars is an old planet with a thin atmosphere; it is almost entirely cloudless, and therefore rain must be very rare. Conse-

quently, irrigation is the chief problem. The Martians must long ago have set up a pacifistic, socialistic system in order to combat the terrible physical conditions on their dying planet, and have built a canal network surpassing anything that has ever been conceived on Earth. The water from the melting icecap of their South Pole is distributed by these canals throughout the entire planet during the Martian summer.

Thereafter the partisans for life on Mars could cite the opinion of a recognized expert. The resultant dispute in the scientific world reached its height at the end of the nineteenth century, but it is not over yet.

Two Americans decided to attack the problem with the full resources of modern astronomy. Percival Lowell had founded the observatory that bears his name in Flagstaff, Arizona, at an altitude of 6,500 feet, in the purest air on the globe; it still remains a model scientific institute. For fifteen years he took at least a hundred photographs of Mars on every day of good seeing. His rival, Edward Charles Pickering, perched on an Andean peak in Arequipa, Peru, at a somewhat higher altitude, worked as hard; during the opposition of 1892 alone he made 375 drawings of Mars.

The upshot of their labors was a series of radical contradictions. Lowell found the canals 12 miles wide; Pickering between 125 and 500 miles. Lowell saw almost every canal as double; Pickering observed this phenomenon in only a few cases, and then for mere seconds at a time. Lowell drew a network denser than Schiaparelli's; Pickering did not note any network at all; by his account the lines kept changing their positions and directions.

These discrepancies led most professional astronomers to consider the canals of Mars as optical illusions. A simple experiment confirmed their opinion. If small, irregular ink blots are placed close together on a page covered with extremely tiny letters, the letters appear to be connected by lines, and even double lines, when looked at from a distance. In high dudgeon, Lowell pointed to the photographs of Martian canals and challenged his critics to prove that the camera would also see lines where there

were only ink blots. They could prove exactly this. Silver bromide reacted to the strong contrasts of black and white in the same way as the retina of the eye.

Thus the problem could not be settled even by photography. In general, photographs of Mars are unsuccessful; the grain of the emulsions is too coarse and the exposure too long, so that currents in the Earth's atmosphere distort the picture. Of every hundred photographs, one may be useful, and this one is far from as clear as a drawing made by a knowing observer after hours of patient looking, comparing, and interpreting.

Observation of Mars is a matter of fathoming riddles. The strongest telescope brings it as close to us as our Moon seen with the naked eye. Anyone who has tried to make out details on the Moon with the naked eye can understand why the problem of Mars has not yet been solved. Recently, the canals have been viewed under the best conditions and with the finest instruments and have disintegrated into grains or spots. This appears to be a confirmation of the theory that they were only optical phenomena, the human eye itself constructing lines and networks.

Schiaparelli's sensation seems to have run its course. But the question remains: is life possible on Mars? Apparently it is, but astrophysical methods have demonstrated that what life Mars could harbor would have to survive frightful conditions. The temperatures of the planet have been measured: from a high of 68–86 degrees Fahrenheit by day to −76 degrees, by night. The annual average temperature at the equator is 27 degrees, elsewhere around 0 Fahrenheit. That is more than a "Siberian" climate; it is an Ice Age climate. Higher forms of plant life cannot endure such alternations of temperature; at best there would be algae, mosses, and lichens.

The reddish-ocher areas on Mars are certainly not "seas." There is virtually no water on the entire planet. The white polar caps are not ice and snow; they may be a thin layer of hoarfrost on the ground, or simply clouds in the atmosphere. For these caps melt in the spring at a speed of fifteen miles daily.

The Martian atmosphere contains a great deal of carbon dioxide, only minimal amounts of water vapor and oxygen. If the in-

habitants of Mars do not go about in divers' suits, or live in sealed dwellings, they can scarcely be living beings of the sort we know.

To sum up, Mars would appear to be a super-Gobi desert with the harshest kind of alpine climate, which would at best permit only simple forms of plant life and highly specialized organisms to survive over a long period. That is the most we can say about the planet at present.

Our other neighboring planet, Venus, is wrapped in a dense mantle of clouds. No one has ever seen anything of its surface. It is safe to assume that any beings dwelling on Venus would rarely, if ever, see the Sun. Darkness alternates with foggy days and long twilights. The atmosphere is composed of carbon dioxide and water vapor. If oxygen is present, we can imagine life on Venus existing in a hothouse atmosphere, dripping wet, a climate for moisture-loving plants and swamp animals—rather like the picture we have of the Earth in the Carboniferous Era.

These two planets are the only ones in the solar system which might support life as we know it. Mercury and the Moon possess no atmosphere; their low gravitation could not hold one. They must be dead worlds of frozen lava. Jupiter and Saturn have dense atmospheres, but are extremely cold. The outer planets, Uranus and Neptune, have a poison-gas atmosphere. Pluto is certainly too cold for life.

If this is a depressing prospect, we must not forget that in the Galaxy with its hundred billion suns there may be innumerable solar systems with any number of planets like Mars and Venus; hence there is every probability that there are "Earths" among them also, bodies on which the development of high types of life, in unimaginable variety and abundance, would be fully possible.

An Event on the Moon

Our satellite is not only without life. Nothing whatsoever happens there; it is a totally frozen sphere with a motionless crust. Consequently, the large gray spots around the Moon's equator,

which to the naked eye merge into the "Man in the Moon," are most inappropriately named "seas," *maria*. Their substance was determined by a clever experiment. First, a calculation was made of the amount of sunlight falling upon such spots; then the amount of reflected sunlight was measured. No more than 7 per cent is reflected, the same percentage reflected on Earth by volcanic rocks such as obsidian and lava. The "seas" of the Moon are therefore frozen masses of lava. They could not have been hurled out of volcanoes, however; they must have boiled up out of faults, for their surface is almost mirror-smooth. When they congealed, crevices formed, especially on the edges.

These rills, some 300 feet deep and at most 3,000 feet wide, march in straight, curved, or serpentine lines up to the mountains, often extending several hundred miles. They are also to be found in the centers of the basins of lava; in such cases they may pierce the crater walls or continue again on the other side of a crater. Undoubtedly they are similar to the cracks that appeared on Earth after the earthquake at San Francisco; these, too, ran for many miles.

They were discovered in the late eighteenth century by J. H. Schröter, a magistrate of Bremen, Germany, and the only jurist among the amateur astronomers. He demonstrated that patience rather than the size of the telescope was the vital factor in lunar observation. There was no point going beyond 500-fold magnification, for then the image began to oscillate. A flea cannot very well be studied while it is hopping; in such case, a stronger magnifying glass scarcely helps.

Patience is rewarding because the Moon, although it holds its face constantly toward us, does rock slightly, so that occasionally we see a strip of its other side. Moreover, we recognize all objects on the Moon only by their shadows, which move in a circle in the course of the month, lengthening and diminishing. These mobile and distorted silhouettes are not easy to interpret. Consequently, selenography is an art difficult to learn; years of practice are required to judge barely visible, vague shapes subject to constantly changing illumination.

For this reason photography is even less effective for study of

the Moon than for Mars. Even the most modern photographs taken at Mount Wilson show only a tiny fraction of the details drawn on maps by the selenologist Philipp Fauth; these maps provide the best pictures of the Moon in existence, and will no doubt be basic equipment when the first rocket to the Moon flashes into the sky.

The largest complete lunar map dates from 1874 and was the product of forty years of patient labor. Its author was Johann Friedrich Schmidt, who had been fascinated by the geography of the Moon since boyhood. His misfortune was that he was never provided with a good instrument and left in peace. In Germany in the nineteenth-century telescopes were still reverently guarded treasures. Opinion was that the lens would be spoiled if used as inordinately as Schmidt wanted to use it. He wandered from place to place, crying his woe to the heavens, until the gods of Greece had mercy upon him. They aroused in the city fathers of Athens the ambition to buy a fine new telescope and find a man who knew how to put it to use. Schmidt was that man. In the shadow of the Acropolis he drew his portrait of the Moon, a map ten feet across, containing forty thousand details.

The scale corresponded to a map of Switzerland in which Lake Geneva is shown eight inches long. On such a scale the globe of the Earth would be thirty-five feet in diameter; Mount Etna could be distinguished plainly. On such a scale, an ocean liner could be seen on the Moon.

Long before he published the map that was his life's work, Schmidt suddenly won fame by making the sensational announcement: "The crater Linné has disappeared." Crater Linné was an important landmark in the Mare Serenitatis. From everywhere on Earth telescopes were directed toward the Sea of Serenity. They could only confirm the announcement: the small crater was gone, and in its place was only a white spot, completely level, casting no shadows. To this day we do not know what happened to the crater, although some important astronomers do not believe that the crater has actually disappeared. Humanity may have witnessed one change on the Moon: the disappearance of a minor crater. Perhaps our nearest neighbor is not entirely dead. Perhaps

the first visitors to the Moon in their heated space-suits may yet encounter wonders.

The mountains of the Moon are, at any rate, as high as the Himalayas. They gleam white in the sunlight, yet cannot be capped with snow and ice, not only because, during the Moon's two-week day the surface is heated to 265 degrees Fahrenheit, but especially because the Moon has no atmosphere. But at full Moon and in the greatest noonday heat, the crater Plato regularly turns dark, almost black. This is hard to explain unless by a thorough soaking of the mountain. Another mysterious fact is that on very rare occasions something like a veil of mist covers one of the Moon's crevices.

If we add that here and there on the gray seas green, brown, and violet hues are observed, and that there is a parti-colored spot near the crater Herodotus—bright dots upon a green and lavender background—then we have summed up what is known about the Moon.

Sunspot Periods

An apothecary named Heinrich Samuel Schwabe who lived in the sleepy provincial capital of Dessau was usually required to be on duty during the night. Interested in astronomy himself, he approached an astronomer friend to inquire whether there was some kind of astronomical project he could do by day.

"By day?" his friend repeated, and reflected for a while. Then he suggested: "why don't you keep on the lookout for the planet that is conjectured to be inside the orbit of Mercury. If you observe the Sun long enough, and if such a planet exists, you ought to see it passing over the Sun's disc sooner or later."

The planet did not exist. For seventeen years Schwabe drew the disc of the Sun on every day of fine weather. He recorded all the spots and dots upon its face, from tiny points to vast sprawling areas into which twenty Earths might have fitted. But no small planet was to be seen. What perseverance this man must have

had to continue the hopeless search for so long. But in the meanwhile he became obsessed with the drama of the sunspots themselves, which never offered the same appearance twice.

He saw them moving forward from day to day, since the Sun rotates on its axis. In the equatorial region they traveled faster than they did toward the poles, for on the gigantic ball of gas which is the Sun, different zones move at different speeds. It took between twenty-five and thirty-five days for a spot to reappear on the other side of the Sun. Frequently, it did not return at all; it had dissolved. The spots were, altogether, highly inconstant; they increased in size or diminished, flowed together or fell apart. On the rim of the Sun it was possible to see that they were deep holes; Schwabe could see slantwise into them, and recognize something resembling the walls of a crater.

Their numbers also were prone to constant fluctuation. For years the Sun's complexion was almost flawless, then for years badly spotted. Gradually Schwabe detected a distinct cycle, an eleven-year period of increasing and then decreasing sunspot activity. When the apothecary published an account of this, no one paid any attention. This indifference did not dismay him; he went on with his studies for another sunspot period, then once more came knocking at the gates of the scientific world with a thick portfolio of drawings and tables. This time he received a gold medal. For another eleven-year cycle had just come to light, a cycle of "magnetic storms."

These "storms" are somewhat less dramatic than their appellation, since man has no organ for sensing them. Only the sensitive apparatus devised by Karl Friedrich Gauss noted their existence and indicated also that the great magnet Earth is highly changeable. The glorious northern lights, for example, which are a kind of magnetic lightning, vary considerably in the frequency of their appearances. And when these variations were compared with Schwabe's sunspot figures, it was seen that both periods coincided.

The pharmacist rejoiced. "I went forth like Saul to seek my father's ass, and found a kingdom," he declared.

If we think his sense of triumph somewhat overstressed, we

must remember that humanity had for ages dreamed of mysterious relationships with the cosmos. Modern science had discredited that dream. Astrology had become a parlor game, which only a tiny sect took seriously. The Moon was once considered a weather-maker, but statistical studies carried on for decades had showed that its phases had no influence upon changes of weather. There remained a single mysterious effect attributed to our satellite: the menstrual period in woman may be in some way under the dominion of the heavenly body that divides time into months for us. For in the animal world also there occur periodic rhythms, all of a sexual nature, which seem linked with the Moon. The sea urchins of the Riviera coast contain more eggs at full Moon than at other times. In Florida, great swarms of eels appear with the last quarter of the Moon; in Japan, similar swarms come on the day after the new Moon or full Moon. And natives of the Samoan and Fiji islands set out at dawn in hundreds of boats exactly one week before the October and November full Moons, in order to catch the palolo worm, which then comes to the surface in enormous numbers to breed. This event occurs, moreover, exactly one week after the land crabs, the "coconut thief" among them, have marched down to the beach to deposit their larvae in the water.

Thus there are at least a few striking examples of a clear relationship between the cosmic order and the life rhythms of terrestrial beings. Consequently, a great deal of attention was suddenly focused upon Schwabe's sunspot periods when the correlation between them and the cycle of magnetic storms and northern lights was recognized. Here was a new tie mysteriously linking us to the Sun, which nourishes all life on Earth. The eleven-year alternation in sunspot activity undoubtedly gave rise to the eleven-year cycle of magnetic activity on Earth. Why should there not be other, as yet unrecognized effects?

Everything imaginable was examined for a relationship to the sunspot cycle: the Ice Ages and the prices of whiskey, the skins of Australian rabbits and South American revolutions, rainy years and epidemics. The supposed seven-year rhythm of human life was to be replaced by an eleven-year cycle. But none of the

fancied relationships would bear examination, except for the following remarkable facts: tree rings were consistently wider in periods of heavy sunspot activity, and Lake Victoria in Africa reached a higher water level. Nature, then, does react in some manner to Schwabe's periodicity.

What astronomers wanted to know, of course, was whether the sunspots were merely concomitants of terrestrial magnetism, or whether they had direct casual influence upon it. The answer to this question was provided by the son of a British brewer, Richard Christopher Carrington, who succeeded Schwabe as foremost observer of the Sun. He was unbelievably lucky, for he was privileged to see what no one ever saw again: a flash of light upon the Sun's disc, an outburst of light in the greatest light of our world. Within four minutes the phenomenon came to an end, and there remained two connected, normal sunspots. Carrington had witnessed an eruption of twin craters on the Sun. And in those same four minutes the magnetic needles in every observation station throughout the world gyrated in a wild dance. For an entire week the world experienced unprecedented magnetic storms; northern lights were observed as far south as the tropics. Astronomers on the Moon would have seen the Earth wrapped in darting blue sheets of light.

But what was the force that emanated from the eruptions on the Sun and produced such dramatic effects upon Earth? Many years passed before this question could be answered. The sunspots had to be probed by the intricate astrophysical methods of the twentieth century, by photometry, spectrum analysis, and especially by photography in the light of a single chemical element. An American astronomer, George Ellery Hale, invented the spectroheliograph for this purpose, and obtained pictures of the seething interior of sunspots, and at the same time pictures of various cross sections of spots. It was learned that the vapors rising from these craters form a whirlwind on the Sun's surface, a maelstrom of furious motion.

When we study such photographs, we are strongly reminded of the patterns of lines of force formed by iron filings in the presence of a magnet. Two adjacent sunspots correspond to the

positive and negative poles of the magnet. Hale suspected that actual magnetic forces were at play, but it took him twenty years to prove his hypothesis. In 1913 he succeeded in demonstrating that sunspots are sources of intense magnetic lines of force along which ionized particles and electrons from the surface of the Sun spiral into the Earth's atmosphere. These lines of force interact with the Earth's magnetic field, which is why they influence our magnetic needles and northern lights. Moreover, the sunspots change polarity in a regular cycle, every eleven years. Thus the eleven-year period is a symptom of some transformation within the solar organism.

Protuberances and Corona

In the year 1842 there was a total eclipse of the Sun. Solar eclipses occur at least twice a year, but they differ widely in character. Usually the Moon only passes across the edge of the Sun, rarely across its center. That it then completely covers the Sun's disc may be considered a remarkable dispensation of nature. Were the Moon only slightly smaller, a narrow band of sunlight would show all around its edges, and the eclipse would be robbed of its dramatic effectiveness. Such a band in any case often shows when the Moon happens to be a few miles farther from Earth than it is during total eclipses.

Total eclipses are seen only in narrowly limited regions of the Earth. In 1842 the grandstand fortunately happened to be situated in Southern France and Italy. Weeks before, astronomers from all countries moved into the zone of totality, laden with gear. They set up their disassembled telescopes and waited for the event. What they were expecting, they themselves scarcely knew. They did not suspect that they would shortly learn what has since become an astronomical proverb: "One can really see the Sun only when it is obscured."

They might have left their telescopes home, for the première of modern solar research showed in its full glory to the man in

A

B

C
D

E
F

G

H

1   2   3   4   5

Composite 100-inch photograph of the Moon at last quarter. The crater Copernicus (D2) has a diameter of about 55 miles. Mare Imbrium, the Sea of Rains (B2), is the largest lunar "sea." Some other craters shown are Kepler (D1), Eratosthenes (C3), Herschel (E4), Ptolemaeus (F4), Hipparchus (E5), Halley (F5), Tycho (H3), and Archimedes (B4). Note the Lunar Alps (A5) and the Mare Nubium, the Sea of Clouds (G2).

PLATE XVII

F

G

H

3   4

Portion of the Moon at last quarter from Ptolemaeus (F4) to Tycho (H3); 100-inch photograph. Diameter of Ptolemaeus, the largest crater on the Moon, is about 90 miles. Photo shows clearly that craters are sunken bowls, many of them containing tiny craters and/or central mountains.

PLATE XVIII

A

B

C

D

2   3   4   5

Northern portion of the Moon at last quarter; 100-inch photograph. The streak in the Lunar Alps (A5) is a valley 200 miles long. Copernicus (D2), Eratosthenes (C3), Archimedes (B4), and Mare Imbrium (B2) are also shown.

PLATE XIX

Meteorite crater near Winslow, Arizona. This famous crater was made five hundred centuries ago when a ten-million-ton meteorite struck. Three fourths of a mile wide, the crater measures three miles in circumference, and is six hundred feet deep at its deepest point.

PLATE XX

Bright lines and shadow lines in spectra of iron (TOP) and Sun (BOTTOM).

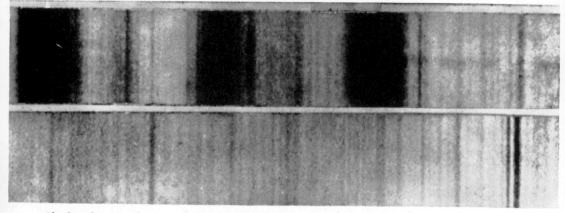

Shadow lines in the spectrum of Uranus (TOP), indicating an atmosphere largely methane gas. Lunar spectrum (BOTTOM) shows no atmosphere, only Moon's reflection of sunlight.

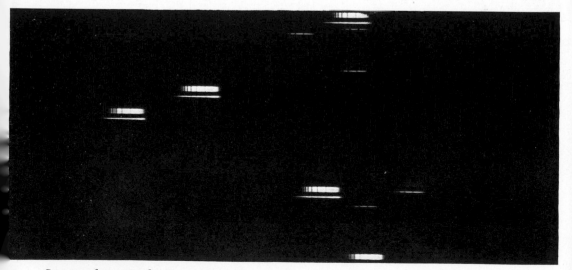

Spectra of stars in the Coma group. Spectra show that up to 90 per cent of total mass of stars is hydrogen.

PLATE XXI

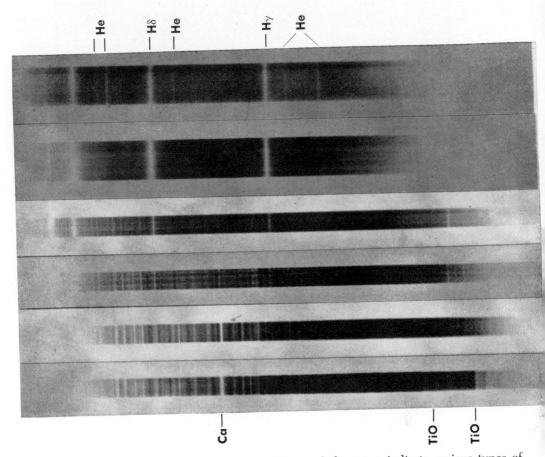

The six primary spectral classes of stars. The symbols at top indicate various types of hydrogen lines and helium; those at bottom, calcium and titanium oxide. Type B stars are hot and white in color; M stars are cool and red.

PLATE XXII

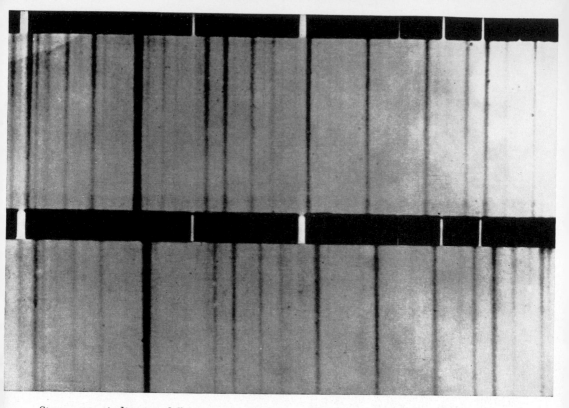

Star spectra indicating difference in velocity. Spectrum at top shows shift from standard comparison spectrum of iron (white lines at extreme top and at center), indicating a stellar velocity of about 50 miles per second. Spectrum at bottom shows twice that velocity.

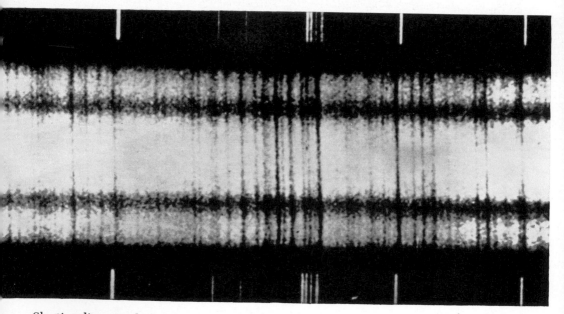

Slanting lines in the spectrum of Saturn's rings prove that the velocity of the rings diminishes toward the outside. This demonstrates that rings are composed of many small bodies.

PLATE XXIII

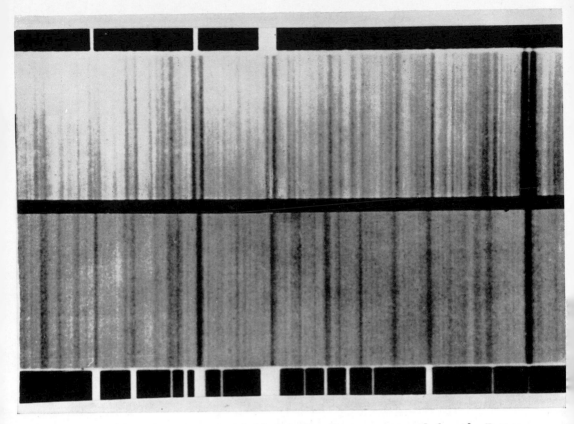

Spectra of twin stars. At top, double black lines indicate stars are side by side. Bottom: lines are fused when one star is behind the other.

Spectrum of the star Altair (top) shows broad, faded lines, indicating rotation at great speed. (See page 335.) Center and bottom, the changing spectrum of a nova.

PLATE XXIV

PATH OF A TOTAL SOLAR ECLIPSE ACROSS THE EARTH. DARKNESS IS
COMPLETE ONLY WHERE THE MOON'S SHADOW IS CONCENTRATED
ALONG THE BLACK STRIP. THIS DRAWING IS NOT TO SCALE; HOWEVER,
THE SUN IS TO BE IMAGINED A CONSIDERABLE DISTANCE OFF THE
PAGE.

the street also. The people shouted "Ah" and "Oh" and cheered the astronomers, apparently feeling that these were the directors of the spectacle. The astronomers themselves, however, were deeply discomfited, for they had been as greatly taken by surprise as the general populace. And afterwards they were still more ashamed when they read up on the matter in old books, and found that the performance had taken place frequently in the past. They had been altogether too supercilious in regard to the observational skills of the past.

But it is best to let one of them describe what he saw. First the light dimmed as in a theater. "The meager illumination which remained was of a bluish-black cast. Objects seemed to be smeared with the lees of wine, and our faces had a greenish hue. Oxen and asses stood still, cows stopped grazing, and even ants ceased their activity. Horses, on the other hand, continued plodding forward as reliably as locomotives. Many flowers closed, but the sensitive mimosae did not."

A cry arose in the streets. "At that moment, the Moon became surrounded with an aura, as large and glowing as a saint's halo. Pure-white rays shot out, darting and flickering, in all directions. We had been expecting an extraordinary sight, but we were unprepared for anything so magnificent. I confess that the weird and wonderful spectacle alarmed me. But in a moment all that we had seen was far surpassed. From the black rim of the Moon there suddenly shot forth three gigantic, purple-red tongues of flame. They paused, motionless, like jagged mountain peaks in an alpine sunset. Each was different from the others, but all were many times larger than the white circlet of rays. It was as if the Sun, behind the Moon, were flaring up in monstrous volcanic explosions."

The length of these fiery tongues was afterwards estimated at half the distance between Earth and Moon. At the end of the eight-minute performance their color turned violet, then white, and then they faded away.

They were forthwith baptized protuberances or prominences, and the halo was called corona. From the first the astronomers realized that this phenomenon had not been produced by the eclipse, but rather that the Sun must constantly be shooting forth

such red streamers and must always possess a corona. Apparatus for observing the corona independently of an eclipse has since been developed by a French astronomer, Bernard Lyot, who employed a moon-shaped disc placed in the telescope to form an artificial eclipse. Lyot took photographs of the prominences every two minutes, and then ran off these stills in rapid succession as a motion picture. It was a spectacle for kings, one that Le Roi Soleil would have delighted in. In Lyot's motion pictures the sheaves of flame can be seen leaping forth, then after a few minutes, subsiding. Heavy banks of clouds condense, swell, alter their form, or remain stable for days, usually connected by a narrow stalk to their place of origin in the Sun. We can grasp the proportions of these cosmic eruptions only when we imagine the Earth in the picture; it would vanish among the solar prominences like an airplane in thunderclouds.

Probably the prominences emerge from the glowing white areas on the surface of the Sun which Galileo was the first to observe, and which he called torches. The name was apt, for his torches shoot flames.

The inner part of the corona is thought to consist of free electrons with an admixture of protons, repelled by the same radiation pressure that produces the tails of comets. Its outer part is not actually part of the Sun at all, but a cloud of extremely fine dust that merely reflects sunlight. This dust, however, is not comparable to anything on Earth; it is believed to be more tenuous than the finest vacuum we can achieve.

The zodiacal light that is visible at twilight in the tropics, shooting up from the ground almost to the zenith in the form of a faint shimmering pyramid, is thought to be due to a similar cloud of dust. The Gegenschein (counterglow) or reflection of the zodiacal light is supposed to be situated outside the orbit of Mars, while the dust cloud that causes the light is within the orbit of Venus.

Thus our solar system is far more complex than is generally realized. It swarms with minor planets, comets, and hordes of meteors; the Sun affects the Earth magnetically with the radiation from its spots, spews forth red smoke and ionized atoms, and holds three clouds of the most tenuous dust floating in space not far from us.

TRIUMPH OF PRECISION

The Perfect Telescope

THE YOUNG MAN'S CAREER can be said to have begun on the
momentous day in the year 1801 when he was caught in the
ruins of the house of his master, Weichselberger. The house had
collapsed, for no discernible reason, and the entire neighborhood
flocked to the scene of the disaster. The Prince Elector in person
directed the rescue operations. When the optician's apprentice
was finally dug out of the ruins alive, the Prince asked whether
there were any favors he might grant him. The boy blurted out
forthwith: "Time to do my assignments for night school."

It turned out that Herr Weichselberger thought the lens-grind-
ing machine provided all the education any boy needed. The
Prince solemnly enjoined him to allow his apprentice, Joseph
von Fraunhofer, enough leisure to keep up with his lessons, and
to read the pile of books the Prince presented to him.

Later employers found the young bookworm even more of a
problem when he moved on to the optical firm of Utzschneider &
Reichenbach; the head of the mechanical division rebelled against
following the suggestions of the youngest journeyman in the
place. But Fraunhofer's proposals were always so clever that they
could not be overlooked, and his superior's resignation was requested. Guinand, the manager of the company, suffered a similar fate. He took his leave of the firm, and went to France,
where as things turned out, he became the founder of the French

optical industry; apparently he preferred to start again from the beginning rather than have Fraunhofer tampering with all his ideas.

Finally Reichenbach himself left the firm when the twenty-one-year-old journeyman put through a total reform of the company, and received a share in the business, as he had requested. There was, in fact, nothing he could not do better than the established masters in the field. He was constantly rebuilding Guinand's glass furnaces, altering the direction of the flame, lengthening the vent pipe, trying various spouts. Eventually he produced the first completely unstreaked and flawless glass. On the other hand, the glass became quickly misted over, even in dry air. No matter how often it was wiped, the thin film of moisture returned. After endless experiments, he reduced the amount of potash in the original compound. The glass stopped gathering condensation, but was now filled with fine air bubbles. Fraunhofer declared that this would not affect its optical properties. He was right; the air bubbles are found to this day in the finest telescope objectives.

Reichenbach's gauges and meters had surpassed all others of the day; they were supreme achievements of precision work. Fraunhofer found ways of replacing them by instruments using pure light. For example, he dispensed with calipers, and checked the curvature of lenses by a hollow glass device into which the lens was placed; if there were the slightest deviation from the proper curvature, the Newtonian colored rings, which formed in the air space between the two pieces of glass, would be visibly distorted. Instead of using a forceps for centering, Fraunhofer employed a ray of light which bobbed back and forth on a rotating lens until it fell upon the exact center; there it stood still.

These extremely sensitive and rapid methods of checking quality have become indispensable in modern mass manufacture of objectives and eyeglasses. The optical industry was founded upon Fraunhofer's inspirations. He also improved the grinding and polishing machines until they operated with the highest precision.

At the age of twenty-five Fraunhofer was in charge of a crew of forty-eight select workmen. His telescopes, in red morocco

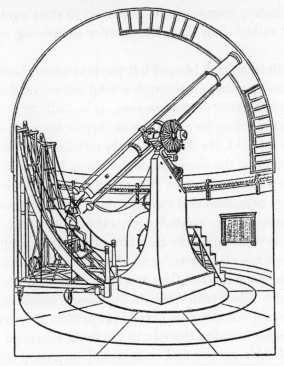

FRAUNHOFER TELESCOPE IN USE AT HARVARD OBSERVATORY DURING
THE NINETEENTH CENTURY.

cases, sailed the seven seas. Even the captains of British naval
vessels took pride in the possession of "a Fraunhofer."

His great ambition was to surpass Herschel's mirror telescope
with a lens telescope. Over a period of fifteen years he solved
most of the complicated problems of producing a flawless telescopic lens, and established the basic type of modern refractor.
In addition, he solved a good many nonoptical problems. For
example: how can a twenty-foot tube weighing many tons be set
up so that the pressure of a finger will move it in any direction?
Surely this is a problem for artillery- and crane-engineers, but it
was solved by Fraunhofer. He employed ball bearings, then
largely unknown, and balance-weights with correction screws to
modify the equilibrium should extra apparatus be added to the
telescope. How important this was, only the future revealed. For
the modern astronomer uses so many types of extra instruments
that the telescope is little more than a vehicle for them.

The vehicle requires a motor, since the sky moves. Like snow-flakes, the stars float out of the visual field of large instruments; a mere quiver of the telescope tube can make stars leap away like so many grasshoppers. In addition, the frictional resistance of the tons of metal and glass changes with the altitude of the tube. This must be automatically compensated for. In short, the motive apparatus for a big telescope would have been a lifetime's work for a skillful precision engineer. In Fraunhofer's busy life it was a mere incidental.

Micrometers are needed for precision measurements. There are a dozen types of them; most of them were given their present form by Fraunhofer. He provided for the heat expansion of a lens by devising a split elastic frame. He produced two master-pieces that for decades were copied unchanged, except for some-times being built on a larger scale: the eleven-inch Königsberg telescope, and the ten-inch Dorpat telescope. At the age of thirty-nine he died of consumption. On his gravestone were inscribed the words: "*Approximavit sidera*—He brought the stars closer."

Spectral Lines and Wave Lengths

Fraunhofer did more than found the optical industry, produce the first flawless glass, and solve mechanical problems in the building of large telescopes. His greatest achievement was a mathematical one: calculation of the formulas for faultless lenses. He kept these formulas a close secret, and to this day it is not known how he managed to fulfill certain mathematical conditions for well-corrected lenses two generations before these fundamen-tal laws of modern geometrical optics were formulated. He even eliminated the astigmatism of the oblique rays of light in his eyepieces. Three generations of theoretical research were neces-sary to catch up with this innovation of Fraunhofer's.

During his lifetime he made public only the third of his secrets: the method for calculation of an achromatic objective. In ordinary lens images, colored fringes are extremely troublesome; they make

exact measurements of the angular distances of stars virtually impossible. Newton had declared the problem insoluble, but his countryman, John Dollond, gave this the lie by making lenses in which different types of glass were combined. Nevertheless, an achromatic objective remained a matter of happy chance until Fraunhofer learned how to determine mathematically the light-dispersing characteristic of different varieties of glass. For this purpose he made a number of experiments which in their clarity and simplicity are strongly reminiscent of Newton's famous experiments. In the course of them he had the finest inspiration of his life. It occurred to him to examine a spectrum under magnification.

The result was an instrument that has since become indispensable to every physics laboratory and observatory throughout the world: the spectroscope. It is essentially a tiny telescope mounted on a turntable; the observer looks through the telescope at a fixed

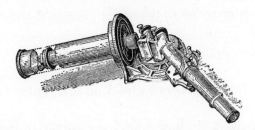

DOUBLE-PRISM SPECTROSCOPE. LIGHT ENTERS THROUGH A SLIT AT LEFT, IS BROKEN UP BY THE PRISMS IN THE CENTER, AND IS VIEWED THROUGH THE TELESCOPE AT RIGHT.

prism, and examines one color after the other under magnification.

What was the point of magnifying the colors of the spectrum? Fraunhofer could scarcely have answered that question; he simply followed the beckoning of his imagination.

At first glance his spectroscope showed him the spectrum of the Sun marked by a great number of fine black lines of varying thicknesses—which are still called, after him, Fraunhofer lines. These spectral lines have become for science the hieroglyphs of a mysterious language, the language of light, which reveals the

innermost nature of matter and the character of the remotest heavenly bodies.

Their discoverer did not know how to read them; to his dying day he never suspected that he had found the philosophers' stone. He was content to make drawings of 576 of the lines with the greatest possible precision. They served him as a tool for measuring the chromatic dispersion of every type of glass—a technical feat of the greatest value. Henceforth objectives for telescopes could be calculated beforehand with as much certainty as solar eclipses. The optical craft became as exact a science as astronomy.

Thereafter, Fraunhofer felt himself to be a scientist. He used his spectroscope in conjunction with one of his best telescopes, and examined the spectra of planets and stars. In the former he saw broad dark bands instead of lines, in the latter dark lines. He found many bright lines in an electric spark, but in the flame of a candle only two yellow lines. These discoveries laid the foundation for the fabulous conclusions that science was later to draw from spectral studies. In addition, he measured the brightness of the colors of the spectrum in the same way they are still measured. He also observed that the human eye is itself not "achromatic" —that is, it does not form images free from extraneous colors— and took this flaw into consideration in making his last telescope lenses.

In 1827 he wrote a small book entitled *New Modification of Light.* It so impressed physicists and astronomers that the professors of the Munich Academy appointed him a corresponding member. Overjoyed, Fraunhofer turned up at the next meeting of the Academy. He was received rather coolly; the academicians were averse to sitting down with "that glass grinder." After some embarrassed discussion, Fraunhofer was seated as a "guest observer," without the right to vote or speak.

But at one of the sessions he was unable to hold his tongue. A professor of physics reported on a remarkable event at the French Academy of Sciences in Paris. A young road construction engineer named Augustin Fresnel had applied for the prize being offered for the best explanation of the fact that light deviates from a straight line; when passed through a fine slit, several colored

images of the slit appear to the right and left of the white image. Fresnel contended that the phenomenon could only be explained by the wave theory of light, which Newton had so strongly rejected.

The professor of physics proceeded to point out the implications of this argument. If there were light waves, then Huygens's ether with its preposterous properties—perfect elasticity and utter frictionlessness—would have to be accepted again as a fact, not dismissed as an historical curiosity. Still, the mathematician Siméon Poisson in Paris had been unable to refute the engineer's equations. He had, however, conceived a diabolically clever practical test: according to Fresnel's wave theory there ought to be a bright spot in the center of the shadow cast by a small sphere.

"Then," continued the professor, "came the astonishing denouement. The simple experiment was tried at that very session—and Fresnel was proved correct. In the center of the shadow cast by a small sphere was a brilliant bright spot.

"Fresnel, moreover, claims that he can calculate the wave length of light rays. He maintains that red light has a wave length of 635–640 millionths of a millimeter."

At this the corresponding member sprang to his feet, crying: "Correct, correct! The man is right."

The academicians were so startled that even the chairman forgot to reprove Fraunhofer for his unseemly conduct. "How do you presume to judge?" he asked sharply.

"I have determined these same figures," Fraunhofer replied, "only I did not suspect that they represented wave lengths. My line B in the red part of the solar spectrum has a wave length of 637.8 millionth of a millimeter."

"Are we to understand that you have already performed Fresnel's experiments, and that you are able to measure millionths of a millimeter exact to one decimal place?"

Fraunhofer explained that he had likwise worked with slit images, and had taken account of the spectra produced. In order to obtain brighter spectra, it occurred to him to place several slits side by side. He therefore made gratings of wire mesh; but these turned out to be much too coarse. Then he tried drawing

lines on gilded glass, soon omitted the gilt, and constructed a precision machine that employed a diamond to make three hundred lines to the millimeter on glass. With this grating he obtained very long and bright spectra, and was able to make exact measurements—but he had not until this day known that he had been measuring the wave lengths of light.

Henceforth, the restriction of silence imposed upon the "lens grinder" was lifted. The academicians even condescended to return his visits and to inspect Fraunhofer's gratings. They then decided to print an account of the gratings in their proceedings, and to send a copy to Paris, so that the members of the French Academy of Sciences would see that the Bavarians were a little ahead of them.

Fraunhofer's diffraction gratings have become part of the regular equipment of modern observatories. They have since been greatly improved, but the wave lengths he measured with them deviate from the now current figures only by ten millionths of a millimeter.

Solitude of the Stars

Once the world had Fraunhofer's precision telescopes, a man was wanted who would know how to get the best results out of them. That man was already at work in Germany. Friedrich Wilhelm Bessel, former businessman, amateur astronomer, had been launched on his scientific career by Olbers of comet fame, had been trained by the selenographer J. H. Schröter, taught the subtleties of mathematics by Karl Friedrich Gauss, and appointed by the King of Prussia to the state observatory in Königsberg, the first such institution in Germany. Bessel developed into the greatest of German astronomers—an improbable combination of practical observer and theoretician.

His insistence on exactitude went beyond all bounds. Due to him the operation of telescopes has become so complicated that beginners may well despair. Not even the best instrument or the

best observer can be trusted, he taught; we must even be wary of the air we breathe and the ground on which we stand.

The Earth's axis shifts and wobbles slightly; the atmosphere bends light rays differently at differing temperatures and pressures, so that thermometer and barometer must be consulted whenever a figure is noted down. The most important instrument for measuring angular distances, the meridian circle, has an optical axis and an axis of rotation. These are supposed to be perpendicular to one another, but a perfect right angle is not easy to obtain; the axis of rotation does not lie perfectly horizontal and point absolutely east and west. In addition, there are a dozen other faults of the telescope which it would be useless to correct because the constant vibration of the ground and the air in any case make mathematical precision an illusion. Finally, every human being has an individual way of noting times and judging the coincidence of a dot of light and a fine thread; this "personal equation" must always be taken into consideration.

Bessel took all these possible sources of error and couched them in formulas and tables which henceforth every astronomer had to heed in order to give exact data for the position of a single star. Bessel himself determined some 50,000 positions. In addition, he corrected all those listed by Bradley, so that the positions of stars a hundred years before could be compared with their present positions, and the movements of the stars not only be demonstrated, but measured in terms of angular distance, direction, and speed. This fanatic of precision was responsible for the present absolute certainty of astronomical data.

Bessel formulated his principles in a magnificent statement: "Every instrument is made twice, first in the workshop and then in observatory, first by the technician and then by the astronomer, first out of glass and steel and brass, and then on paper through correction tables." Thus he breathed life into the wonderful "Fraunhofer" that he had been given. He studied its peculiarities, noted its small weaknesses, trained it like a child, and brought it into harmony with his own personality like a beloved wife.

His efforts were rewarded. The instrument presented him with two of the most significant discoveries of the century.

That Sirius moves had long been known, but Bessel was able to measure the angular distance of the movement from one year to the next. He found that the star moved in a curve, and between 1830 and 1840 determined an extremely small deviation in the curve. Bessel concluded that Sirius must revolve around an unseen companion whose gravitation drew the star alternately to one side and to another.

If this were true, there must be dark stars—a premise that aroused a good deal of skepticism. Bessel coolly commented: "There is no compelling reason why radiation of light should be considered an essential characteristic of a heavenly body." In principle he was right, although wrong in the specific case; the companion of Sirius was later detected as an extremely tiny dot radiating white light.

The wonderful precision of his instrument led him to attempt once more to realize the classical dream of astronomers, albeit no one yet had carried out that dream: to measure the linear distance of a star.

His strategy was based upon the Copernican interpretation of the planetary loops as reflections of the Earth's voyage around the Sun. If the stars are not infinitely remote, it should be possible to observe a similar reflection of the Earth's motion; in the course of a year stars ought to describe an extremely small apparent ellipse. The attempt to demonstrate these parallaxes, as they are called, had often been made, but always without success.

Bessel chose Star No. 61 in the Swan, 61 Cygni, which he considered to be unusually close because it changed its position so very rapidly—5 seconds of arc per year. This is as much as a point seen from a distance of one mile would appear to move if it actually changed its position by 1.4 inches. Superimposed upon this motion is the apparent parallactic motion of about 0.3 seconds of arc arising from the Earth's motion around the Sun. This is what Bessel measured by noting the change in the position of 61 Cygni in six or seven successive half-year periods. From the amount by which the star appeared to shift, as measured in the eyepiece of his telescope, and from his knowledge of the focal length of his telescope, Bessel was able to measure the angle of

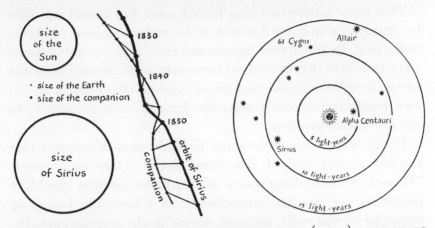

ORBITS AND SIZE OF SIRIUS AND ITS COMPANION (LEFT). THE STARS
NEAREST OUR SUN (RIGHT).

shift, or parallax. This angle coupled with his knowledge of the
distance of the Earth from the Sun enabled him to calculate
geometrically the linear distance to the star, a distance of eleven
light-years from the Earth. The first actual measurement of
interstellar linear distance had been achieved.

This one measurement was promptly followed by another, also
made with a Fraunhofer telescope, by F. G. W. von Struve.
Struve, the founder of a dynasty of astronomers which has continued down to the present day, had specialized in binary stars.
He quadrupled the number of binaries in Herschel's catalogue,
and measured the angular distances between the pairs with unprecedented exactitude. These successes encouraged him also to
venture the measurement of a linear distance. For his experiment
he chose brilliant Vega in the Lyre, since presumably the brightest
stars were also the nearest. He watched it for three annual trips of
the Earth around the Sun, and was likewise able to determine
the parallax. The angle of shift was so small that the linear distance
of Vega could not be less than twenty-seven light-years.

During the second half of the nineteenth century astronomers
found out, one by one, how far the brightest stars are from us.
Sirius alone comes as close as nine light-years; Altair, the eye of
the Eagle, blinks at us from a distance of fifteen light-years; and
most of the other bright stars are farther away than Vega. But

there are about half a dozen feeble stars which are relatively close to us; the closest of all, Alpha in the Centaur, is only 4 1/3 light-years away, about twenty-six trillion miles.

To have some grasp of what that means, let us imagine the solar system to be the size of a wagon wheel with a diameter of 4 feet. The nearest neighboring sun, Alpha Centauri, would then be not in the next house or the next street, but 2.6 miles away. In between would be absolute emptiness for a distance of about 2.6 miles all around our wagon wheel of a solar system.

We can fully appreciate the significance of this when we learn that the diameter of our Sun at the hub of the wheel is 1/1,000 of a foot. If we raise the diameter of the Sun to an inch, then the nearest star proportionately must be 216 miles away. And that is the average proportionate distance between stars. Frightful indeed is the solitude of the stars. To use another comparison: if a space rocket traveling at supersonic speeds were to reach the Moon in a week, it would take ten thousand years to attain the nearest star!

The Leviathan and the Rival Discoverers

Leviathan was the name of the whale that swallowed and vomited up the prophet Jonah. There is a constellation known as the Whale, but what is being referred to here is the giant telescope built in 1845 by William Parsons, third Earl of Rosse, at Parsonstown, Ireland. This largest telescope of the nineteenth century was fifty-four feet long, and so wide that a man could walk upright through it. The diameter of the mirror was seventy-two inches.

This colossal instrument, which for the first time brought to light the spiral form of nebulae, took seventeen years to complete. Lord Rosse, a big landowner who trained the sons of his tenants to be technicians and chemists, first built a steam engine with their aid in order to run the tools for polishing the mirror, and then spent five years experimenting with metal alloys in order to

find the right material for the mirror. The finished disc weighed four tons; yet merely the pressure of a hand upon its back could make constellations wobble wildly. The most difficult task proved to be the construction of a mobile and yet stable bed. Rosse solved this by mounting twenty-seven cast-iron plates upon a base of oak tree trunks which in turn rested upon a ball and socket let into

LORD ROSSE'S LEVIATHAN, 1845. THIS COLOSSAL INSTRUMENT WAS FIFTY-FOUR FEET LONG, AND THE DIAMETER OF ITS MIRROR WAS SEVENTY-TWO INCHES.

solid rock. The telescope was moved awkwardly to the right or left with a chain drive. Only a tiny segment of the sky could be observed with it. To shield it from the wind, two walls were erected on either side, so that the resultant structure looked like a medieval castle, complete with drawbridges, assault ladders, and the Leaning Tower of Pisa in the center.

But it would have been a grave error to judge from outward appearances that this structure was the crude work of an amateur. The polish of the metal disc was rightly considered an optical marvel. It had been necessary to remove an even layer 1/10,000 of a millimeter thick from the prepolished mirror, all the way from center to edge. This was a remarkable feat of precision.

A rich Lancashire brewer named William Lassell decided to surpass Lord Rosse's instrument in accuracy if not in size. He constructed a telescope only twenty-four inches in diameter, with the frank aim of putting Fraunhofer's in the shade. Ever since Newton the British had sworn by the reflecting telescope. Mirrors have much the same aberrations as lenses, but they must be made parabolic and thus have small fields of view. On the other hand, they could be made far bigger than was ever possible for lenses. Lassell was bent on proving that a mirror could equal and surpass the much-admired German lenses, especially in regard to sharpness of the image.

His experiment succeeded beyond expectations. At the first test, on October 10, 1846, Lassell observed not only Neptune, which had been discovered less than three weeks before, but a tiny dot alongside it. In a space of five days this dot circled around Neptune; plainly, it was Neptune's moon. Here was a striking demonstration of the power of his new telescope; a refractor would hardly have shown Neptune itself, Lassell thought. But a few weeks later Neptune's moon was seen at Harvard Observatory, where a German instrument with only a twelve-inch objective was in use. The director at Harvard, America's first observatory, was the onetime watchmaker G. P. Bond. Inadvertently, he selected the same objects for investigation as the brewer on the other side of the Atlantic, so that a rivalry began which yielded several of the most remarkable examples of the "duality of discoveries" so common in science.

Lassell was determined to find a new moon of Saturn. Six had already been discovered. They adhered to the curious distance ratios that Bode had discovered for the planets, and also displayed the same striking gap as the one between Mars and Jupiter. Lassell

insisted that there must be a moon in that gap—and one night in 1848 he found it.

That very night the small moon was also observed by Bond at Harvard—the very same night.

An even stranger coincidence was to follow. The Englishman thought he was slightly ahead of his American rival when he observed a diaphanous black veil within Saturn's ring, a dark inner ring, as it were. All night long he sat at the telescope making sure that he was not the victim of an optical illusion. At breakfast he wrote out a report for the newspapers, and then settled down, with the satisfaction of a man who could rest on his laurels for a while, to read the morning *Times.* And there was a detailed article on the latest discovery at Harvard Observatory: Mr. Bond had succeeded in demonstrating the presence of an additional dark ring within Saturn's ring.

It would almost seem as if a humorous world-spirit had thrust the same objects into the fields of vision of both rivals simply in order to prolong the competition between the two types of telescope. Temporary victory, however, was won by the refracting telescope, which accomplished as much as the reflector with half the aperture, and in addition was handier, cheaper, and more adaptable. Until the end of the century the refractor dominated in observatories; then, in the twentieth century, the pendulum swung he other way, as we shall see in a later chapter.

As for moons—new ones are still being discovered occasionally. More than thirty satellites are already known; Jupiter alone has eleven, Saturn ten. As far as can be determined, most of them range around the size of our own Moon, between two and three thousand miles in diameter. However, there are some more like the minor planets in size, being only a few hundred miles or less in diameter. Compared to their mother planets, all the moons in the solar system, with a single exception, are absurdly tiny; the various satellites of Jupiter possess between 1/10,000 and 1/100,-000 of the planet's mass, and some of Saturn's are only a millionth of its mass. The sole exception, so far as is known, is our own Moon, whose diameter is nearly 1/3 and whose mass is about 1/80 of the Earth's. That is indeed an impressive fraction when

we consider that the largest of the planets, Jupiter, amounts to only 1/1,000 the mass of the Sun, and that all the planets taken together come to only 1/800.

The Deviation of Mercury; the Discovery of Neptune

Long before, in the year 1753, a young French astronomer named Le Français de Lalande, full of pride in the infallibility of his science, had asked his king to witness a transit of Mercury across the face of the Sun. Louis XV inquired how it was possible for such an event to be calculated in advance with such precision, and appeared punctually at the observatory. Mercury, however, was not so punctual. When the Sun set, he had still not made his transit. The delay amounted to eight hours, and as it turned out, the phenomenon was not visible at all in Paris.

Lalande felt utterly disgraced, and cursed the wretched tables that were to blame for it. In this, he was being distinctly unjust. The tables were fifty years old. If the error of eight hours is distributed over this period of time, it amounts to two minutes for each revolution of Mercury. Two minutes deviation out of three months certainly cannot be considered "wretched" calculation.

But modern astronomy demands a far greater degree of precision—and was vouchsafed it in the person of Urbain Leverrier of St. Lo, a chemist who unexpectedly turned astronomer. In the year 1837 he was busy preparing some new phosphorus compounds when he was asked whether he would consent to be instructor in astronomy at the Ecole Polytechnique at Paris. He accepted the post with utmost satisfaction, although he knew little about the subject.

After a brief spell of orientation in the new science, Leverrier took it upon himself to improve on the work of Laplace, then the pride of France. By and by, he brought out corrected tables for Mercury, calculating the next transit to the minute—his error was only five seconds. This error, too, he judged too large; once

again he revised the entire theory of Mercury's movements, so that his tables coincided with all observations. The deviation now amounted to no more than 38 seconds per *century*.

Does such accuracy seem uncanny? However, he still was not satisfied. "The secular deviation [nonperiodic, and increasing with time] of Mercury must be explained," he insisted. Astronomers had come so far that they could reckon the motions of a heavenly body with absolute precision—for 38 seconds per century are truly less than nothing. Yet they would have it that even this insignificant deviation from theory could be traced to a particular cause. This was tantamount to asserting that the theory was infallible, virtually divine.

For generations the causes were sought. Leverrier postulated the presence of a swarm of asteroids in the vicinity; others suggested that Mercury possessed an invisible moon; others held that the Sun must be somewhat more flattened at the poles than it appeared to be. But none of these hypotheses could be proved. The cause of the zodiacal light, that is to say, a dust cloud within the orbit of Venus, was also proposed as the perturbing element, and for a time this explanation seemed to fit the facts best. But it has lately been demonstrated that the mass of the cloud is too small to account for the perturbations.

The ultimate explanation of the mystery was provided by the theory of relativity: that the gravitational field of the Sun induces a change in the geometry of space which in turn slightly distorts Mercury's elliptical orbit. This interpretation, too, has only been confirmed in recent years after a great deal of discussion and recalculation with electronic computers.

Leverrier, however, not only bequeathed a hundred-year riddle to astronomy; he also won for it a noteworthy triumph.

The problem was the deviation of the planet Uranus from its calculated orbit. The deviation was a serious one: two minutes of arc by 1845, sixty-four years after its discovery. A strong perturbing factor must be present, a body possessing considerable mass, possibly another planet.

Leverrier undertook to calculate the mass and position of the hypothetical planet from the deviation of Uranus. The computa-

tions proved to be a subtle and toilsome business, and when he had finished them Leverrier himself had no great confidence in his results. Nevertheless, he wrote to Professor Johann Gottfried Galle at Berlin, where there was a first-rate telescope, suggesting that the professor look for the computed planet. As it happened, page 21 of the Berlin University star chart had just been printed, and covered the area in question. Armed with this, Galle peered into his telescope on the evening of the day he received Leverrier's letter—September 23, 1846. About a degree from the position proposed by Leverrier was a small star of the eighth magnitude not shown on the map. The following night, it had changed its position slightly; the star moved, was really a planet.

In this way Neptune was discovered, not by chance, like Uranus, but by the visionary powers of pure intellect, by computation from the universal law of gravitation. This was the very summit of prediction; it was prophecy translated into reality, a dream come true in the fullest sense.

The news created well-merited excitement throughout the world. The most curious reaction, however, was that in France, a country that had always taken pride in the accuracy of its astronomers. Several French professors actually reproached Leverrier for having erred by a whole degree in his calculations; he was forced to defend himself like a schoolboy at an examination.

The greatest stir was aroused in England. It seemed that a Cambridge student named John Couch Adams had carried out the same computations, and come to the same conclusions, a year before. But his professor, who had assigned him the task, did not think it worth his while to use the excellent telescope at Cambridge Observatory to look for the planet. At Greenwich, too, the results of Adams's computations were known; but there, at least, the astronomers had an excuse for their sin of omission: their best instrument would not have been good enough to detect Neptune. A new one of the finest sort was promptly obtained for the Greenwich Observatory, but it came too late. A major scientific conquest of the century had been snatched from under the noses of the British.

Leverrier and Adams ignored the nationalistic jealousies. They

congratulated each other, and henceforth remained in continuous friendly association. Both men went on to examine the most minute deviations of the planets from the positions prescribed by the known gravitational forces affecting them; both became directors of their observatories and filled these with the most advanced equipment, so that in the future the triumphs of pure reason could be confirmed on the spot.

Neptune turned out to be a close relation of Uranus, possessing almost the same characteristics: about four times the diameter and seventeen times the mass of the Earth. It requires 165 years for its journey around the Sun, has an atmosphere of methane gas, and a temperature of —330 degrees Fahrenheit. And like Uranus it is perturbed by another heavenly body, although the amount of perturbation is so small that it was not possible to locate this body by sheer computation. After a twenty-year search it was found in 1930 by C. W. Tombaugh, working at Lowell Observatory. He gave this last—for the present—member of our solar system the name Pluto.

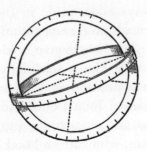

PROBLEMS OF GENESIS

How Saturn's Rings Originated

O NE OF THE FASHIONABLE theories of a few decades back was the birth of the Moon out of the Earth. Unlike Laplace, who assumed an expelled ring of gas which then condensed, this theory described a process of budding: a bulge supposedly formed on the globe of the Earth and was then shaken off. The ostensible scar can still be seen: the basin of the Pacific Ocean has a round, almost circular outline.

The budding or detachment theory was an outgrowth of twentieth-century criticism of the mathematics of Laplace's ball-of-gas theory. According to Jules Henri Poincaré's calculations, the rotation of a ball of gas would not result in an elongating ellipsoid that would ultimately cast off rings, but in a pear-shaped body, which might, in some circumstances, break into a larger and a smaller piece. The budding-off of the Moon would therefore not be impossible; but it would have to have occurred in a gaseous or liquid state of the Earth, and thus no scarified wound would be left behind. Moreover, this new theory applied to no other moon in the solar system, for satellites are generally far too tiny to have originated as the smaller end of a planetary pear.

After the First World War precisely the reverse theory won a temporary popularity: the "world ice" theory advanced by the Austrian Hans Hörbiger. This was an attempt to solve virtually all geological problems by positing the fall of several moons upon the Earth. These supposedly heaped up the mountains

and drowned continents; daily floods piled up the various strata of coal, while each new moon ushered in a new era on Earth, with new forms of life.

What actually would happen if such an event took place was outlined a hundred years ago by the only feasible method: mathematics based on the law of gravitation. In 1850, E. Roche, a French astronomer, computed the result if a moon had attempted to unite with Earth. His principal conclusion: the union would not take place at all. No heavenly body could simply fall from the sky; it would have to approach deliberately in closer and closer spirals. As it did so, the attraction of the Earth would increasingly distort it; at a distance of 10,000 miles its shape would be that of a long egg. From then on our heavier planet would rend fragments from its body. Nor would conditions be very pleasant upon the Earth. Our globe would be distorted, too, by gravitation, would groan in all its joints; earthquakes, floods, rising of mountains and annihilation of continents would be the tamest of the possible consequences. And should any remnant of life have been able to survive this, it would certainly be destroyed in the subsequent disaster, which would suddenly and catastrophically reverse all the recent gravitational stresses. For then, when the half-shattered satellite approached within four times the radius of the Earth, it would burst. The Earth's gravitation would blast it into a thousand pieces; only relatively small crumbs would rain down upon the surface of our planet.

Now came the most curious result of Roche's computations: something would be left of that moon. The smallest fragments would not fall to Earth; they would circle around our globe, distributing themselves in a shallow disc. In other words, we would find ourselves with rings like Saturn's.

Roche believed that Saturn's rings had actually been created in this manner. In basic terms, Saturn had captured and shattered its nearest moon, converted the remnants to dust, and set them whirling around its equatorial zone in the form of the well-known rings.

No doubt it amused Roche thus to revive the ancient Greek myth of Saturn, who devoured his children. It is noteworthy

that Saturn's rings are closer to the planet than four times its radius, and this within the zone that Roche held to be fatal. Nevertheless, his atrocity tale of the annihilated moon cannot be accepted out of hand. A number of points remain to be proved. The first of these is whether the rings actually consist of fragments. When they are observed through the telescope they appear as a glistening white disc surrounding the yellow sphere of the planet, and might easily be taken for a solid mass.

That the rings could not be solid was demonstrated by the British physicist James Clerk Maxwell in 1856. A solid ring, he computed, would be caused to oscillate more and more wildly by the least disturbance; ultimately it would dash itself to pieces. If, on the other hand, the rings were fluid or gaseous, their rotation would lead to the formation of waves which would swiftly tear them apart. The only remaining possibility is a collection of fragments, a heap of bricks, as Clerk Maxwell put it. And since according to Kepler's third law (the squares of the times of revolution of bodies are in the ratio of the cubes of their mean distances from the center of revolution) the outer fragments must revolve more slowly than the inner ones, Saturn's rings must be comparable to the inside of a concrete mixer in which the aggregate is constantly being shaken up. These rings are extremely thin—less than a hundred miles in thickness as against a diameter of 170,000 miles. In order to represent Saturn's rings, we would have to conceive of a twelve-inch phonograph record less than seven thousandths of an inch in thickness. And this record would have to consist of independent motes of dust whirling around and around, each zone at a different speed. How, one wonders, could so strange a body have originated, and how could so seemingly impossible a structure last?

Roche answered this question with a second mathematical triumph: the Roche disc.

He turned again to Laplace's rotating sphere of gas, this time with a particular premise: that the principal mass of the sphere was concentrated in the center. In that case a central globe would remain intact through even the fastest rotation; the outer layers, however, would spread out into an increasingly thinner disc. Thus

Roche demonstrated mathematically that a structure like the rings of Saturn could come into being, and last.

There remains the question: are we still obliged to accept Roche's hypothesis of the shattered moon? Is that really the only possible origin of the famous rings?

Laplace held the directly opposite viewpoint, that a ring would be the primary form from which the moons developed. He held that the solar system evolved out of a rotating sphere of gas with the Sun in the center. This perforce became a Roche disc, from which small rings broke off and, because of uneven cooling, rounded out into new spheres, our present planets. In the case of some planets the process repeated itself, leading to the birth of satellites. Accordingly, Saturn's rings would constitute the preliminary stage of a moon that, exceptionally, cooled uniformly and therefore remained in the form of a disc.

Whose account is right, that of Roche or of Laplace?

Probably that of Roche. For the Laplace theory has been falling more and more into disrepute since 1850.

The Birth of Planets

Of the swarm of new members the nineteenth century brought into our family of planets, the numerous satellites must be regarded as gifts from Pandora's box. They caused endless trouble in the realm of cosmogony. Laplace's marvelously simple and harmonious theory of the origin of the planets had been derived from four striking basic facts: that all bodies in the solar system revolve in the same plane, in the same direction, in almost circular orbits, and that all rotate in the same direction. But after 1850 satellites turned up which did not obey these rules. The four moons of Uranus deviate far from the plane of the zodiac. The outermost moon of Saturn revolves in an elongated, cometlike ellipse. Two moons of Jupiter and one each of Saturn and Neptune move backward, in the retrograde direction. Phobos, one of the moons of Mars, circles its planet in seven hours, while Mars takes twenty-four hours for his own rotation. If the moon had begun

its career by detaching itself from the planet, it should not have a faster speed of revolution than the parent's speed of rotation. This is so because in general the momentum of rotation must be conserved; the momentum of rotation of a planet and satellite at any time therefore cannot exceed its value originally.

Evidently, Laplace's theory no longer complied with the facts. But if the theory of the birth of moons from whirling, gaseous protoplanets was no longer tenable, neither was the conception that the planets had been born from the Sun. Still other weighty reasons stood in the way of this latter hypothesis. Laplace had done well to place his famous cosmogony in a footnote. "In all things," this farsighted man remarked, "the last steps to perfection are the most difficult." This aphorism was tantamount to a sentence of death upon his own theory, for it was those last steps to perfection on which the theory foundered.

Truly, this was a pity. Until the present day no comparable substitute for it has been found, although recent theories have been quite successful in accounting for many features of the solar system. Among the aspirants for Laplace's crown, the late Sir James Hopwood Jeans distinguished himself by a truly Laplacean knack for perceiving something plainly apparent which no one else had noticed: that the entire family of planets, together with their satellites, assumes the form of a cigar when placed together, thick in the middle and coming to a point at both ends. At these ends we may place the small, moonless planets; next in line would come the Earth and Neptune, with their one outsize moon apiece, then Mars and Uranus, with two and four moons. The center is formed by the two giants, Jupiter and Saturn, with their large assortment of satellites.

This is a striking image—but how did this particular order come about? Jeans suggests a pretty story to replace the rejected tale of Laplace: that the cigar was pulled out of the body of the Sun when a visiting star passed nearby. Supposedly, the increasing and then diminishing gravitation of this star drew a spindle-shaped cloud of gas out of the globe of the Sun; this cloud afterwards condensed into the astonishingly regular progression of planets and satellites.

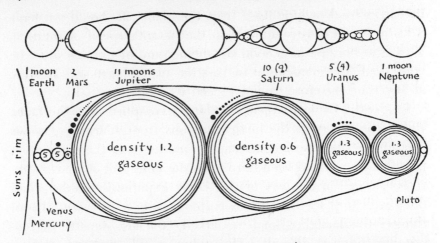

JEANS'S PLANETARY CIGAR (MOONS IN BLACK) AND THE SATELLITE
CIGARS. THE ENTIRE FAMILY OF PLANETS, TOGETHER WITH THEIR
SATELLITES, ASSUMES THE FORM OF A CIGAR WHEN PLACED TOGETHER.
AT BOTH ENDS ARE THE SMALL, MOONLESS PLANETS; NEXT IN LINE
FROM BOTH ENDS ARE THE EARTH AND NEPTUNE, WITH THEIR ONE
OUTSIZE MOON APIECE, THEN MARS AND URANUS. THE CENTER IS
FORMED BY JUPITER AND SATURN, WITH THEIR LARGE ASSORTMENT
OF SATELLITES. JEANS SUGGESTED THAT A GASEOUS, CIGAR-SHAPED
CLOUD WAS PULLED OUT OF THE BODY OF THE SUN BY THE ATTRACTION
OF A PASSING STAR. THE GAS CLOUD AFTERWARDS CONDENSED INTO
THIS REGULAR PROGRESSION OF PLANETS AND SATELLITES.

The criticism was quickly raised that such an encounter between two stars was highly unlikely, because of the relative isola-
tion of the stars in the vastness of space. Astronomers calculated
the probability and came up with a staggering figure: two stars
would approach close enough to disrupt one another by tidal
forces only once in 10^{20} years—a period far longer than the assumed age of the universe. Jeans replied that this was of no account; the solar system might well be a special creation and the
Earth a special case, a phenomenon not duplicated anywhere
else in the Galaxy.

Since the little lords of this Earth are always glad to hear
that they occupy a special place in the universe, Jeans's theory
met with a warm reception. Nevertheless, it does not adequately
replace the nebular hypothesis, since it explains little more than

Jeans's cigar. An acceptable cosmogony must account for a great deal more—among other things, for the geometrical succession of the planets' distances from one another, which is duplicated in the distances among the satellite systems of Jupiter and Saturn. Moreover, the four basic Laplacean facts still stand. In spite of a few small moons that misbehave, these remain the fundamental facts of the solar system, and failure to explain them is failure to explain anything.

The situation has now been further complicated; any new cosmogony must now account for additional peculiarities of our solar system, such as Jeans's cigar and Bode's law. At the same time, any hypothesis must leave room for exceptions. The first step in this direction was taken by Karl Schwarzschild, who proved himself one of the most ingenious astronomers of the twentieth century before he was killed in the First World War. He began by abandoning the unproved dogma that the planets originated in the Sun, and painted a picture of our system's evolution which can be roughly summarized as follows:

In the Kantian primal nebula there first arise, by mutual attraction of the particles, small nuclei; the cloud becomes transformed into a swarm of meteors. The biggest pieces soon sweep their vicinity clear by their gravitation; several of the dark globes may already possess satellites, but as yet everything is a wild confusion of motion, without goal or fixed direction.

Suddenly, into the midst of the rotating swarm, there rushes a new star. We have reasons for supposing that stars arise with great suddenness, and are at their utmost brightness from the first. The Sun, then, supplies light and a central mass at one and the same time. Its gravitation gradually brings order into the dark swarm of meteors; they begin to revolve around the Sun. Some few satellites may escape the general direction of motion, but the larger planets can hardly do so.

There then follows the evolutionary situation described by Roche: the entire cloud becomes a disc, flattening out more and more; the planets revolve more and more in the same plane, and their ellipses are rounded out. Once again a few small moons may behave eccentrically, especially if they are far enough from

the controlling gravitation of the Sun. The Sun also distributes the planets in order of increasing and then decreasing masses, forces them into orbits at geometrical intervals—although how it does so is as yet unknown. At any rate, the Laplacean facts come into being subsequently, by a kind of process of selection, just as the astonishingly teleological adaptations of living creatures have evolved.

Bombs on the Moon

Our long-dead Moon has a very lively story to tell. Its pockmarked face composed of masses of lava provides us with our first direct insight into the youthful adventures of a heavenly body.

The outstanding characteristic is the great number of craters. They vary so greatly in size that lunar topographers have not been content with the term "crater," and speak of "ring mountains" and "walled plains." If we will, the so-called "seas" may likewise be regarded as great walled plains, for almost all of them are circular and more or less framed by mountains. In that case the surface of the Moon appears as an unbroken succession of similar shapes, the smallest having a diameter of a few hundred yards, the largest many hundreds of miles. What these shapes mean and how they came into being is the most interesting problem of selenology.

There were three principal theories in the past: the volcanic theory, the bubble theory, and the bombardment theory. These held that the lunar craters arose either by volcanic eruptions, by the bursting of bubbles of gas when the surface of the Moon was still plastic, or by the impact of innumerable meteorites over a long period of time.

The most beguiling of the theories was the volcanic, since this assigned to the craters the same origin as those upon Earth. But J. H. Schröter, the German magistrate, long ago recognized that the comparison would not hold. Neither the size nor the shape of

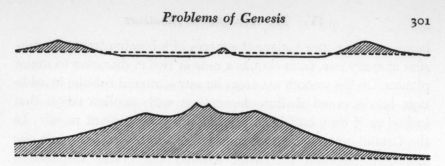

CRATERS OF THE MOON DO NOT RESEMBLE VOLCANOES. PROFILE OF LUNAR CRATERS (TOP), PROFILE OF VESUVIUS (BOTTOM).

the craters corresponded. Vesuvius and Etna rise above the surface of the Earth in the form of cones with a small, funnel-shaped crater at the top. Lunar craters, on the other hand, are sunk into the ground like bowls floating in water. Their floors are always at a lower level than their surroundings, as a rule about 10,000 feet lower. The peripheral walls contain just about enough material to fill in the depression.

The volcanic theory might explain the smallest of the craters, but no eruption of a volcano could create a crater thirty miles in diameter, not to speak of walled plains the size of whole countries.

The same objection applies to the seductive conception that the craters resulted from gas bubbles in a plastic Moon. Such bubbles, of the kind that burst out of the hot mud in the California desert, would leave behind only miniature scars. Not even the smallest crater could result from such a process.

Thus nothing remains but the idea of a hailstorm of meteorites on the Moon. Until recently—when Harold Urey and the late Enrico Fermi worked on the problem—this has always seemed fantastic to astronomers; they have usually left it to outsiders to work out the details. Among the foremost of these is the geographer Alfred Wegener, author of the interesting theory that the American continent broke loose from the Afro-Eurasian land mass, and has been sailing westward ever since.

Wegener studied the wonderful photographs of the Moon in the *Atlas Photographique de la Lune,* published in Paris early in this century. These entirely convinced him that our satellite

bears over its entire surface the traces of a bombardment by missiles of every size, from chunks a mile or two in diameter to minor planets. On the smooth sea areas he saw scattered rubble; in addition, he discerned shallow depressions with swollen edges that looked as if they had been pricked out with a giant needle. In the Cassini crater were two such holes side by side, the left one distinctly punched slantwise. Around the crater Copernicus the terrain looked torn up as if by a series of shell holes. On the walls of craters and the slopes of mountains he saw more holes, sometimes pear-shaped, with broken edges and jutting lips; these, too, could only be interpreted as the effect of missiles. There were successions of holes as if a string of bombs had been dropped one after the other. Then there was the so-called valley in the Lunar Alps: perfectly straight through the mountains, 200 miles long; this could scarcely be explained as anything but the result of a missile hitting the mountains.

But if all these effects were caused by the impact of meteorites, why are most of the craters so shallow? Wegener found a plausible reason for that: meteors are torn apart before they strike the Moon's gravitation, as Roche's theory of the creation of Saturn's rings stipulated. The larger masses thus break up into a hail of fragments which only scrapes and furrows the Moon's crust, while the resultant debris is pushed up into an encircling wall, so that the round, sunken basin is left.

Wegener decided that the process could be demonstrated in the laboratory. The scale being so much smaller, he would have to use smaller materials—fine powder, say, to imitate both the missile and the bombarded moon. Wegener cleverly employed two powders of different colors; he dropped a spoonful of plaster into carefully smoothed powdered cement. The plaster scattered, and so did the topmost layer of cement powder, forming a circular wall around a smooth-floored concavity. The concavity was astonishingly similar in appearance to a lunar crater. Pear-shaped, slit craters with jutting lips could also be produced by adroitly throwing the plaster at the cement.

Wegener's most striking discovery was this: if the layer of cement powder were thin enough, the outstanding characteristic of

many lunar craters resulted, the central mountain. In photographs of the Moon such peaks can be seen everywhere, neatly in the center of the basins. It is astounding that a spoonful of plaster should be able to heap up a ring wall, and even pile a sugar-loaf mountain in the middle, exactly like the walls and central peaks on the Moon.

In order to obtain a perfectly clear picture of this remarkable phenomenon, Wegener deposited a bright-red layer of cinnabar under the cement; he then dropped the spoonful of plaster, produced the ring wall and central mountain, and examined their composition. Both consisted entirely of cement powder strewn with a fine coating of plaster. But at the bottom of the crater the plaster lay directly on top of the cinnabar; the cement had been completely swept away, partly to the outer wall and partly toward the center, where it formed a tiny peak. This is what must have happened on the Moon when a meteorite struck vertically upon a smooth surface; the mineral matter of the Moon was swept out to the walls, and in toward the center.

This skillful experimenter with his simple methods also reproduced another of the unique lunar phenomena: the irregular wreaths of rays such as radiate in particularly beautiful fashion from the Copernicus crater. These rays are nothing more than meteoric dust scattered unusually far. Evidence for this supposition is the fact that they are seen only when the sunlight falls vertically upon them, just as glass dust on a plate of glass is seen only under vertical illumination.

The entire theory is well illustrated by a terrestrial model: the famous crater of Arizona, which was undoubtedly caused by the impact of a meteorite. It has the typical profile of a lunar crater: a shallow basin below the level of the surrounding plain. Its slopes are dusted with fine powdered stone, just as Wegener's walls of cement were covered with plaster. It contains innumerable iron fragments one half to fifteen tons in weight. Fragments, including rocks as tall as houses, were hurled to great distances when the meteorite burst. The explosion therefore must have taken place in the air, but was forceful enough to break open the crust of the Earth and sweep all stones away from a

circle five hundred feet in diameter, and dispose the debris in a
ring wall. The existence and shape of the crater is strong evidence
for the bombardment theory of the origin of the lunar craters.

But then why did not the Earth suffer a similar fate? We do
not, in fact, know whether it did not. When it was a larger and
hotter body than it is now it may, in a fluid state, have received
a rain of missiles which left no scars. Only in the earliest stages
of its history can a heavenly body be bombarded by meteorites of
such size and numbers—or rather, draw them down upon itself
by its excessive gravitational attraction. This must have occurred
when it formed out of the primal nebula, a nucleus that pulled
to itself all smaller, neighboring masses, until it had cleared the
space immediately around it, had become a round, completed,
solitary globe, and could begin its eternal journey within the
gravitational field of a still mightier globe.

The Moon is more than our lamp of the night, more than the
generator of our tides, more than a frozen, lifeless satellite. It is
a surviving document out of the first day of Creation, from a day
that perhaps even antedates the birth of light. It bears upon its
face a runic script that tells us of how in the darkness of earliest
genesis the heavenly bodies of the solar system, moons and Earth,
and all the rest, emerged out of the primal nebula and grew
great under a hail of meteorites.

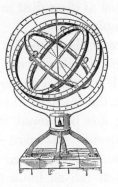

Book Five

REJUVENATION

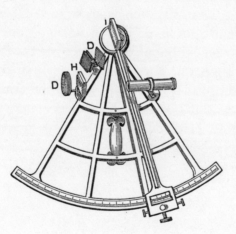

ORGANIZATION AND TECHNOLOGY

Astronomy Becomes Astrophysics

SINCE 1870 astronomy has undergone an astounding metamorphosis. To appreciate this we have only to compare the textbooks: at the end of the last century the fixed stars were treated in a modest final chapter; today two thirds of the book is allotted to them, five sixths if we count in the model specimen of them all, our Sun. Astronomy has literally become the science of the stars.

There has developed something we might almost call a zoology of the stars. They have been divided into genera and species; classified by size as though they ran the gamut from mosquito to elephant; they have been weighed, had their temperatures taken, had their metabolism investigated. Some have been shown to breathe, and others to excrete at regular intervals. Their tendency to pair off, their dances, their herding and flocking, have been discussed. The birth of stars has been witnessed, three stages of their evolution described; the characteristics of senility among them are known, as are their illnesses and outbursts of temperament. Astronomers have even recorded a case of cannibalism. In short, more is known about these specks of light, which even in the strongest telescope remain no more than specks of light, than is yet known about our near neighbors Venus and Mars.

This extraordinary increase in knowledge, astronomy owes to physics.

Physics is the daughter science of astronomy. It was tutored and apprised of its tasks by men like Kepler, Galileo, Newton,

and Huygens. Thereafter, it went its own ways, explored unknown territories like thermodynamics and electricity, joined with
the rising young science of chemistry, and became the acknowledged sovereign among the natural sciences. The former queen
abdicated her throne; she seemed to have reached the end of
her career, and entered a period of honorable shadow-existence
as a second-rate scientific discipline. No one suspected that she
was maturing rapidly, that a rebirth was impending. For astronomy then went through a stage of pupation in which she was
totally rejuvenated. Like a beginner, she went back to school,
learned from her daughter, and became modernized to an extent
no one would have thought possible for so full-blown an observational science.

The metamorphosis was wrought by a band of pioneers from
all nations: Secchi in Rome, Faye in Paris, Janssen in Meudon,
Ångström at Uppsala, Vogel at Potsdam, Zöllner at Leipzig, Huggins at London, Lockyer at South Kensington, Young at Prince-
ton, Pickering at Harvard. These men lived in a fever of exciting
discoveries, revolutionary ideas, magnificent conceptions—all of
which were only a foreshadowing and prelude of what was to
come. They themselves did not see the mature fruit of their work.
Virtually nothing still stands even of Lockyer's towering achievement; his famous book on the Sun today has only historical
value, and the same is true of his conception of the life history of
stars.

Such is the fate of pioneers. But they did not think it a hard
one; they certainly would not have changed places with their
successors, who harvested what they had sowed. Modern man is
happiest in the midst of the creative act and loves striving more
than he does fulfillment.

Those early astrophysicists had a glorious *élan*. When Paris
was encircled in 1870, Pierre Janssen could not bear the thought
of missing the total eclipse in Italy for so trivial a reason. He
piled his instruments and himself into the gondola of a balloon,
and landed safely far beyond the German lines. Another time he
suffered shipwreck, but arrived at his destination in time to observe a conjunction of Venus. It was truly a youthful period for

modern astronomy, a chrysalis stage of the astronomers' science, when the caterpillar was changing into a butterfly.

Around 1900 the butterfly emerged. Astrophysics came forth, armed with apparatus and methods that would have bewildered the amateur astronomers of 1850: with photometers, spectroscopes, motion pictures, photoelectric cells, monochromatic photography—above all, with those devices that analyze light, which made chemical analysis seem crudely primitive by comparison. Chemistry and physics were now practiced over distances of many light-years.

Thirty years later this rejuvenated astronomy startled blasé twentieth-century man with assertions that made even physicists jump. Astronomy, it seemed, was in the forefront of modern thought. Decisive proof of the theory of relativity was provided by astronomers; Einstein's vision was checked and amplified by men with telescopes.

Today there is a close alliance between the observatory and the physics laboratory, an alliance based on reciprocity. The astronomers take their tools and their principles of interpretation from the arsenal of the physicists; the physicists use the stellar spaces as a kind of vast laboratory where they can test their theories under conditions that never occur in terrestrial experiments. The macrocosm of the stars and the microcosm of the atoms have moved close together. For a time it was thought that the atom presented an exact counterpart of the solar system. This concept proved to be an oversimplification, but the most striking similarity remains: the incredible emptiness of both universes. In both, infinitesimal dots of matter are separated by vast spaces and nevertheless compelled by forces operating over great distances to move around one another in prescribed orbits.

That most important of scientific methods, spectrum analysis, is common to both physics and modern astronomy, and progress in it comes alternately from both sides. It is difficult to say whether the solar spectrum means more to astronomers or to physicists.

The Camera Revolution

When a Parisian showman released the secret of photography in exchange for a life pension, astronomers were quick to see how it could serve them. The camera was attached to telescopes to photograph the Sun, Moon, and stars. The Sun caused difficulties because its harsh light burned the film. For that reason an English paper-manufacturer, Warren de la Rue, invented the shutter to make possible extremely fast exposures. In London, at the World Exhibition in 1862, he displayed much-admired stereoscopic pictures: an eight-inch Moon that arched toward the observer, and sunspots seen in depth: great craters with bulging, protruding rims.

As a result of these successful experiments, special telescopes were constructed exclusively for photographic purposes. For instance, the objective of a telescope used in photographic work must be corrected differently from an objective used in visual work. But astronomical photography did not really hit its stride until after 1870, when the silver bromide plate was invented. There followed a more radical revolution in astronomy than that brought about by the telescope itself.

Present-day astronomers virtually do not see the sky except on photographic plates. Seated at the view finder of a telescope, their sole activity consists in holding the guiding star in the cross hairs, so that the picture will not be spoiled by wobbling. The famous giant instruments on Mount Wilson, Mount Hamilton, and Mount Palomar are actually nothing but teleobjectives for tiny cameras that cling to some point on the huge structure like monkeys to a palm tree. Astronomers now rarely observe directly with the eye; every favorable night the telescopes are set to photographing the heavens on a carefully planned schedule.

The research material of modern astronomy is a library of glass plates. Virtually all the discoveries of our century have been read off such plates. It is a weird situation: here is a science that has voluntarily given up looking directly at its subjects. Imagine a zoologist who studied animals only from reproductions. Tycho

Brahe would have been horrified at this mechanization, this stripping of physical reality from a profession that had once placed man face to face with the countenance of God.

But the result remains the same whether the observer, like Brahe, goes for an evening walk and suddenly sees a star that is new to him, or whether he bends over a microscope on a laboratory table and identifies, among a thousand dots, one that was not present in the last photograph taken of a sector of the sky. And the modern method is incomparably more efficient. The astronomer is no longer dependent upon chance; the tiniest change in the sky is noticed. No observations are ever lost; they can be examined and compared decades later. Important discoveries often come to light by merely leafing through files.

Moving objects distinguish themselves from stars by making small dashes on photographic plates that are given long enough exposure. This is the way asteroids and comets are searched for nowadays. A sweep of the firmament, which took Herschel years, can now be accomplished in a few nights, and remains preserved forever on glass plates. Certainly astronomy has lost nothing by entrusting observation to the camera. Photography does a better job.

Silver bromide is superior to the retina of the eye in three ways:

1. It possesses greater sensitivity to gradations of light. The very first photographs of the Sun showed something no eye had ever seen: the darkening of the solar rim. This proved that the Sun has no solid core, that it is a ball of gas throughout. Better photographs then showed the apparent granulation of its surface, and pictures by hydrogen light revealed tremendous eddies of gas.

2. Silver bromide reacts to invisible ultraviolet radiation; it can also be made sensitive to particular colors. When Mars was photographed in red and in blue light, it turned out to be considerably larger on the second photograph: it possesses a far deeper atmosphere than was formerly thought.

3. Silver bromide can store up and summarize feeble light-impressions, so that smaller, more remote objects can be seen if the film is exposed long enough. (On the other hand, the flicker-

ing of the atmosphere makes serious difficulties, for which reason modern observatories are built higher and higher in the mountains.) This advantage is the greatest of all; the camera has multiplied manifold the telescope's range. Without it, the universe would be incomparably narrower, and we would be aware of only a fraction of the number of stars and island universes we now know.

The extraordinary power of the camera has been most brilliantly made manifest by its detection of some thousand nebulae in the Galaxy. Previously, only dim spots had been seen; on photographic plates these were revealed to be wonderful, extremely variegated clouds strongly resembling our terrestrial clouds. Any layman can study them just as well as the professional astronomer.

It seems somehow reassuring that the tremendous reaches of interstellar space display precisely the same types of cloud formations as our insignificant little Earth: heavy clumps, diaphanous veils, fleecy backs, and dark, menacing reefs of thunderclouds. We must keep in mind, however, that this similarity is a miracle, for in interstellar space there are no winds, no air, no water vapor. Those "clouds" have in reality nothing in common with ours. They are cosmic matter, inconceivably tenuous. The central part of the Orion Nebula has a diameter of about 30 light-years and has enough material in it to form 50,000 solar systems such as ours.

Within these clouds there is a shifting and pulsation at a speed that would make a raging typhoon seem as slow as the growth of grass. And yet to our eyes the whole cloud is motionless, and our grandchildren will find scarcely any changes in it—so far away does it lie.

The cosmic clouds glow, moreover, like their miniature copies on Earth, not by their own light, but by the light of nearby stars. A nebula near Antares, the red eye of the Scorpion, therefore glows with a reddish light. In themselves they are invisible; there may be countless dark clouds among the stars.

This conjecture found vivid confirmation when the *Heidelberg Photographic Atlas of the Milky Way* was published. On many

of the plates small white nebulae could be seen, from which proceeded long black channels, as if the nebulae had swept up all stars in their path. That could never have happened because the gravitational attraction of nebulosities is too small. Rather, the nebulae trail behind them streamers of dark gas which effectively block off all light.

It is difficult for the observer to comprehend that the dark places on such photographs are indeed nebulae much closer to us than the stars. Instinctively, we imagine that we are looking beyond the stars into empty space. Herschel once had such an experience. One night he called to his sister in great excitement: "Come quick, look at this. Here is truly a hole in the sky." In the middle of the Milky Way was an inky black spot without a single star to be seen in it. It was dubbed the Coalsack. Every spot in the sky showing a diminished density of stars indicates the presence of a dark nebula; there are innumerable such clouds, curtains of greater or less opaqueness in the sky. A Swiss astronomer, Rudolph Wolf, was able to estimate how many light-years distant they are, and what their thickness must be, simply by counting the stars of all magnitudes on his plates—an application of Herschel's ingenious statistical method. (See pp. 237 ff.)

Thus the camera has made us acquainted with a tribe of space dwellers whose existence had been previously only vaguely suspected. The Galaxy has become a good deal more homelike with its bright and dark nebulae that remind us so strongly of terrestrial clouds. Photography has given back to us the picture-book skies of our childhood, in which little angels sat upon white puffs of cotton, scouring the nearest stars. Only we must now draw in a lot of black puffs also.

Planned Research, and the Two Rivers of Stars

After 1870 the nature of astronomical research changed. The number of professional astronomers, which had remained almost static for two centuries, increased manifold. State-supported obser-

vatories sprang up everywhere, and were outfitted by a rapidly developing optical industry with bigger and bigger telescopes, equipped with ingenious supplementary apparatus. Considerable personnel was needed to man these precious instruments. Years of specialization were necessary before an astronomer could venture to undertake independent research. There was no longer any room for hobbyists. Nowadays, the amateurs at best take over minor tasks such as counting meteors and observing planets. In general, they engage in their hobbies as a sport, and are so obsessively devoted to polishing mirrors that their wives have been jocosely called "glass widows."

The age of gay and gallant celestial hunts, in the manner of Herschel, is past. Original discoveries and inspirations on the part of outsiders are almost without exception relegated to oblivion, after perhaps creating a brief stir. Professionals do not take the trouble to disprove them; they know that such sensations spring up once every five years, on the average.

I myself have witnessed the transition from amateur to outsider in the career of Philipp Fauth. A wealthy lady presented him with a wonderful telescope and a private observatory; he used them well to draw up the finest lunar maps we have. But he devoted the major part of his lifework to the "world ice" theory put forth by the Viennese engineer Hans Hörbiger; he enlarged upon this theory, adding details and developing it into an exciting "glacial cosmogony." But none of it stood up under the superior methods of astrophysics. The astrophysicists long ago promulgated, and proved, the universality of cosmic dust rather than ice.

The inevitable trend toward specialization began fairly early in astronomy. After 1850 it received its impetus from a powerful personality, Sir George Biddell Airy, the reformer of Greenwich. He completely reorganized Greenwich into the model observatory of Europe, and conferred upon it the character it still possesses. Airy established no less than six new institutes. Each was charged with a whole program of research. There was an institute for chronometer testing, one for magnetometeorological studies, one for astrography, one for heliography, one for spectroscopy,

and one for analysis of binary stars. Airy personally designed and tested all the instruments but scarcely ever made observations. He had enough to do directing this large-scale enterprise. In addition, he carried a burden of duties as government inspector of railroads, canals, bridges, lighthouses, as supervisor of surveying and weights and measures. He fixed the boundary between the United States and Canada, determined the longitudes of Cambridge, Edinburgh, Brussels, Paris, Altona, and Valencia, and organized five astronomical expeditions.

Airy was an archpedant who tyrannized over his assistants as though they were so many schoolboys. They had a twelve-hour workday, and their mealtime was measured by a chronometer. If the crew were setting out on an expedition, each member was handed a schedule with train numbers and transfer stations; in addition he received a cake of soap and a numbered towel. A new pane of glass for a window took as much space in the annual report as a new telescope. In his leisure hours this man, who for forty-six years dominated Greenwich like a despot, busied himself labeling used boxes "empty." Malicious gossips whispered: "When he wipes his pen on a blotter, he writes down the date and notes the incident in his diary." But his organization became a model for all of Europe.

The major work at Greenwich remained the measurement of the positions of stars. But this, the oldest task of astronomy, was gradually exceeding the capacity of a single observatory. The last person to undertake it alone was a professor at Bonn, Friedrich Wilhelm Argelander, that paragon of astronomical patience. His famous *Durchmusterung* (1859–62) listed the positions and magnitudes of more than 324,000 stars. And no sooner was he finished than he founded an association, the Astronomische Gesellschaft, expressly for the purpose of repeating the work in collaboration with many observatories.

This task required the labor of more than a generation. Meanwhile a second international project began, this time with cameras. On more than 22,000 plates the entire sky was covered twice and more than thirty million stars recorded. The catalogue for this work was based upon microscopic analysis, and was far

from finished when a third undertaking was started with wide-angle cameras; the photographs taken with these were evaluated by a punched-card process.

In addition there are several hundred special catalogues. The work is still going on.

The purpose of all this is to determine, by comparison with older maps and catalogues, changes of position among the stars. Modern man wishes to see everything in movement, including the eternal firmament. The motions of the Galaxy must be traced as, long ago, the motions of the planets were revealed. Modern man is passionately seeking the law that governs the millions of dots of light in the heavens above him.

Around 1900 the first results of these tremendous endeavors began to be harvested. For a few hundred "near" stars it became possible to mark little arrows showing the direction and apparent distance traveled. Since every such arrow in the diagram on the next page represents the movement of a star in 10,000 years, it is easy to see how minute the change of position must have been in the fifty years at the disposal of the observers.

At first the entire picture seemed hopelessly confused. Every arrow pointed in a different direction. But then Lewis Boss made an analysis of the Hyades group and showed that 50 of the 150 stars were flying definitely toward a single point. This point was only an effect of perspective; in reality these fifty stars were moving in parallel lines. They were actually a swarm, impelled by a mysterious force toward a common goal.

To appreciate the remarkable character of this discovery, it must be remembered that the stars are relatively as isolated in space as pinheads at distances of sixty miles from one another. In the Hyades the pinheads are merely "twenty miles" apart; nevertheless it seems magical that they should all, in this enormous void, fly strictly in the same direction. Such swarms of stars—for several more have since been found—are an impressive illustration of uncanny forces operating over great distances.

Even more exciting was the discovery by a Dutch astronomer, Jacobus Cornelis Kapteyn, of the Ursa Major cluster: eighty stars, strewn over the entire firmament, which apparently belong to a

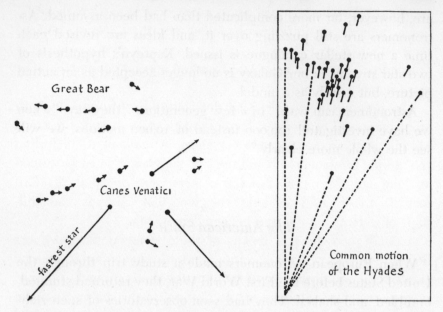

CHANGES OF POSITION AMONG THE STARS. LEFT: REGION OF THE
GREAT BEAR. THE ARROWS INDICATE THE POSITIONS OF THE STARS
10,000 YEARS HENCE. RIGHT: THE HYADES GROUP IN TAURUS. THESE
STARS APPEAR TO BE MOVING TOWARD A SINGLE POINT, BUT IN REAL-
ITY THEY ARE MOVING IN PARALLEL LINES.

single flock. Their destination is the Eagle; their motion is precisely opposite to that of the Hyades swarm.

Thereafter, Kapteyn succeeded in reducing the confusion of
starry motions to order. Aside from a few eccentrics, all the stars
relatively near us are moving in two great streams flowing in opposed directions, one toward the Eagle and the other toward the
Great Bear. The first is larger and flows somewhat more swiftly.

Hail them though they did, the astronomers were secretly troubled by Kapteyn's findings. For there really should have been
only one stream of stars, representing the rotation of the Galaxy.
That it actually does rotate in the course of 200 million years
was tremendously difficult to demonstrate. Not until 1927 did
another Dutch scientist, J. H. Oort, succeed in calculating, from
thousands of individual motions, the common direction of rotation. He placed the center of the unimaginably vast movement
in the Archer. The details of the movements of our sidereal system

are, however, far more complicated than had been assumed. Astronomers are still puzzling over it, and ideas are revised each time a new stellar catalogue is issued. Kapteyn's hypothesis of two star streams in our Galaxy is no longer accepted as an actual picture, but merely as a model.

Astronomers can wait. "In a few generations," they say, "when we have investigated 100,000 instead of 10,000 motions, we will see the whole more clearly."

The American Spirit

When European astronomers made a study trip through the United States before the First World War, they returned stunned, humbled, and shaken. They had seen observatories of such richness and efficiency that they almost lost heart at the prospect of continuing their work back in their homes.

Most impressive of all was the Yerkes Observatory at Lake Geneva, Wisconsin. Built in the shape of a double cross, crowned by a dome like that of the Pantheon in Rome, it contained the largest of all refracting telescopes, with a focal length of sixty-four feet and an objective as wide as a door. In addition it was equipped with a large number of magnificent special instruments, a physics laboratory, a machine shop, and a staff of assistants composed of astronomers from all countries who had flocked here to study the Yerkes methods on the spot.

Certainly one of the most significant of these was the method for finding money to support so luxurious an institution. "No European government would ever approve such lavishness," a visitor sighed. "Nor does the American government," he was told. "The entire observatory has been privately endowed by Mr. Yerkes." And the Europeans learned to their astonishment that Charles Yerkes had been a millionaire who had not previously been known for liberality. How had he happened to provide so generously for this ideal monument to his name?

It seemed that George Ellery Hale, then a young astronomer,

had once arranged matters so that he was seated beside Yerkes at an official dinner. He began to bewail the fact that the University of Chicago could never rival Harvard so long as it did not possess a decent telescope. And as ill luck would have it, the university was about to pass up a unique opportunity. It had been offered a yard-wide block of glass from Paris which he was sure could be ground and polished into the biggest lens that had ever been made.

Hale left the dinner with a check for $20,000.

While the big telescope was being built, the question of what to do with it arose. An observatory was going to be needed. The rich patron had not expected his contribution to lead him deeper and deeper into enormous expenses for unknown ends. But Hale succeeded in converting him into an enthusiast of science—an achievement so extraordinary as to be considered on a par with the astronomer's later scientific triumphs.

The observatory exemplified the spirit of America, something which was quite other than the spirit of Greenwich, but ideally consonant with the new technological era of astronomy. From it sprang the marvelous instruments of the twentieth century which have done the major share of astronomical research. It bred, too, the new type of scientist, the idealist who is nevertheless versed in the art of eliciting enormous donations from a rich, utilitarian-minded society—donations for the least utilitarian of sciences, for greater knowledge of the sublimest works of God.

The American scientists also had a far more personal relationship to their hard-won instruments than did their European colleagues. They looked upon them as something more than means to an end; they could feel equal passion for technical problems and for the flights of "pure" science. A perfect example of this attitude was provided by the physicist Albert A. Michelson of the University of Chicago. He loved his instruments as if they were beautiful women, maintaining that they had human characters, and distinctly feminine ones at that. "They react to flattery, persuasion, and threats. Handling them is as fascinating as a game of chess. They come up with unforeseen maneuvers, take advantage of every mistake like a woman."

This remarkable scientist played the violin and painted water colors. As an infant he had been brought all the way from the German section of Poland to San Francisco; as a boy of seventeen he had gone to Washington to see President Grant because the Naval Academy had not accepted him in spite of his passing the examinations. He had his interview and was admitted. In the course of time he invented the graduated spectroscope, measured the international standard meter at Paris in terms of the wave length of cadmium light (a task of incredible delicacy), and with his interferometer made one of the most important scientific experiments of modern times—whose negative outcome banished the ether from scientific theory. In his last years he crowned his career by doing what no astronomer had yet done: determining the diameter of seven stars, seven infinitesimal dots of light.

These American astronomers engaged in a new kind of dilettantism, not in their own science, but in technology. They were not content with the equipment provided by the optical industry; in their view, only the scientist himself could decide what he really needed. Instruments should adapt to them, not they to the instruments, and they set about designing what they wanted. Their devices would have unknown flaws, they realized, but the known advantages would compensate.

Professor Henry A. Rowland of Johns Hopkins supplied all observatories with his diffraction gratings. He guarded his production methods so jealously that it was five years after his death before engineers were able to duplicate his 5,000 lines to the millimeter.

Samuel P. Langley had invented a thermometer so sensitive that it registered the heat radiations of a grazing cow at a distance of ten miles. With this he determined the temperature of the surface of the Sun at 10,405 degrees Fahrenheit. But when colleagues came to see his fabulous apparatus, he filled their ears with accounts of his newest hobby, the construction of an airplane, and vowed that the would willingly give them the whole of astronomy in exchange for the glory of being the first man to fly in a heavier-than-air craft.

At the beach in East Hampton, Long Island, Professor

R. W. Wood had the most original telescope in history: a well shaft. At the bottom he rotated a tub full of quicksilver; the mercury rose up around the edges of the tub, forming a flawless parabolic mirror that was capable of resolving the closest of binary stars.

The most remarkable representative of the American spirit, however, was undoubtedly George Ellery Hale. He had specialized in solar research. While still a student he conceived the idea of taking monochromatic photographs by the light of single lines of the spectrum. For this purpose the magnification of the forty-inch lens at Yerkes Observatory was not sufficient; he therefore constructed a special telescope. In order to render it absolutely free of vibration, Hale placed the objective on the ground and directed the sunlight into it by means of a mirror kept focused on the Sun by clockwork. Wisconsin's air proved to be too misty; Hale moved to a mountain picked out by the best American meteorologists, who took all possible climatic factors into consideration. This was Mount Wilson, near Los Angeles.

Here the Sun was guaranteed to shine three hundred days a year. But the lens on the ground became so overheated in consequence that every picture was distorted by eddies of air. Hale decided to abandon his new principle and build a chimneylike telescope. This was not troubled by heat eddies, but on the other hand it swayed in the wind. A third type of construction was tried: a framework of steel crossbars contained within a tower. Although this was 165 feet high, it no longer swayed. Its length was further extended by a deep subsurface structure. Here, protected from all temperature changes, Hale succeeded in capturing the Sun in photographs the size of a Mexican sombrero.

In the telescope towers on Mount Wilson, the gigantic telescopes of the Baroque Age lived again. No one but Hale had understood that they might be turned to useful account—though only for study of a single object, the Sun. With these monsters, he went beyond anything European astronomers had done in the field of solar research. Leadership in astronomical science passed definitely to America.

FABULOUS SPECTRUM ANALYSIS

Light and Dark Lines

IN THE YEAR 1859 the Heidelberg physicist Gustav Robert Kirchhoff examined flames of various origins with the spectroscope. Yellow sodium light yielded a yellow line, red lithium light a red and an orange line, green barium light four lines of various colors. Every element produces such a spectrum when vaporized. The number of lines varies enormously; for iron there are over a thousand. But the lines of one element never coincide with those of another.

Kirchhoff recognized at once that he had discovered an extremely sensitive test, far superior to chemical analysis. The tiniest grain of salt, when heated, at once betrayed itself by the yellow line in the spectroscope. The same line flashed into view if he merely dusted a book near his Bunsen burner—dust evidently contained a good deal of sodium.

The most exciting thing about this subtle test for various elements was its application to astronomy. It made possible chemistry at a distance, to the very limits of the visible universe. Wherever such lines appear in the spectrum of a heavenly body, they instantly signalize the component elements.

Few of the stars show many-colored lines in their spectra. But nebulae do; in the Great Nebula in Orion, for example, the presence of oxygen and nitrogen has been demonstrated by spectroscopy. It is somehow a consolation to man that out there in space, in an area millions of times the size of our solar system, an "at-

mosphere" like that of Earth exists. This atmosphere would be scarcely breathable; it is extremely tenuous.

Incredibly small quantities of matter can be analyzed by spectral lines, for example, the tails of comets through which the Earth would otherwise have passed unbeknown. Comets' tails proved to be a mixture of carbon monoxide and nitrogen which would have been deadly to the human race if it had not been so rarefied. Should fate ever bring the head of a comet across our path, there would no doubt be a sizable fire, for the head of the comet is like a mighty gas flame; its spectrum is the same as illuminating gas: colored bands of carbon compounds, colored lines of carbon and sodium. It is the Sun's heat that elicits such flames from comets, transforming them into virtual torches.

For a time it appeared that astronomers would be able to introduce the chemists to some entirely new elements. In the spectrum of the solar chromosphere—the gaseous layer around the Sun—a bright line was discovered which occurred nowhere else. Its discoverer, Sir Joseph Norman Lockyer, attributed it to an unknown solar element that he called helium. Twenty-six years later helium was found in Texas and is now used for lighter-than-air craft. It is also produced artificially as a result of the fusion process in a hydrogen bomb.

These are only a few examples of long-distance chemistry by spectrum analysis. If only bright lines had been examined, spectroscopy would have remained a rather esoteric scientific specialty. For by far the majority of all heavenly bodies, including 99 per cent of the stars, emit the ordinary Newtonian spectrum, a continuous ribbon of color from red to violet, like that of our Sun. Such spectra do not serve as a test for elements because the colors, that is the wave lengths of the radiation, pass without transition into one another.

Fortunately, there are sharply demarcated, observable lines in the Sun's spectrum: the Fraunhofer lines. These are, it is true, black, not colored; but each black line has a fixed wave length and can therefore stand for a colored line of the same wave length. Kirchhoff took account of this, and in addition learned how to transform colored into black lines. He did so in a very simple ex-

periment of fundamental importance. With a calcium-light lamp
he produced a continuous spectrum without any lines. He then
placed a flame containing sodium in the path of the rays. One
would expect a still brighter yellow line to appear in the yellow
part of the spectrum. However a black line appeared instead.

Kirchhoff explained the paradox as follows: from the spectrum
of calcium light the sodium vapor absorbed precisely the color
it would itself emit. Against the brighter source of light, the vaporized sodium cast shadows.

It might therefore be assumed that the Fraunhofer lines in the
solar spectrum would likewise be shadow lines deriving from the
vapors of a great variety of elements surrounding the glowing core
of the Sun. And, in fact, when Kirchhoff placed his sodium flame
in the path of a solar spectrum, Fraunhofer's D-line in the yellow
showed even darker. The hypothesis appeared to be proved.

There remained only to demonstrate that the converse was
true: to make colored lines out of dark lines. If the vapors around
the Sun could be isolated, they should show bright emission lines.
This *experimentum crucis* was arranged by Nature herself during
the solar eclipse of 1868. On this occasion an American physicist,
Charles Augustus Young, for the first time viewed an eclipse
through a spectroscope. At first he noticed only that the ribbon of
color, with its Fraunhofer lines, became feebler. But the moment
the Moon entirely covered the solar disc, he beheld a wonderful
spectacle: all at once the whole spectrum glowed with bright
emission lines instead of the dark shadow lines. The hot core of
the Sun was momentarily veiled, and only the vapors around it
were emitting their light. These yielded normal colored spectra,
just as they did in Kirchhoff's laboratory.

The marvelous phenomenon lasted but two seconds. But
thereafter there could be no doubt: the lines, whether they are
colored or black, can be used for chemical analysis and interpreted
in the same sense. Now there was practically no celestial body
whose elements could not be determined.

The Sun became, for the time being, the chief object of research.
A whole generation of scientists endeavored to capture as wide as
possible a spectrum with the fullest complement of dark lines.

Kirchhoff himself determined 2,000, Ångström 6,000, Rowland 21,000. This was far from the maximum; the lines continued into the infrared and ultraviolet, and Langley cleverly measured them in these regions of the spectrum with the bolometer, an instrument for measuring minute quantities of radiant heat. In recent times solar radio waves have been detected.

Each of the lines had to be assigned to some element. This was in the main a task for physicists, and they are still engrossed in it. They are also attempting to explain the various lines in terms of the internal structure of each element; atomic physics developed by leaps and bounds out of this sport. It is perhaps fair to say that atomic physics is entirely based on spectral lines.

The Chemistry of Celestial Bodies

Unknown lines also appeared in the solar corona. They have been explained only recently; but scientists have long been convinced that they did not represent unknown elements. The Sun contains precisely the same elements as the Earth. They are, moreover, all in the elementary state, for in such heat no chemical compounds can exist. That is, there are no molecules in the Sun, only atoms and ions.

Molecules always reveal themselves in the spectrum by bands because groups of atoms instead of individual atoms are radiating, and the lines unite. From study of these bands astronomers have been able to study the chemistry of the planets.

The planets, of course, are not radiant bodies; their light is only reflected sunlight. But this sunlight is sifted twice through the atmosphere of the planet, and therefore reveals the chemical compounds in that atmosphere. Hence, we know nothing about the chemical composition of the solid mass of the planets, but we do know the character of their atmospheres quite well.

The atmosphere of Venus would scarcely be comfortable for animals or human beings, since it contains only water vapor and carbon dioxide. Dwellers on Mars would have to be content with

very little oxygen in their thin, cold, Himalayan air. On Jupiter
and Saturn there would be nothing to breathe but ammonia
fumes and methane; the latter gas is almost the sole atmospheric
constituent on Uranus and Neptune and gives to Uranus its sal-
low green coloring. Mercury and the Moon have no swathing of
air, for they reflect pure sunlight.

All this scarcely opens up a pleasant prospect for space-travelers.
But as we have said, only the atmospheres have been analyzed;
the soil of the planets may hold undreamed-of treasures.

The stars have been a great disappointment to the spectrum
analysts. They yielded such fascinating spectra that a host of
chemical discoveries was expected. But what in fact emerged
from closer study was the sobering rule that stellar chemistry is
virtually the same everywhere in the universe. Only atoms and
electrons can exist in these hot globes of gas—just as on our Sun.
And to all appearances every star contains all the known elements.
Only in the cooler red stars have black bands in the spectrum, representing a few carbon compounds, titanium oxide, and zirconium
oxide, been observed.

Recently, however, astronomers have had a surprise that gave
a piquant note to this rule: it now seems most probable that the
elements in all the stars are to be found in the same quantitative
proportions as on Earth. Whether a celestial body is bright or dark,
small or large, young or old, gaseous or solid—quantitative analysis of it leads to the selfsame result: it is composed of carbon,
oxygen, and nitrogen, a supply of light metals and elements of the
iron family, and traces of the heavy metals. Few scientists had
counted on so thoroughgoing a simplification of the universe.

Only in a single point does the chemistry of the Earth differ
from that of the universe as a whole: our Earth possesses compar-
atively little hydrogen and almost no helium. Yet these two elements make up the major part of the mass of the stars. However,
this circumstance does not invalidate the general relationship.
The Earth, after all, is a solid globe that has cooled off, and her
hydrogen and helium, the lightest of the elements, have escaped
into space. A similar process must also have taken place on the
Moon and in the planets.

On the glowing spheres of gas we call stars these two elements are absolutely dominant. Up to 90 per cent of the total mass of the stars is hydrogen; this element is the chief building block of the universe. The second most important is helium; these excepted, the other elements follow in the same proportions as on Earth.

Thus, remote analysis of the stars resulted in a highly dramatic conclusion: that nine tenths of their mass—and nine tenths of the Sun's mass, therefore—is composed of the most ethereal of all material things: hydrogen.

A Stellar Thermometer

If the chemistry of the stars is the same throughout the universe, what accounts for the extraordinary differences in spectra? Sometimes the entire left side of a spectrum is invisible, sometimes the right side; sometimes only spots of color here and there remain. The lines are usually black, but a few are colored; some are wide bands with dark borders, so that the spectrum looks like a row of illuminated windows by night. The black lines, too, can be broader than usual; in some circumstances they may appear faded. What does all this mean?

Interpreting these messages from outer space has taken as long as the deciphering of cuneiform script. Details are still being puzzled over. In the beginning the whole subject seemed so complex that scientists sought only to collect the various spectral types and find some reasonable classification system for them. Not even that was possible. They could not gather enough data because a spectrum is obtained only by the use of a narrow slit, so that photographs require hours of exposure. The few samples taken of unusually bright stars did not provide enough information.

At this juncture Edward Charles Pickering of Harvard Observatory hit upon a brilliant solution. Instead of attaching the spectroscope behind the telescope, as the Europeans were doing, he placed a giant prism in front of the objective. Thus his plates

recorded nothing but the spectra of stars instead of white-light images. His images were extremely tiny, but they were so clear that the types could be recognized without difficulty. There proved to be so many types that almost the entire alphabet was used up in naming them, and each letter still required ten sub-divisions. This Harvard classification was the work of three women astronomers, Mrs. W. P. Fleming, Miss A. C. Maury, and Miss A. J. Cannon, who examined more than 200,000 spectra.

When they were finished, it turned out that 99 per cent of all stars could be classified under six letters that in fact constituted a temperature scale.

How they arrived at this simple solution becomes immediately apparent when we consider that a spectrum is an analysis of various colors. The differences among spectra derive from the different colors of the stars—and the color of an incandescent body is determined by its temperature. It is common knowledge that white heat is far hotter than red heat. The stars show us the gradations in between: orange-yellow, pale-yellow, all the way up to bluish white. Each color of a star indicates that the star is of a particular spectral type and temperature. The temperatures could be determined by comparison of the spectra of terrestrial substances.

SPECTRAL TYPE	CHARACTERISTICS	COLOR	TEMPERATURE (DEGREES CENTIGRADE)	EXAMPLE
B	H and He lines	blue-white	20,000	Star in Orion
A	H lines	alabaster-white	11,000	Sirius
F	H and metal lines	pale-yellow	8,000	Polaris
G	metal lines	yellow	6,000	Sun
K	few bands	pumpkin-colored	4,000	Arcturus
M	many bands	poppy-red	2,000	Antares

Thus the astronomer need only look at the spectrum of a star in order to determine how hot it is. The second virtue of spectrum analysis was, therefore, that it served as a universal thermometer.

Temperature also often indicates the age of a star. The white stars are young, the red ones old. Class B and A stars are very frequently seen in the midst of bright nebulae, out of which

they probably originated. These extremely hot globes of gas are evidently burning up swiftly and should therefore lose their radiance in a relatively short time.

There is also a special class of white stars, the O group, whose temperatures run considerably higher than 20,000 degrees Centigrade. Their spectra contain bright lines instead of dark lines; it is not possible to determine their temperatures exactly, but they probably are consuming themselves. Such stars are very rare. They are not distributed uniformly over the firmament, but are grouped in some twenty families, as if there were hothouses in the heavens where seedlings of stars are being raised. Certain Soviet scientists believe that they scatter from these concentrations in all directions. Class B stars also are found in such clusters.

The aged, cooled-off red stars are by far in the majority. On the average they appear to move faster than the hotter stars—but this is only apparent because these red stars are stragglers that belong to the central core and are moving in very elongated orbits.

Some of our red neighbors, like Antares, the eye of the Scorpion, have outer layers at a higher temperature than the inner strata, as if they were wrapping themselves in heated coats against the —262 degree Centigrade cold of space. How they manage this is not known. It is, after all, cause for wonder that scientists can read so much from spectral lines.

Dust in the Milky Way

In the course of these investigations astronomers encountered a troublesome irregularity: at times the spectral type did not coincide completely with the color. A Class B star ought to glow blue-white according to the above table. But an astonishing number of B stars displayed the redness characteristic of the M type. Somehow, the astronomers had to prove that these red-polled B stars had a right to exist.

Everyone has seen "blood-red" sunsets. They are caused by the layers of dust in the atmosphere absorbing light of short wave

lengths so that only the long wave lengths of red light reach the eye. Obviously, the fact that B stars appeared red must be caused by a similar phenomenon. Only the red light was passing through layers of dust, invisible nebulae. Invisible dark clouds had earlier been recognized on photographs by a reduction in the number of stars observable in certain portions of the sky. Now an incomparably more sensitive method for studying these dark nebulae had been found. The redness of stars that should not be red was an excellent detector of dust.

With the aid of this reasoning, a further unexpected discovery was made.

B stars show the greatest redness when they are in the galactic belt. There whole clusters of stars may be seen glowing redly. But this applies only to the rim of the belt; in the center star clusters as well as spiral nebulae are conspicuous by their absence. This fact had long puzzled astronomers because elsewhere in the Milky Way star clusters and spiral nebulae are distributed with fair uniformity. Suddenly, the cause became apparent. Right through the center of our Galaxy extends a narrow layer of cosmic dust which blocks our view of the galactic belt. Everything lying beyond this veil of dust, all the star clusters and nebulae, are dimmed by it, and the brightest stars of our system are discolored by it.

In addition to the single bright and dark clouds, then, there is a continuous sheet of cloud in the center of the Galaxy, dividing our wheel-shaped island universe in two. Curious as this discovery was, it was confirmed by the appearance of other galaxies seen edge-on. On photographs they show as a white double line, split by a dark line throughout their entire length. These external galaxies also possess a continuous layer of dust in the center.

A Stellar Speedometer

Even before the three Harvard ladies finished preparing their thermometer scale, an English astronomer named William Hug-

gins perceived a third application of spectroscopy: as an indicator of direction toward us or away from us.

The idea is based upon a principle of physics. As a locomotive passes by us, the pitch of its whistle rises and then falls again. In approaching, the sound waves pile up in front of the locomotive, as it were; more vibrations reach our ears, and the pitch rises. This effect, known as Doppler's principle, can be applied to light; spectral lines shift toward the violet if the source of light is approaching us, toward the red if the source is retreating from us.

Huggins was able to demonstrate a shift toward the violet of the spectral lines of Sirius. Hence, Sirius is approaching us. Even the speed can be calculated from the displacement of the lines, although this calls for extremely fine measurements, measurements in millionths of an inch. Hermann Vogel at Potsdam in 1890 succeeded in dealing with these infinitesimal distances. He perfected photography of the spectra of stars, so that he could actually measure with the aid of a microscope such minimal deviations from the normal positions of the lines.

Ever since, spectral lines have also served as speedometers built into the composition of every star, every nebula, even the most tenuous of cosmic dusts. When we consider how extraordinary this is, we might almost think the cosmos itself in league with modern man's desire to see movement in everything, and analyze it quantitatively.

It will be recalled that astronomy had succeeded in discerning tiny shifts in the positions of stars in the course of a century or so. These movements were only to the right or left, or up and down on the celestial sphere. The third dimension was lacking. Now the astronomers had found a way to investigate motion in the third dimension, and the speed of that motion. Every possible motion in space could be quantitatively examined. This was an unhoped-for miracle.

The velocities were a disappointment at first; everyone was by now so used to "astronomical" figures. On the average, however, the stars apparently move no faster than from five to twenty miles per second—about the same speed as the Earth's in its annual journey, and as the Sun's on its voyage toward Hercules. A few

rapid stars were singled out; these seem to reach as high a speed as forty and seventy-five miles per second. But the high-velocity stars are not really moving at high speeds. It is the solar system that is rushing away from them as it revolves around the Galaxy at a speed of 134 miles per second. The period of this revolution of the Sun around the Galaxy is 250 million years.

Our Galaxy as a whole is rotating around itself. For the stars in our vicinity this rotational motion amounts to somewhat less than 200 miles per second. The stellar speedometer does not indicate this, however, for the simple reason that we are participating in the motion. A person inside the train does not hear the pitch of the locomotive whistle rising and falling. The spectroscopic speedometer, then, is no absolute measuring instrument, any more than our terrestrial meters in automobiles and airplanes; these register only motion relative to the Earth and do not record the fact that automobile and plane are being carried along by the Earth around its axis and around the Sun.

Aside from this inherent limitation, however, the spectral lines have proved to be dependable and highly sensitive instruments. Not even the most sanguine of scientists foresaw how many questions the spectral lines would answer. There is space here for only a few examples.

When spectrographic pictures were taken continuously during an eclipse, the lines were seen to be displaced as soon as the Moon covered all but a narrow rim of the Sun's disc. It was soon realized that this effect was caused by the Sun's rotation; the edge of the Sun was moving away from us. The velocity of rotation determined by the displacement exactly equaled that determined by tracking sunspots across the face of the Sun.

Would it not be possible also to prove uneven rotation of Saturn's rings by the same method? For if the theory were correct that the rings are composed of myriad small bodies the size of bricks, then the rotation would not be uniform, but would be slower on the outside than the inside of the rings. Careful spectrographs were taken of Saturn's rings—and showed slanting lines. That is, velocity diminished at a steady rate toward the outside of the rings. The theory was beautifully confirmed.

The Diffusion of Metals

In 1906 Johannes Hartmann noticed two calcium lines in the spectrum of a star which did not share the displacement of all the other lines. There could be only one explanation for this behavior: the lines did not belong to the star, but to a calcium cloud between the star and ourselves. The spectroscope was proving itself a remarkably fine detector of interstellar gas.

During the next twenty years a large number of such "lazy" lines turned up, lines of various metallic vapors in addition to the universal gas, hydrogen. From this phenomenon Sir Arthur Eddington concluded that metals were diffused throughout the Galaxy. Perhaps this diffuse vapor filled all the space between stars, and even the atmosphere of our own planetary home. We would then be breathing it constantly, and escape poisoning only because it is inconceivably tenuous, only an atom to a thimbleful of space.

Far pleasanter for the speculative mind was the discovery of the twin stars in close embrace made by Antonia C. Maury of Harvard Observatory in 1890. On one of her innumerable photographs of spectra she observed that all the lines were doubled. She brought this puzzling phenomenon to the attention of her chief, Edward Pickering. Pickering ordered a series of pictures of this same spectrum to be taken. It turned out that the doubling of lines occurred at intervals. Evidently, two spectra were actually being observed, one displaced to the right and one to the left. That is, here were two stars, one approaching, one retreating from us: a pair of dancers. At intervals the images fused, and the photograph would then show only one spectrum. It was then impossible to say which lines belonged to which star. Theoretically, the lines should draw apart from one another and then close up the gaps, in accordion fashion. That is precisely what they did on the series of photographs.

A new class of stars had been discovered: dancing twins. These are much more peculiar than binaries which revolve around one another at respectful distances; the twins cannot be separated

even by the strongest telescope. Only the splitting of the spectral
lines proves their existence. Measurements of the spectra of some
1,300 such pairs showed how remarkably close these stars were.

First of all, a mad pace was noted, far faster than normal. The
record is held by V Puppis: 375 miles per second. If the Earth
were to race at such a rate around the Sun, our seasons would
each be over in a month. Moreover, these stars complete their
orbits far too quickly to make astronomical sense. They take
only a few days for a revolution. This is utterly bewildering,
indicating as it does a minuscule ellipse, approximately the size
of the Moon's orbit around the Earth, for stars which must in themselves be far larger than the entire orbit of the Moon. From this
it is apparent that the twin suns are so close that in most cases
they must be in actual contact with one another.

Let us imagine that we had V Puppis for our sun: two gigantic
lights in our sky. Today they would be moving side by side, tomorrow or the day after one sun would be behind the other, and
we would receive only half as much light, half as much warmth as
before. Every few days our climate would change. What consequences this would have upon clothing, the structure of our
houses, our whole mode of life; what flexible creatures we would
have to be, how adaptable and ready for change. Perhaps our
minds would work differently also; we might be faster-thinking,
more versatile, wittier.

Among the close binaries there are some whose partners are
almost dark, much fainter than the bright component. These be-
tray their presence not by splitting but by oscillation of the lines.
Sometimes, when the faint star almost hides its partner from our
view, the lines suddenly leap back for a moment, as they do in an
eclipse of the Sun. That is to say, they reveal the rotation of the
star. Even the period of rotation can be measured.

Modern Fables of the Stars

In the past thirty years spectrum analysis has become an exceedingly refined system that calls for precision measurements of the

Filamentary or veil nebula in Cygnus; 60-inch photograph.

PLATE XXV

Great Nebula in Orion; 100-inch photograph. This glowing cloud of gas can be seen by the naked eye as a tiny smear in the "sword" of Orion.

PLATE XXVI

A nebula in Orion north of the Great Nebula; 100-inch photograph.

PLATE XXVII

Horsehead Nebula in Orion; 200-inch photograph taken in red light. The "horse's head" is a cold cloud of gas and opaque dust.

PLATE XXVIII

A section of the Milky Way in the region of Cygnus. Our Sun is only an average-sized member of this enormous group of stars.

PLATE XXIX

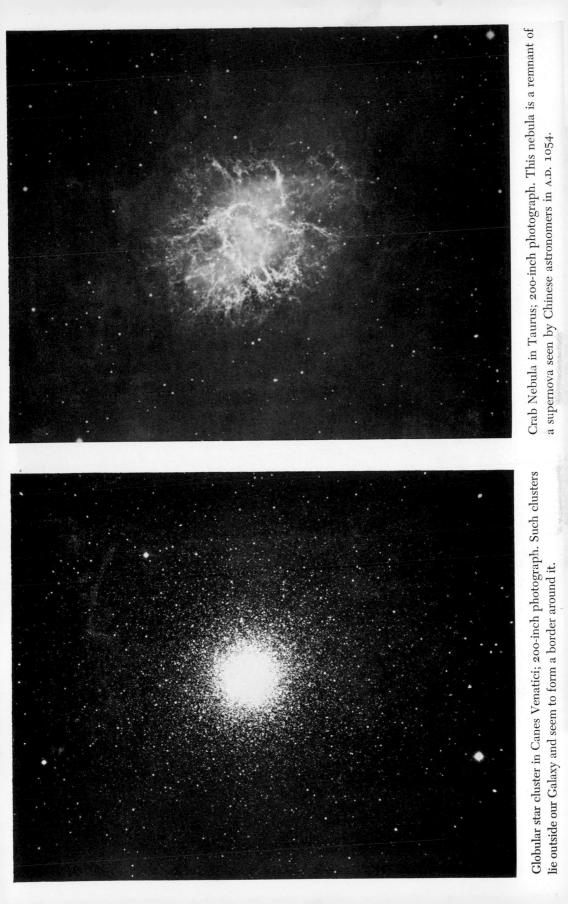

Globular star cluster in Canes Venatici; 200-inch photograph. Such clusters lie outside our Galaxy and seem to form a border around it.

Crab Nebula in Taurus; 200-inch photograph. This nebula is a remnant of a supernova seen by Chinese astronomers in A.D. 1054.

Edge-on view of the spiral galaxy in Coma Berenices; 200-inch photograph. Note characteristic shape of the galaxy: bulge in the middle and layer of dust through the center.
(Compare illustration on page 347.)

PLATE XXXI

Great Galaxy in Andromeda, M 31; 48-inch Schmidt photograph. The two bright blobs of light are satellite galaxies. This galaxy is the nearest large system of stars comparable with our own, which also has two satellites.

PLATE XXXII

Tip of the Great Galaxy in Andromeda, M 31; 100-inch photograph, resolving lower end of galaxy into stars. Bright spot at left appears below the smaller satellite in Plate xxxii.

PLATE XXXIII

Evolution of spiral nebulae: M 51 in Canes Venatici; 200-inch photograph. Here the spirals are distinctly marked off, representing a development midway between the spirals in Plates xxxv and xxxvii.

PLATE XXXVI

Evolution of spiral nebulae: M 81 in the Great Bear; 200-inch photograph. Here the spiral arms have already approached the nucleus, and the entire system has evolved into a closed, elliptical disc.

PLATE XXXVII

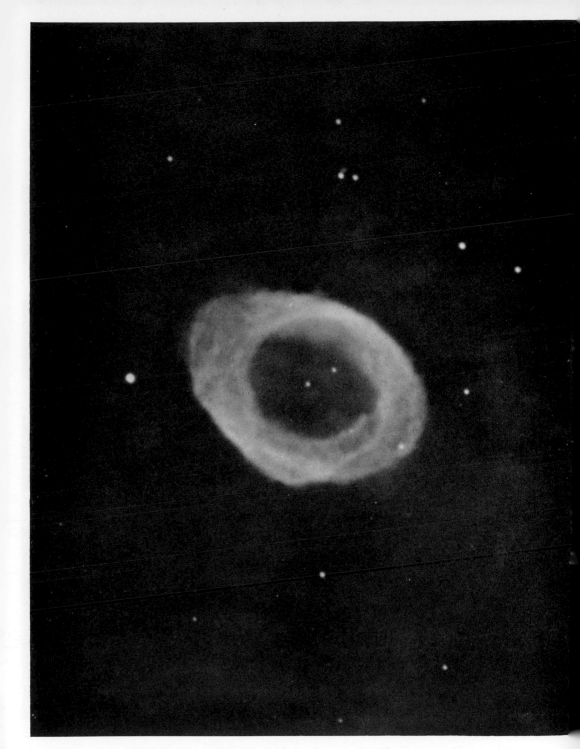

Planetary nebula in Lyra, M 57; 200-inch photograph. The gases making up the ring are illuminated by stellar light.

PLATE XXXVIII

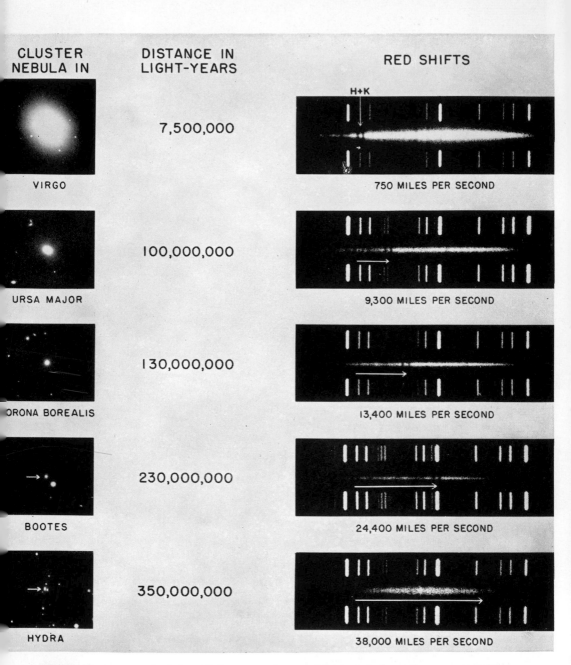

CLUSTER NEBULA IN	DISTANCE IN LIGHT-YEARS	RED SHIFTS
VIRGO	7,500,000	750 MILES PER SECOND
URSA MAJOR	100,000,000	9,300 MILES PER SECOND
ORONA BOREALIS	130,000,000	13,400 MILES PER SECOND
BOOTES	230,000,000	24,400 MILES PER SECOND
HYDRA	350,000,000	38,000 MILES PER SECOND

Relation between red shift and distance of extragalactic nebulae. The arrows indicate shifts of calcium lines H and K. One light-year equals about six trillion miles.

PLATE XXXIX

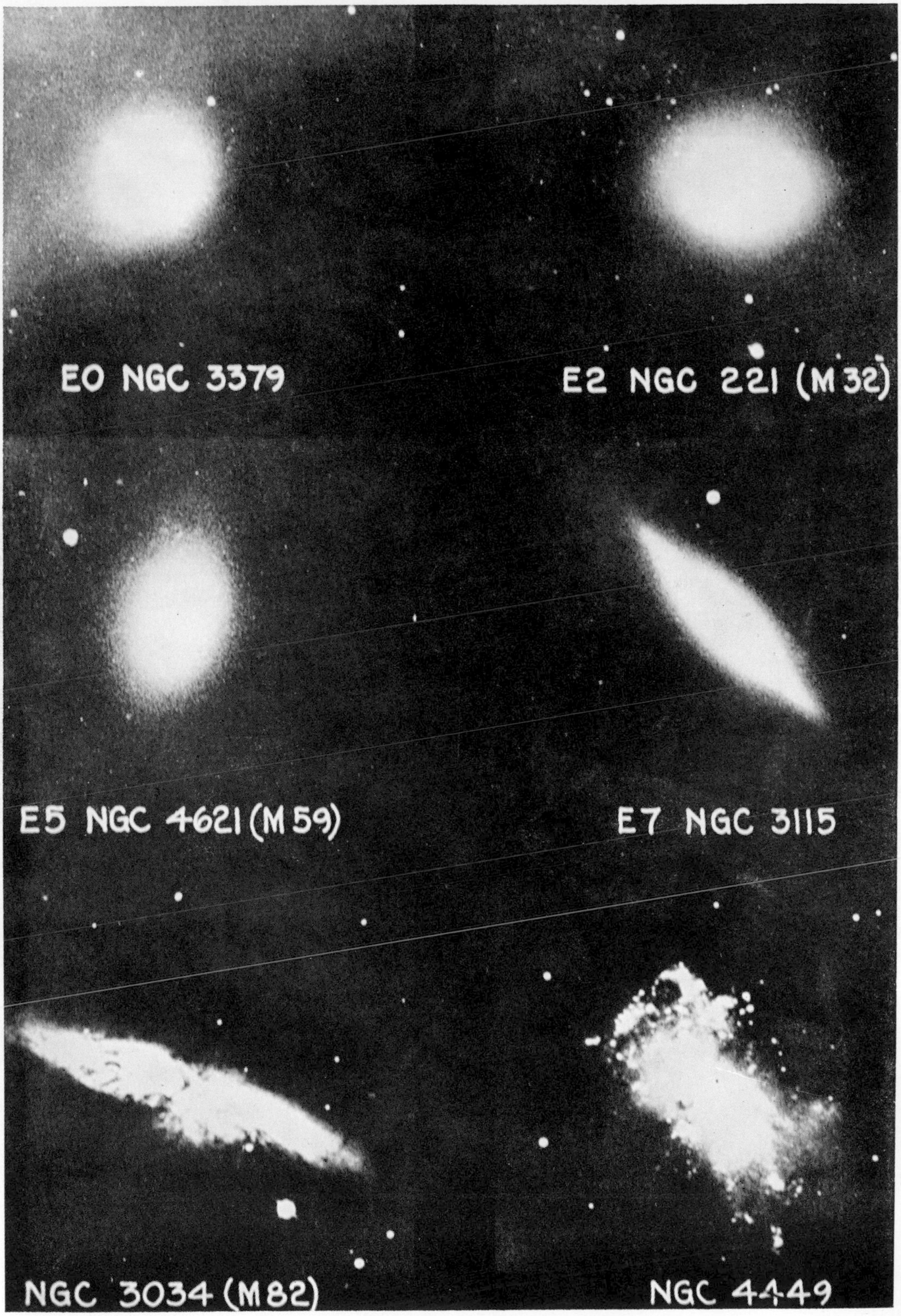

EO NGC 3379

E2 NGC 221 (M32)

E5 NGC 4621 (M59)

E7 NGC 3115

NGC 3034 (M82)

NGC 4449

Types of elliptical and irregular galaxies.

PLATE XL

greatest delicacy and mathematical formulas of the most complicated sort. Virtually every peculiarity of the Fraunhofer lines has been exhaustively studied; the tiniest variations from the normal can be interpreted. It is now known that not only motion influences the lines, but also heat, pressure, and atomic processes. These and other factors can now be clearly distinguished, and thus the sought-after new facts determined.

Recently, spectrum analysts have come to examine microscopically individual lines as biologists do individual chromosomes, measuring the degree of their blackness, and the decrease of blackness from the center to the edge of the.lines. On the basis of such analyses astrophysicists draw conclusions about conditions in the interior of stars, as if the great globes of gas at vast distances were high-temperature ovens in a laboratory provided with sensitive dials to record the slightest changes.

As a result of this work, the first modern fables of the stars have been written. They may not be so pretty as the Greek tales of Perseus and Andromeda, of the hunter Orion and the fleeing Pleiades. But on the other hand, they are true—and far more original. Here, in brief, are examples of five of the most curious of them.

Altair and His Belt

The broad, faded lines of Altair, the Eagle's eye, attracted attention early in the history of spectroscopy. They proved to be a fanning out instead of a splitting of lines; this suggested various states of motion simultaneously, now to the right, now to the left. Interpretation showed Altair to be rotating at great speed, whirling his vast body around in a single day. His surface must be moving 125 times faster than the Sun's—too fast to hold together. Apparently part of the sphere of gas was torn loose by the rapid rotation and now sails around Altair in the form of a flat girdle, like Saturn's rings. Thus there are Saturn suns—and perhaps our grandchildren will see them in their telescopes.

Fat Zeta Aurigae

If spectral lines are deep black instead of gray, a rapidly rising

and falling, seething atmosphere can be deduced. Fat Zeta Aurigae is one such star, and in 1932 it apparently boiled over; Zeta increased in girth by one half—a sizable compass indeed, since it was normally as big as the circumference of the Earth's orbit. It fattened out until it would have filled the orbit of Mars. That seemed to be the limit, and by 1934 it had contracted again. Zeta is easy to find in the sky. Above Orion sits the Drayman. Below the bright star forming his right shoulder, Capella, is a triangle formerly called the three Kids; one of these, the small dot below and on the right, is Zeta. The star twinkles so gently and modestly that no one would dream it could boil over.

Cannibals in the Lyre

Somewhat below Vega the pair may be seen. The partners whirl around one another in four hours. As a result, both are distorted; they form a kind of double egg, with ends almost touching. The smaller of the two stars has emitted a gaseous appendage that is wrapped around its big partner. But horrible to relate, the big one is sucking the substance out of the little one, as a spider might a fly. The end, however, will not be fatal, said astronomer Paul Guthnick. Soon the smaller star's turn will come, he maintains, and it will feed on its partner for a few years, until the big one is only a skeleton of its former self. Then the whole procedure will begin over again.

Clockwork under Glass

The star in question forms the central point of the big W known as Cassiopeia. In its spectrum broad colored bright bands are to be found lying inside faded dark lines; these bands in turn possess a sharp black central line. This complicated spectrum points to the presence of three layers of gas wrapped around one another. The innermost layer rotates fastest, the middle one is slower but hotter, and the outside layer is motionless and cool.

In periods of four years the bright lines move around: the hot layer shifts; the middle stratum swells and shrinks. This star breathes like a panting boxer. This is not all. In 1935 the bright bands abruptly flared and the black middle line disappeared: gas

had erupted through the cool outer skin. This eruption did not end until 1938; then the globe of gas shrank and the motionless, cool outer skin once more protected the two inner spheres that move inside one another at different speeds.

Stellar Explosion

In 1918 astronomers succeeded for the first time in following spectroscopically the flaring of a "nova," a "new" star. Since then it has been clear that the nova actually represents a tremendous outburst of flames. The extreme shift toward the violet of all the spectral lines denotes a billowing mushroom cloud of smoke which rolls toward us at the staggering speed of about 1,500 miles per second. Suddenly bright lines flare up in the spectrum; the intensity of the heat has abruptly mounted. The mushroom of smoke becomes a cloud of fire, but only for a few hours. Then the bright lines vanish in a brilliant continuous spectrum: the core of the nova shines through the cooling flames. It constantly emits fresh masses of gas which whirl wildly through each other; the chaotic state is recognizable by doubled and tripled absorption lines.

After a few days, the continuous spectrum also fades; there remain emission bands that grow steadily wider: the internal heat is pouring out. This pattern may persist for months. By and by only a few thin bright lines remain; by their light the nova looks like a greenish cloud. Finally, after years, a small star appears in the midst of this cloud, shining an innocent white, and all is stable again.

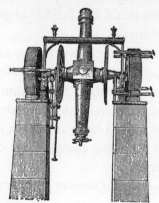

THE REVELATIONS OF PHOTOMETRY

Lighthouses and Glowworms

T HE MOST PROMINENT characteristic of the stars is the variance in their brightness. Hipparchus, as we have seen, classified them by brightness into six magnitudes; these the telescope increased to some thirty. But the question of what these classes really mean, how great the difference in brightness is, was first raised in the eighteenth century by Heinrich Lambert. He did not succeed in answering it, but he learned how to measure the luminosity of two lamps. Thus he created photometry, the second principal tool of modern astronomy.

The mere concept that light can be measured was a great step forward. How to go about measuring it was still far from obvious. Nowadays every amateur photographer buys a selenium cell, which transforms radiant energy into measurable electrical energy. But Lambert was dependent upon the subjective sensations of the human eye. How could this fallible organ yield an objective measurement of brightness?

Lambert's trick was to place two lamps at different distances until the shadows cast by them were equally dark. He then expressed the luminosity in terms of the distances. Once again man was using numbers to grasp an intangible natural phenomenon.

But stars cannot be moved back and forth at will. It was a long road from Lambert's primitive comparisons of lights to exact astronomical photometry.

The first useful stellar photometer was devised in 1860 by Jo-

hann Zöllner, who cleverly employed an artificial star for comparison. The tiny, pointlike image of a lamp was reflected into the telescope alongside the actual star. By a complicated screw-mechanism, the light of the lamp was made progressively weaker until both points were of the same brightness; the number of turns provided an exact measure of the brightness.

But Zöllner soon found photometry of one star after the other a bit of a bore; he shifted to the more attractive field of spectrum analysis, then to spiritism, until he was associating with ghosts instead of stars. Consequently, another forty years passed before a fresh start was made in the field on which all of astrophysics depends. Then, however, there was a great burst of activity in observatories all over the world. In 1907 Potsdam and in 1908 Harvard published photometric catalogues; in 1910 came the Göttingen Actinometry and in 1912 the Yerkes Actinometry—each catalogue more precise than the previous one. Finally Pickering developed his "north polar sequence," a fundamental comparative scale of magnitudes as much prized by astronomers as is the standard meter at Paris by physicists.

The huge magnitude catalogues could not have been drawn up with only Zöllner's cumbersome technique to go by. The method employed was, in fact, even older than Zöllner's. It occurred to an American astronomer, G. P. Bond, that the comparative brightness of stellar images could be measured on photographic plates. Silver bromide has the same flaw as the retina of the eye: it sees brighter stars as larger; it forms disc images of them—and the size of these discs constitutes a remarkable measure of the amount of light received. Since a few hundred or a thousand stars can be taken on a single photograph, it is very convenient to measure the magnitudes of the images rather than of the stars themselves.

The degree of blackness of the discs can also serve as a measure of the light. Hence, a shadow scale was copied onto the plate, and a microphotometer to measure the blackening, a microscope to measure the size of the discs were constructed. In order to test the luminosity from the tiniest and most remote stars, Karl Schwarzschild deliberately jiggled his camera, obtaining a smeared image

of the star. Einar Hertzsprung measured the brightness of the spectra. In short, the subtlest combinations of photography and photometry were devised.

The figures being determined with so much effort did not represent the actual luminosity of the stars. A modest-appearing star very far away from us may actually be brighter than Sirius, which is close by. In order to obtain the absolute magnitude, therefore, the linear distance had to be reckoned with. And since measurements of linear distances are the most difficult of astronomical tasks, even today we know the true magnitudes of only a few thousand stars. The differences among them are indicated by the following table.

STAR	LUMINOSITY IN COMPARISON WITH THE SUN	RELATIVE TERRESTRIAL LUMINOSITY IF THE DISTANCE IS CONSTANT
S Doradus	500,000 ×	lighthouse
Capella	120 ×	100-watt bulb
Sirius	30 ×	25-watt bulb
Sun	1	candle
Sirius' companion	1/300	glowing coal
Wolf 359	1/5,000	glowworm

If we could suspend all the stars at equal distances, the darkest would bear the same relation to the brightest as a glowworm to a lighthouse beacon. The differences in luminosity are so enormous that we can partly grasp them only by examining a few practical examples.

The brightest star we know at present, S Doradus, belongs to a neighboring galaxy. If it were in the position of the Sun, it would soon heat the Earth to a temperature of several thousand degrees Centigrade; our terrestrial home would burst into flame and be burned to a crisp.

The feeblest star, on the other hand, Wolf 359, would at our Sun's distance provide as much heat for us as a bonfire on a remote mountaintop. If it were our orb of day, our temperature would drop almost to absolute zero (−273 degrees Centigrade); Earth's

atmosphere would be liquefied. How fortunate we are to have been assigned a good average star for light and heat.

Most impressive of all, perhaps, is the fact that clusters containing about 17,000 stars radiate no more light than a single "lighthouse" star, even though they contain many suns equal in luminosity to Sirius. Whole clusters of this sort may be compared to the multitudinous lights of a large city, which flush the clouds red but are far surpassed in total brightness by a single searchlight beam.

A star like S Doradus is equivalent in luminosity to five hundred thousand of our suns!

Variable Stars

Around the year 1600 the Frisian pastor David Fabricius saw a star in the constellation of the Whale which he had not, as far as he knew, ever seen before. Day after day the star faded, until after a few weeks it disappeared. The pastor thought himself a conscientious observer, but he could not have been quite so conscientious as he imagined, or he would have noticed the dot of light reappear the following year. As it was, it did not attract his attention again until thirteen years afterwards. Then he named it Mira Ceti, the wondrous star in the Whale. Had the telescope been invented by then, he would have seen that Mira never entirely disappears; its brightness merely changes. It is a flickering fire, a variable star.

By 1800 four of these variables were known. Herschel discovered three more. In the nineteenth century the number of them gradually increased; photometry has by now located nearly ten thousand. They constitute by far the most interesting species among the hosts of stars, but also the most mysterious. They exist also in innumerable varieties.

Ordinarily, their brightness waxes and wanes by small amounts, from one and one half to five times their norm. But sometimes a star relatively as luminous as a candle will temporarily flash forth like a searchlight. There are strictly periodic and entirely irregular

alternations of luminosity. Their periods can be years or decades, days or hours. We might put it that some flicker, some are like blinker signals, and others flare.

Light curves are employed to make comparisons. If the measured luminosities are graphed against time intervals, we obtain highly characteristic images of the course of the flickering, blinking, or flaring. Some of the graphs show neatly geometrical wave lines, others repeated depressions or humps. Frequently, the picture resembles a fever curve, a mountain silhouette, a collection of noses, the zigzags drawn by an unpracticed child's hand, or an attempt to draw lines made in a jolting vehicle.

The interpretation of such curves has become a special branch of astrophysics, much like the interpretation of electrocardiograms in modern medicine. But this detective work is only in its beginnings at present. Astronomers have made all kinds of guesses about the underlying causes of variability, but for the most part their theories cannot yet be proved. Occultation of stars by neighbors, planets, meteor swarms, or clouds have been suggested. It is thought that some stars actually swell and shrink because of erupting gases that then cool and relapse. There has been much speculation concerning the nuclei of stars. In short, the variables have stimulated the imaginations of scientists like nothing else in the heavens.

At present the variables are divided, according to their light curves, into seventeen types. Only one of these types has been convincingly explained: the eclipsing variable.

Algol, the eye of the Medusa, is in the constellation of Perseus. The Medusa of legend would turn anyone who looked at her to stone. When astronomers took the risk, they were rewarded by observation of a variable star. It is normally of the second magnitude, hence easily visible. Within 4 1/2 hours its brightness diminishes by two classes, then returns in the same period of time to the original magnitude. This phenomenon is repeated every third day. The explanation: Algol is a binary composed of two very different companions, one bright and the other about fifteen times fainter. Every third day the darker star passes in front of the brighter one, producing a partial eclipse.

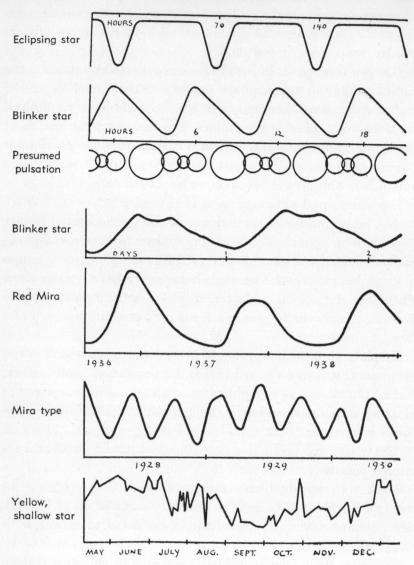

REGULAR AND IRREGULAR LIGHT CURVES OF VARIABLE STARS. THE
BRIGHTNESS OF THESE STARS WAXES AND WANES IN CHARACTERISTIC
PATTERNS ACCORDING TO TYPE. BLINKER STARS ARE IMPORTANT FOR
THE CALCULATION OF STELLAR DISTANCES.

In the course of time over a thousand such regular stellar
eclipses have been discovered with the aid of photometers. Their
periods vary between a few hours and several years, depending

upon the closeness of the companion. Ordinarily, both are bright, but of different magnitudes; hence their light curves alternately display deep dips, depending on whether the brighter or the darker star is eclipsed. In addition, more delicate variations in the curves result from the reciprocal radiation of the stars. Frequently, such stars are the same pairs that have already been recognized from the splitting of spectral lines. By combining the results of photometry and spectrum analysis, some intimate details of their life cycle have been discovered. The stories of the cannibal stars and of Zeta Aurigae are based on such data.

The counterpart to the eclipsing stars is afforded by the blinker stars. The brightness of these does not drop periodically; rather, they blaze up periodically. Their brighter phase appears as punctually as a revolving searchlight on a lighthouse, though the tempo is somewhat slower—the intervals being every few hours or days. The light curves of these blinkers display a swift rise and a gentle descent, usually smooth; only a few show small humps here and there.

Simple as the matter appears to be, it was extremely difficult to assign its cause, and the solution is not yet entirely satisfactory. At first the cause was thought to be rotation; but in that case the blinking variables would have to have one dark side, and no one could believe that of a star. In preference, the bold theory of A. Ritter was accepted: that the blinkers actually swell and diminish, pulsate.

These stars are monstrous creatures, many times larger than the Sun. It is difficult to imagine how they can puff up and shrink again within a few days, or even hours, and do so, moreover, with clockwork regularity.

The more that is known about blinkers, the more mysterious they become. Some leave off varying for a time, others begin to flicker irregularly, and in others the period seems to be lengthening. But although they have by no means yielded all their secrets, they have conferred one great boon on astronomy, and this has made them the most respected of all the variables. They have revealed themselves as milestones of the Galaxy.

Milestones of the Galaxy

What astrophysicists most fervently desire to know about a star is its distance from the Earth. This they must know if they wish to calculate its mass or its true luminosity. But as we have said, measurement of linear distance is the most difficult problem of astronomy. From 1850, when that exemplary astronomer Friedrich Bessel made the first such measurement, only sixty more were added by 1900. Lewis Rutherfurd had discerned on photographs displacements of stars by means of which he was able to calculate the distances without much trouble. By use of his method the number of measured stars rose to 5,000. But that was about the limit, for trigonometry could not be employed for distances beyond three hundred light-years.

If investigation of the stars and the Galaxy were to make progress, new methods for determining distance would have to be found. The number of solutions proposed cannot be described. Virtually every feature hitherto discovered about the dots of lights in the sky was employed in one way or another to provide at least some estimate of distance. From the motion, the brightness, the color, the spectrum, and even from single spectral lines astronomers learned, by ultrafine computations, to draw some conclusions about the distances of stars. On no other astronomical problem has so much ingenuity been lavished.

The prize in this unofficial world-wide competition was won by Harvard Observatory in 1912. There, our two neighboring galaxies were being studied, the greater and the smaller Magellanic clouds. These are regular nests of stars; raggedly shaped, they consist of innumerable dots of light of every type and magnitude. Unfortunately, they can be seen only in the Southern Hemisphere, but Harvard Observatory had a station in the Peruvian Andes. Innumerable photographs were taken there, and over the years these were studied and compared photometrically.

Miss Henrietta Leavitt, who did much of this work, discovered that many of the dots of light showed a regular variation in lumi-

nosity. They presented perfect blinker curves. More variables
were in this cloud than in all the rest of the firmament—some
three thousand of them. Here was a unique opportunity to get to
know this interesting species. All three thousand were, since
they belonged to the same cloud, approximately the same distance
from the Earth. That meant that if the brightness were measured,
the absolute magnitudes could be easily computed. The brightness proved to be amazingly high: the variables ranked among the
hundred-watt lamps, and some of them were even lighthouse
power.

Because they were so numerous, Miss Leavitt tabulated their
apparent brightness against their periods, and at once discovered
the close relationship between the two characteristics. Later in-
vestigators, among them Harlow Shapley, translated this into a
relationship between period and luminosity. Each luminosity
corresponded to a particular period of variability. Brighter stars
blinked more slowly, feebler stars faster.

This seems a thoroughly reasonable rule whose counterpart is
to be found both in nature and technology. Big clocks tick more
slowly than little ones; the stork's wings make fewer beats than a
hummingbird's. But of course it could not be predicted that the
rule would also apply to variable stars in outer space.

Naturally, the rule also holds for all the variables in our own
sidereal system. This fact is of vital importance: no matter where
a variable is, if its period can be determined, its absolute luminosity can be read off from the Leavitt table. If, then, its photometric brightness is measured, the distance from the Earth is at
once given. For the amount by which the true magnitude is greater
than the apparent magnitude depends on the distance.

These blinker stars, then, constitute regular milestones scattered
throughout the Galaxy. Distances may be read off them with great
ease and reliability, quite as if they bore in illuminated lettering
the words: "So and so many miles to Earth." Astronomers could
not have asked for anything better. The period-luminosity relationship, as it is called, is one of those lucky finds that so frequently incline us to believe that astronomy must enjoy especial
favor from on high.

The consequences for galactic research are almost unimaginable. By the aid of the variables, the Galaxy can be surveyed almost like a terrestrial continent. At once it was possible to confirm the figures for the length and width of the Galaxy which had been calculated on the basis of Herschel's stellar statistics. In addition, two new facts were learned which materially altered our picture of our own sidereal system.

The first of these is that the Galaxy has a bulge in the middle on both sides, like the protruding hub cap of an automobile wheel. The region of the Archer, which had long been noted for its unusual concentration of stars, forms a raised center in the otherwise uniformly flat disc of the Galaxy. This unexpected novelty was splendidly illustrated by photographs of other galaxies, which we see edge-on. In these, too, the central bulge is distinctly visible, as well as the layer of dust which splits them in two along their entire length.

EDGE-ON DRAWING OF THE MILKY WAY, SURROUNDED BY VARIABLE STARS AND STAR CLUSTERS. NOTE THE DISC SHAPE OF THE GALAXY, WITH THE CHARACTERISTIC CENTRAL BULGE AND LAYER OF DUST SPLITTING THE GALAXY IN TWO. (SEE PLATE XXXI.)

The second fact of great interest concerned the globular star clusters, in which ten or one hundred thousand dots of light are so close together that toward the center they can scarcely be re-

solved even by the most powerful telescopes. In these, too, a few variables are regularly found, so that the distance of the clusters can be reckoned precisely. It turned out that these globes of stars— about one hundred of them are now known—for the most part form a vast sphere around the outskirts of the Galaxy. Consequently, a new picture of our sidereal system emerges; the globular system is not flattened, but if we were to look down on our Galaxy from a point above its hub, it would appear, in two dimensions, to resemble an elongated South Sea island, framed by a wreath of tiny coral islands. Amid these, like bathing Polynesian girls, float numerous RR Lyrae stars, as the smallest and fastest of the variables are called. The diameter of the island amounts to about 80,000 light-years. Our Galaxy is about 1,000 light-years thick in the region of the spiral arms, where our Sun is, and in the denser center it is some 10,000 to 15,000 light-years thick. The Sun is 30,000 light-years distant from the galactic center. The spherical shell of the globular clusters with their RR Lyrae stars is about 150,000 light-years in diameter.

This entire system revolves around itself, but many individual stars fly like comets in and above the cluster region, periodically returning to the main island.

In order to complete this picture, we must remember that this island is practically "empty": every star is so far away from the next nearest as a grain of sand in one city is from a grain of sand in another city. On the other hand, the whole of the intervening space is apparently filled with extremely tenuous matter that takes four forms:

1. Bright clouds; about one thousand large ones and countless very small ones whose presence has only been demonstrated by their spectra.

2. Dark clouds of all sizes. There are vast numbers of these.

3. A galactic mist composed of metallic vapors and the universal gas, hydrogen.

4. A stratum of dust running down the center of the Galaxy which obscures our view of the galactic circle.

Most recent research goes so far as to assert that our island universe consists only half of stars, that the other half of its total

mass is made up of the thin matter between the stars. This seems a startling thought—and, indeed, it has astonished the astronomers.

Giants and Dwarfs

In 1905 the Danish astronomer Einar Hertzsprung compared the luminosities of stars with their colors. Only a few luminosities were then known, but he assumed from the start that the two characteristics were connected. White heat is brighter than red heat. Presumably the white stars would be the "lighthouses," the red stars the "glowworms." Yellow stars like our Sun would lie somewhere in the middle.

However, Hertzsprung soon discovered a few exceptions. Among the red stars, almost all were at the lower end of the luminosity scale, just as might be expected; but a few rivaled the white stars in brightness. Obviously, this could only happen if they were of unusual size: a very large red lamp *can* produce as much light as a small white bulb. The red stars of this type must be enormously larger than the white ones.

Red stars of spectral type M are, therefore, a class to which the very smallest and the very largest stars must belong. But the class contains no intermediate sizes, only giants or dwarfs.

Among yellow stars, also, which are normally "candles," there are some "lighthouses." The difference is not so great, but again there are only two types, without intermediate stages: small stars and giants.

Apparently Hertzsprung did not quite dare to present this tale out of *Gulliver's Travels* directly to his colleagues; he published his theory in a journal of photography, where it remained obscure until 1914. Then Henry Norris Russell hit upon the same typology of the stars. He diagramed his findings—and the matter became indubitable. The "Hertzsprung-Russell diagram" plays a part in modern astronomy comparable to the Law of the Twelve Tables in ancient Rome. It is reverently commented upon, con-

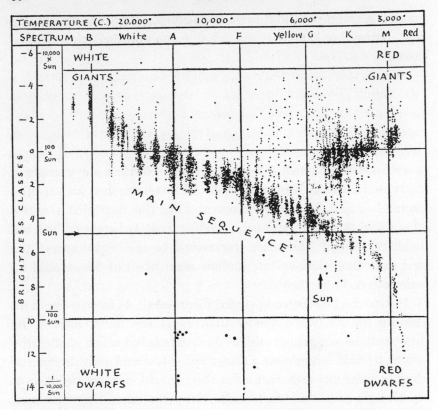

HERTZSPRUNG-RUSSELL DIAGRAM OF THE THOUSAND NEAREST STARS.
COLORS, SPECTRAL TYPES, AND TEMPERATURES ARE INDICATED ON THE
HORIZONTAL; LUMINOSITIES AND ABSOLUTE MAGNITUDES ON THE
VERTICAL. EVERY STAR IS PLACED ON THE DIAGRAM AS A DOT.

stantly cited, applied to special cases, provided with amendments, and held in high affection by theoreticians who like to
show that it is inherent in the structure of the universe.

The diagram shows as abscissas (horizontally) the colors of
the stars, which are simultaneously their spectral types and their
temperatures. It shows as ordinates (vertically) their luminosities
and absolute magnitudes. Every star is placed in the diagram as
a dot; the result is an arrangement by color and brightness simultaneously.

By far the majority of stars lie on a single branch that slants
upward. These are the normal stars, which follow the rule of in-

creasing brightness with increasing temperature. On the right, at the bottom of the diagram, are the coolest and darkest stars, the red dwarfs.

Above this slanting branch a more horizontal group extends to the right. The density and uniformity are less than in the main sequence, but stars of all colors, white, yellow, orange, and red, are to be found in this group. Here are the "lighthouses." And as we move to the right along the diagram, their size steadily increases; the biggest are at the red end, on the upper right.

It remained to be proved that the stars in this section were actually giants. The true diameters of stars had to be determined. This was done by extremely complicated computation. Around 1920, however, Michelson succeeded in measuring seven red giants directly with an interferometer attached to the Mount Wilson telescope—an instrument which divides the light from a star into two beams. From the fringe patterns formed by the interference of the two beams of light, the angular diameter of the star can be calculated—if the star is near enough and bright enough. This instrument confirmed the assumption that the red, highly luminous stars were also the biggest. Betelgeuse, the star in Orion's left shoulder, has 250 times the diameter of the Sun; it would contain the whole orbit of the Earth. Antares, the blood-red Scorpion's eye, is still larger; it would fill the orbit of Mars. If we imagine the Sun as a ping-pong ball, this giant would be as big as a captive balloon. Compared to it, the red dwarfs are like grains of sand. Hertzsprung's Gulliver fable was true; not only are there differences of brightness like that between a glow-worm and a lighthouse; there are also differences of size like that between a flea and an elephant—and in stars of the same type.

Around 1925 an additional group of dots was added to the left-hand corner of the Hertzsprung-Russell diagram: white dwarfs. These, it was reasoned, must be extremely tiny, since in spite of their bright color they yield no more light than the red dwarfs—and this logic led to exciting consequences.

The foremost example of the type was the companion of Sirius, a tiny star whose existence had been deduced only from certain perturbations in the orbit of Sirius. When it was at last seen in a

good telescope, it was, of course, promptly examined by photometric and spectroscopic methods. It proved to be a pure-white dot of improbably small luminosity. It became possible to calculate its mass and diameter. Its mass is about the same as the Sun, but it is only twice the size of the Earth; it would take sixty thousand such stars to fill in the globe of the Sun.

This was a staggering set of facts: the same mass and only 1/60,000 of the volume of the Sun! That meant a specific gravity forty thousand times that of water, three thousand times that of lead, two thousand times that of platinum. A pint of the material of Sirius's companion would, if placed on Earth, weigh twenty-five tons.

When the aging Michelson was informed of this conclusion, he declared that it was impossible; the theory must be wrong. Yet the conclusion was not a theory; it was a calculation based upon photometry and spectrum analysis, whose results had been incontrovertible in thousands of other cases.

When the physicists recovered from their amazement, they found that the incredible density of the white dwarfs fitted neatly into their conception of the atom as a planetary system in miniature, with (relatively speaking) astronomical distances between the circling electrons. They had long asserted that so solid a thing as a stone consisted of practically empty space, a field of force of infinitesimal points of matter in vast solitudes of empty space. If the atom were shattered, if the field of force collapsed, the points of matter would scarcely need any space; a boulder could shrink to the size of a grain of sand.

Such is the situation in the white dwarfs. Their atoms have been shattered, their matter has become "degenerate," completely clotted together.

Physicists did some theoretical calculations of the specific gravity of such degenerate matter—and arrived at figures that coincided exactly with those discovered observationally for Sirius's companion.

The white dwarfs demonstrate what awaits us if physics ever reaches the point of shattering all the atoms on the Earth.

Novae and the Evolution of Stars

A nova is a star that suddenly bursts into visibility. Hipparchus saw one. Tycho Brahe wrote two weighty volumes on the new star of 1572, which was brighter than Venus and visible even by day. No nova ever shone so brilliantly again. Kepler also saw one; thereafter, only three appeared up to 1900.

Not until photography came to the fore as the principal method of observation did it become apparent that novae were regular occurrences. Again and again astronomers discovered on their plates dots of extraordinary luminosity which had not been there before. But when older photographs were carefully compared, it turned out that in the place of every nova a small star had stood previously, an inconspicuous white star usually, within the brightness range of our Sun.

These stars, then, were not new births; instead, they represented a sudden flaring, an explosion in a star, a cosmic hydrogen bomb.

What happens in the course of such an eruption is indicated by spectrum analysis. Photometry supplies the light curve: in the course of a few hours the luminosity rises ten thousandfold. A candle becomes a lighthouse—in a few hours! This is probably the most thrilling phenomenon that takes place in the heavens. It is terrifying to think that our Sun might explode in this fashion. Humanity would at any rate enjoy a solemn and dramatic doom as the entire planet went up in a puff of smoke.

As a matter of fact, the danger seemed much more real than any of the catastrophes so dreaded in the past: collisions with comets; the fall to Earth of giant meteors; prolongation of the Earth's day, and thus overheating of the planet; or prolongation of the Earth's orbit, and thus freezing of the planet. An eruption of the Sun into a nova seemed, in fact, absolutely inescapable after it was learned that two dozen novae flare up annually in the Galaxy, one every two weeks on the average. Statistical probability would indicate that sooner or later the turn of every star

would come, including that of the Sun. And it might happen at any moment.

Fortunately, close investigation of several hundred novae showed that only a certain spectral type inclined to explode, chiefly the white and in some cases the pale-yellow stars. In every case the star's appearance was the same before and after the eruption. In spite of the catastrophe, its luminosity remained practically unchanged—a highly reassuring fact. Apparently these celestial eruptions were much ado about nothing. It was calculated how much mass a nova lost in the course of an eruption. It turned out to be insignificant, perhaps one hundred thousandth of the original mass. That is why novae can undergo several explosions. The nova of 1898 flared again in 1933; another repeated its eruption in twelve years and then again eighteen years later. In short, there are stars that behave something like volcanoes. And these, happily, are limited to the spectral types B, A, and F. Consequently, the Sun does not appear to be in danger.

Since astronomers have become better acquainted with novae, they have simply classified them among the variable stars. Their light curves show more or less regular oscillations that are reminiscent of certain variables. In fact, one subspecies of the variables, the type of U Geminorum, have recently been characterized as miniature novae; these do not explode so violently as the typical novae, but they do erupt regularly, as often as ten times a year. These, too, are small white stars.

The white stars, then, are peculiarly temperamental. It seems apparent that their many eruptions would gradually destroy them. In a sense, this is what happens—for they presumably become white dwarfs. These celestial hydrogen bombs gradually shatter their own atomic structure, lose their hydrogen, condense into fantastically heavy, radiant spheres of degenerate matter.

This is, of course, only a hypothesis. But in astronomy "historical" statements must always remain hypothetical. We cannot expect developments that take millions of years to unfold before our eyes. Nevertheless, the astrophysicist is tempted again and again to write the life history of stars. The Hertzsprung-Russell diagram with its slanting branch and its level crest virtually cries

out for historical explanation. Russell himself viewed the diagram as the image of stellar evolution. His interpretation was as follows:

Out of a dark nebulae there is first formed a red-hot giant star relatively low in temperature. As it contracts, it grows steadily brighter, its color shifting up the temperature scale through yellow-white. Once it reaches maximum heat, its temperature begins to decline again along the path indicated by the diagonal branch; it radiates away its substance, becomes darker, smaller and cooler, and finally ends as a red dwarf.

Neat as this explanation of the diagram seemed to be, it could not be sustained. It is evident from the most recent data that stars may begin their lives almost anywhere along the main sequence of the Hertzsprung-Russell diagram. What happens to them from that point on depends upon how massive they are, how thoroughly mixed their matter is as they evolve, and finally, whether they were formed primarily of hydrogen with no dust or from hydrogen with an admixture of the heavier elements. Most of the stars in our Galaxy, which are also the oldest stars and which are found in greatest concentration toward the center of the Galaxy, were formed primarily from hydrogen and started their lives as red dwarfs in the lower right-hand corner of the diagram. As they used up their hydrogen these stars moved up the main sequence until they became about three or four times brighter than our Sun. They then moved off the main sequence into the giant region. These then are the oldest stars now, in which the heavy elements are being cooked. Stars like our Sun were born from a mixture of hydrogen and heavy material, and are really "second-generation" stars. These stars spend most of their lives in the neighborhood of the main sequence. Type O and B stars are among the youngest, no more than a few million years old. They were formed from the great clouds of gas and dust in the spiral arms of the Galaxy.

What will happen to our Sun? That depends on whether the material inside it is thoroughly mixed or not. If it is, the Sun will remain in the region of the main sequence which it now occupies, but at the very last stages of its life, when it has but a small

amount of hydrogen left, it will move rapidly up the main sequence, becoming thousands of times brighter and probably
ending its life as a white dwarf. This process will take billions of
years. If the material inside the Sun is not thoroughly mixed, it
will move off the main sequence toward the giant branch, and
if it can collect enough material by gravitational accretion our
Sun will become a giant star moving toward the red end of the
diagram. This process, too, is a matter of billions of years.

Supernovae

For some thirty years a constant photographic vigil has been
kept upon the remotest celestial structures of all, the extragalactic
nebulae. Again and again a dot of light will appear in these, and
within a few days swell so mightily that it will outshine the entire
nebula.

To outward appearances nothing much happens. The photograph will show a dim line amid many dots of light of every
imaginable size, and in this line a medium-sized bright spot. But
that line is in reality far beyond the surrounding stars; it is a

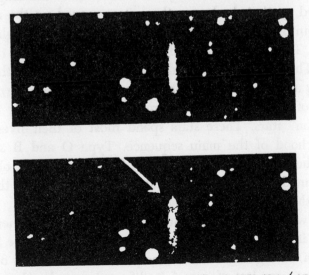

A SUPERNOVA BECOMES VISIBLE IN A DISTANT NEBULA (ARROW).

galaxy composed of millions upon millions of stars which we never see. And the bright spot inside it represents something almost inconceivable: a supernova whose radiance rivals that of an entire galaxy, outshining all its stars put together, including its giants and supergiants.

Astrophysics sometimes excavates its most exciting finds from humble soil. Centuries of intellectual endeavor were required before human beings understood the pictorial message from the depths of space. What is recorded on the two photographs reproduced above is probably the most tremendous event in the universe: an outburst of light compared to which ordinary nova explosions are like the flicker of a match. It would take about ten thousand of the former to approximate the radiation of a single supernova.

One such monster star radiates in a single month as much light as our Sun in a million years. Recent computations indicate that it squanders all at once the entire energy at the disposal of a normal star. Nevertheless, the event takes place with majestic deliberation. After flaring up, the light curve descends uniformly, without the vacillation and flickering of an ordinary nova.

This remarkable phenomenon has been the subject of a variety of speculations. A once appealing theory held that a "nova" in the literal sense, a new star, is actually being born. Presumably, dark masses of gas have clustered together, been condensed more and more by their own gravitation, until they become so heated that the newborn star blazes up with ultimate brilliance. It cannot hold this peak of radiation very long; within a short time it dissipates the major part of its matter and energy, and there remains a white giant surrounded by a self-generated cloud. But novae cannot be stars in the process of birth. All contemporary evidence is against this.

In general, supernovae are very rare. On the average, one every three hundred years appears in an aging nebula. At first thought this seems seldom enough. But astronomy reckons in redoubtable periods of time; even at such a rate, in a billion years more than three million new stars will spring into existence.

But in the young spiral nebula NGC 3184 three supernovae

have appeared within seventeen years—certainly a lively rate.

In the Milky Way, too, supernovae ought to appear occasionally. The occurrence of one has been demonstrated by an interesting combination of circumstances. Chinese chronicles report a new star of unprecedented splendor that appeared in the year A.D. 1054 in the constellation of the Bull. The Chinese annalists described the position of the star with great care. Modern charts record for this same position a curious cloud with many tentacles that appear to be crawling in all directions. They are indeed crawling, steadily expanding outward. Using their velocity as measured now, astronomers extrapolated backward in time and found that the Crab Nebula was no bigger than a star in A.D. 1054. Undoubtedly the nebula is the product of a star which, according to descriptions of its brightness, must have been a supernova.

There are in the Milky Way, moreover, about 150 curiously shaped little clouds with white stars in their centers. They look like smoke-rings, and they expand like smoke-rings. Their ages, too, can be calculated from the rate of expansion; they are within a range of 15,000 years, and apparently one of them was formed every few hundred years. If this is correct, a supernova is formed in our Galaxy every few hundred years, flares and fades rapidly, and remains as a white giant surrounded for a time by a self-generated cloud. This expands steadily, and is probably dissipated after a few thousand years.

Such is the nature of one of the greatest of cosmic events, a tremendous outburst of light, a blaze of radiation enormously surpassing all the other radiant phenomena of the universe.

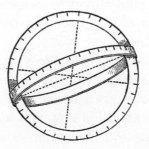

REVOLUTIONARY THEORY

Is Anything at Rest in the Universe?

IN THE YEAR 1851 cultivated persons in cities throughout Europe went to the largest cathedrals to attend an unusual sort of worship. They were coming to witness Jean Foucault's pendulum experiment, which he had first performed for the public in that year under the dome of the Panthéon in Paris.

From the highest point in the cathedral a heavy weight hung suspended on a thin rope, so that it was free to swing in all directions. It was given a push in a northerly direction, and began to swing in a north-south line. It continued to swing for days, but ever so slowly the direction of its swing shifted. And it continued to do so visibly. Those who waited long enough were able to see the plane of the pendulum's swing turn in a full circle in the course of a day.

Actually, however, the plane of oscillation had not changed at all. A pendulum retains the direction of its original motion, as stated by Galileo's law of inertia. Thus the pendulum provided visible proof of Copernicus' doctrine: the Earth was turning underneath the swinging pendulum.

How unfortunate it was that Galileo did not notice this when he observed the chandelier swinging in the Duomo at Pisa. He would have been spared his troubles with the Inquisition; such tangible proof of the Earth's rotation would have silenced all doubts.

Nevertheless, the Frenchman's ingenious experiment stimulated

other ideas, for which the times and the place were ready: ideas on one of the fundamental problems of both philosophy and religion.

Originally Newton had asked himself whether absolute movement existed in the universe, that is to say, movement in itself which we could determine without reference to other movements. His answer was that there was only one such motion: the rotation of the Earth. Ultimately, he maintained, we would have discovered this motion even if there had not been a sky full of stars circling about the polestar above our heads. Even without the polestar we would have found the flattened poles of our globe; we would have understood that they had been caused by the distorting effect of centrifugal force.

From this reasoning Newton drew a profound conclusion. If we imagine our universe with no other bodies beside the Earth, there must still be something to which we can refer the motion of the Earth, something that is at rest in relation to the Earth. Absolute motion presupposes something absolutely at rest. Only space can be this something. Hence, space ceases to be solely a philosophical concept, a mere word; it must have physical existence, for all that its only characteristic is being at rest. This idea of something at rest, ubiquitous, absolutely fixed, suggested the attributes of the Supreme Being; physical space of its own accord intruded itself into the sphere of religion.

Similar reflections may have occurred to the spectators who witnessed the Foucault experiment in 1851. The rotation of the Earth, absolute motion, the existence of space and hence of divine ubiquitousness—they were being granted an actual demonstration of these concepts, not only an intellectual apprehension such as Newton had had.

Ernst Mach, who was a boy of thirteen in 1851, was destined to expose the fallacy of the experiment and demolish the Newtonian argument. Mach was a scientist possessed of an unusual need to unify scientific thought. He challenged Newton's ideas with the Newtonian principle that no superfluous assumptions ought to be made. Among such superfluous assumptions he considered the "persistence in a straight line," which held Foucault's

pendulum to its original plane of vibration, and even "centrifugal force," which everyone could personally experience by twirling a stone on a string. These concepts were needless, he maintained; they could be eliminated, and everything explained by the law of universal gravitation. The force that flattened out the Earth and held Foucault's pendulum to its plane of vibration, so that the Earth turned underneath it, thus betraying its rotation—this force was nothing less than the attraction of all the bodies in the universe, stars and remote galaxies: in short, the total gravitation of the universe. Undoubtedly the Earth turns, Mach argued, but we are not logically forced to regard its rotation as absolute; we may also take it to be relative to the totality of matter in the universe. Inexplicable centrifugal force, the equally mysterious persistence in a straight line, and even Galileo's inertia, could be dropped. All these fundamental concepts of physics could be explained as effects of a single universal force, gravitation.

Newton himself might have assented to this overwhelming simplification of the mechanism of the universe; he probably would have done so under protest, but bowing to his own principles of reasoning. The simpler explanation must always be accepted in preference to one more complex. Ernst Mach was ennobling the universe by reducing all motion to a single principle. But if the Earth's rotation were considered in reference to the totality of matter in the universe, if absolute motion were thus eliminated, then absolute space could no longer be demonstrated; the factor of rest and ubiquity would have to be put aside, and therewith one religious value that Newton had wrested from physics.

There was, however, a second logical avenue one might take in order to establish absolute motion in an absolute: the motion of light in the ether.

Once again it was Foucault who supplied the means for testing this possibility. He succeeded in measuring the velocity of light in the laboratory. In order to appreciate this achievement, we must remember that light can rush around the globe seven times in a second. How can it possibly be timed over a reasonable distance? Foucault set up a tiny mirror to revolve around an axis 800 times a second, so that it tore an impinging ray of sunlight

and scattered fragments of light. One such fragment was caught by a concave mirror; the time it took to go and come was measurable. The velocity of light proved to be very nearly 186,000 miles per second, with a possible error of only one per cent.

With this figure to work with, it was hoped to prove the existence of the motionless ether. The Earth not only revolves around its axis, but moves around the Sun at a velocity of 18.5 miles per second. Hence, a ray of sunlight ought to move 18.5 miles per second faster when measured along the Earth's orbit than when measured perpendicularly to it, because the Earth's speed would be added to that of the light. Such an experiment would not only prove conclusively the Earth's revolution around the Sun (if this were not proved by other methods), but would also demonstrate the existence of something at rest in the universe, the "luminiferous ether."

The test of this concept, the most important experiment of modern times, was undertaken by A. A. Michelson. His first attempts, with apparatus so sensitive that the footstep of a passer-by upset it, yielded a negative result. In 1887, working with Edward W. Morley, he performed the experiment with such accuracy that the final negative result was without question: the sought-after change in the velocity of light did not occur. The Michelson-Morley experiment showed that the speed of light is independent of the motion of the observer and the motion of the source of light.

Consequently, no ether at rest, no ether at all, existed. The physicists were not sorry; they had never felt at ease with this clumsy concept. But when the ether vanished, there vanished with it the last prospect for proving that Newton's absolute space existed. And physics was promptly confronted with a new set of problems. If ether did not exist, how could light be transmitted in the form of waves? And was it conceivable that the velocity of light was entirely independent of the Earth's velocity, that the two sums could not be added?

No solution to the second problem was needed.

A young mathematician in Zürich proposed giving up all attempt at explanation, accepting the fact as inherent in nature,

and raising it to the status of an axiom of physics. The velocity of light, and it alone, would then be the sought-for absolute, he posited. Everything else, motion, space, even time, must be regarded as relative, no matter what conceptual difficulties such a position gave rise to.

Accordingly, the only absolute we can cling to is not something at rest, but something in motion—the fastest-moving thing we know. Here was a hypothesis fully in consonance with our modern urge to see movement in everything—the very ultimate conclusion of that impulse, as it were.

The young mathematician who enunciated it was named Albert Einstein.

Space-Time Continuum

The first third of our century was a golden age of theory such as had not been known since the seventeenth century. In both these periods there was widespread enthusiasm for abstract speculation, for sweeping ideas, for a philosophy of nature. In both the public took a passionate interest in the issues, even though it could not understand some of the theoretical subtleties. In both periods ordinarily calm and objective scientists became highly agitated; each of them felt that basic principles were at stake. And in both periods a single genius became, within a few years, the supreme arbiter; his name became a symbol, he himself the center of controversy and reverence. In the seventeenth century it was Newton, in the twentieth Einstein.

Like Newton, Einstein provided a comprehensive theory which solved a number of problems that had seemed hopeless. He shaped a new mode of thinking, complex, revolutionary, running counter to traditional basic concepts, but so fruitful that the initial resistance soon vanished.

Einstein's thesis was: there are no absolute magnitudes on which we can rely. Our fundamental measurements of length, weight, and time are dependent upon states of motion, change with motion, and mutually influence one another.

Back in the seventeenth century science had come to the disturbing discovery that we can no longer consider weight a fixed characteristic of objects. A pint of water weighs less on a mountain than at sea level. In order to have some fixed magnitude with which to deal, Newton invented the concept of "mass." This led to some strange consequences which, in the course of time, came more and more to trouble physicists.

Einstein dispelled these disturbing consequences by declaring that mass, too, was relative, dependent upon velocity; the faster a thing moves, the more massive it is. This fantastic assertion was confirmed by numerous experiments. In powerful magnetic fields electrons can be subjected to extraordinary accelerations; they can be speeded up until they reach almost the speed of light, and their mass increases enormously in the process. The functioning of modern electron accelerators, which are employed for smashing atoms, is based upon this characteristic of matter.

Time, in turn, is dependent upon mass—or rather, our devices for measuring time, our clocks. Relative time was not altogether new; at the equator Huygens's pendulum clock ran more slowly than elsewhere on Earth. Newton explained this phenomenon as due to the lesser gravity at the equator. Newton's explanation left open the possibility that a better clock, one not dependent on gravity, might eliminate this effect.

The best measures of time we know are the vibrations of electrons. These can be measured quite exactly by spectral lines, that is, by the wave lengths of the light they emit; and they are not ruled by gravity to any great extent. Nevertheless, Einstein's theory required that they run slow if the force of gravity is large enough, because time itself is nothing absolute; time changes with gravitation.

The white dwarf star known as the companion of Sirius is a mass of such unusual density that were Einstein right, the gravitational effect upon time ought to be observable. And right he proved to be; in the light of this star the spectral lines were shifted toward the red. In other words, the vibrations of the electrons are slowed.

Time, Einstein continued with compelling logic, must also be

dependent upon velocity. It ought to grow shorter if velocity is very high. Once again the vibrations of electrons have borne him out; when hydrogen atoms are greatly accelerated, the infallible clock again runs slow.

Most difficult of all to grasp was Einstein's primary criticism of the concept of time: that it is impossible, outside of the Earth, to make true measurements of time. We cannot take time in itself, he maintained; comparisons of time are inseparable from measurements of space, and these are falsified by the observer's motion. A special case of this principle was exemplified by the Michelson-Morley experiment, which showed that the speed of light was independent of the Earth's motion.

All these proofs of relativity would have been mere negations had Einstein not succeeded in building upon them a new cosmology that allowed for the summing up in a few formulas of virtually all the physical facts of experience. These formulas pictured a cosmos in which space and time are inextricably interlocked, dependent upon one another, inconceivable apart from one another: the famous four-dimensional space-time continuum.

This concept cannot be expressed in images. Nevertheless, it is easier to understand than is generally thought. We are accustomed to graphic representations in which the base line indicates years, so that we can see development in time. We need only imagine a physical, three-dimensional structure developing in time, and we have grasped the Einsteinian space-time universe in principle. It is essentially a continuation of Galileo's invention: the introduction of time into a geometrical figure. Einstein inserted time into the geometry of the universe, declared the graphic representation to be a reality of the physical world.

Had not Herschel anticipated this concept? With his telescope he was, he realized, peering not only into space, but into the past, seeing stars as they had been aeons ago, not as they were in his day, seeing each star at another point in its development. This meant, basically, that we cannot obtain a picture of the universe as it now is. Along with the objects in space, we see different times. A simple look at the heavens confirms the fact that

space and time are inseparable; they appear to us in the form of a "space-time continuum."

Naturally, this notion does not get at the heart of the theory of relativity. The true essence of it can be grasped only by mathematicians; it is by no means subject to pictorialization, and every attempt to formulate it in words means falsifying it to some extent. As in the Pythagorean Academies, the portal to relativity bears the inscription: "Entry of nonmathematicians forbidden."

It is a somewhat painful thought that the profoundest truths of physics can no longer be grasped by human reason, not even by the minds of philosophers. The human mind is limited by the words of a language, and in this realm not even the most abstract language will serve. This is a bitter pill to swallow: that our thinking is dependent upon an instrument that is inadequate to formulate ultimate knowledge.

But on the other hand there is no greater triumph of the human spirit than this: that man has been able to shake off the fetters and create a new language of greater range. Mathematics comprehends truths that are no longer susceptible to verbalization, and which nevertheless meet the hardest possible test: that of predicting realities. The theory of relativity does not provide us with a "philosophy" in the old sense; it leads us into an icy, inhuman atmosphere. Yet here concepts that seemed to underlie sharply disparate phenomena merge into a harmonious unity.

Curved Space

For Newton, space was a thing existing in complete emptiness. Leibnitz, on the other hand, considered space nothing more than the relationship of objects to one another. Who was right?

The matter remained a verbal dispute that could not be settled until around 1840, when Michael Faraday, the onetime bookbinder's apprentice, discovered something in space that was not an object and yet could be made visible, which changed like objects and yet was undoubtedly a spatial structure. Faraday

found the existence of lines of force which extend into space from the poles of a magnet, forming shapely curves; these lines are sometimes densely, sometimes loosely packed. Faraday spoke of them as a flow of force.

This demonstration that space has content worked in splendidly with Leibnitz's idea. For lines of force really represent only relations between objects; they link separate objects, provide a vehicle for the effect of a magnet, as it were; they eliminate the concept of force operating at a distance, a concept fundamentally uncongenial to physicists, for all that they must work with such concepts constantly.

One of the great physicists of the nineteenth century, Clerk Maxwell, treated the lines of force mathematically, and conjured out of them his electromagnetic theory of light. Henceforth, space was understood to be a field given over to the play of many forces, permeated with waves of light, magnetism, and electricity. This mathematical vision has been brilliantly corroborated. For modern man space is something almost tangible, filled with waves of all kinds which transmit music, words, and images across vast distances. In our modern view space is a tremendous field of force.

Under the circumstances, someone was bound to ask whether gravitation, that most powerful of all the cosmic forces which operate at a distance, is not also represented in the field of forces in space. The one who asked this question, and answered it affirmatively, was none other than Einstein himself. In his unified field theory he added one more element to the content of space; space was now represented as a gravitational field also, the transmitter of the attraction of masses which guides the motions of all celestial bodies.

In the course of his calculations it turned out that Euclidean geometry did not suffice to account for such a function of space. Einstein tried another geometry.

The possibility of non-Euclidean geometries was recognized by the mathematical genius Gauss. So startling was the idea even to himself that he did not dare to publish it during his lifetime; he feared the outcry of the Philistines, he said. However, the Philis-

tines were not particularly outraged; they paid no attention. Superior intellects, on the other hand, went off on wonderful imaginative explorations of this new territory. Still, no one attributed any practical importance to these divagations until Einstein announced that the concept of space as a gravitational field required a non-Euclidean structure. The fantasies of the mathematicians had been realized, not on Earth, but in the cosmos.

This possibility had been considered earlier. Hermann von Helmholtz, the great German scientist, attempted to convey to the public at large the idea of such a universe by comparing it with the kind of glittering, silvery spheres ornamenting Christmas trees. In such a magic mirror we can see the image of a non-Euclidean universe. If we step up close, our mirror images appear gigantic and grotesquely distorted. If we step back, we see the whole room reflected and apparently floating inside the ball. Distant objects become extremely tiny and seem to hang at the center of the sphere. Infinite space caught in a Christmas-tree ornament—here is a subject that repays thought.

If we had to become accustomed to seeing things actually as they are reflected in such a sphere, we would—though perhaps reluctantly—adjust to such a vision; we would cease to be conscious of the distortions and diminutions. In short, we would live, without feeling the difficulties insuperable, in a non-Euclidean universe.

Einsteinian gravitational space, however, does not have the structure of the space inside a Christmas-tree ornament. It cannot be equated with anything in our experience; only mathematical analysis proves its existence.

A further disturbing conclusion from the theory of relativity is this: the universe has a curved structure. "Two-dimensional beings" who would not know the existence of depth, who could perceive only right and left, would imagine the Earth's surface as a curved "space" whose size could be calculated. In the same fashion, according to Einstein, our own three-dimensional universe can be calculated; it has a definite radius of curvature, a finite content.

How is this conclusion compatible with that necessary element

of our thought we have noted earlier, the idea of infinite space? As soon as we are told that the universe ends at a certain point, we invariably ask: "And what lies beyond?" Einstein cannot stop us from asking. But he does forbid us to thrust our heads outside his curved universe like the man in the illustration on page 111. Einstein proves that it is impossible to do so. For we could only look out with the aid of light rays—and in a curved space, light also travels along a curve. If we could see far enough, we would see ourselves "at the end." Hence, we remain locked within a cage.

Mathematicians can come up with weird ideas. The worst of it is that their theses can be proved. The curvature of light called for by Einstein's theory has already made its appearance in our own back yard, close to the Sun. The Sun's gravitation is large enough to bend passing light rays from stars. It was an act of scientific courage for Einstein to predict this; his entire theory would collapse if this simple, demonstrable effect did not occur.

At the solar eclipse of 1919 the *experimentum crucis* was made. British astronomers undertook an expedition to Principe Island in equatorial Africa, and took photographs of stars whose light was passing close by the rim of the Sun. They compared these photographs with others of the same stars when the Sun was in another part of the sky. The apparent difference in position coincided very closely with the amount of light curvature predicted by Einstein. Later observations by German and American astronomers confirmed these results.

Einstein's gravitational field equations have since been acknowledged the fundamental formulas for the structure of the universe. He next embarked on the task of combining Maxwell's electromagnetic field theory with his own equations in one system that would contain the fundamental concepts of physics; all types of field were to be included as elements of a single universal field, and even matter would appear as a confluence of gravitational lines of force, "places of high field-density."

If we consider these matters in the proper light, such a field theory would in truth restore space to all honor as the prime principle of all things; certainly it would not be an absolute, but it

would nevertheless comprehend all other concepts. Space would assume a new meaning, one that might have consoled Newton for the loss of stasis and ubiquity. We would have to conceive of space as an eternal play of currents and movements which by its very motion generates all the fundamentals of the universe: matter, time, light, gravitational attraction.

Shortly before his death Einstein reached what appeared to him to be the solution toward which he had been striving since 1920. He formulated the quintessence of his new world-view in the words: "Space has devoured ether and time; it seems to be on the point of swallowing up also the field and corpuscles, so that it alone remains as the vehicle of reality."

Ought we not gladly exchange a tangible, conceptual view of space and time in return for this philosophical insight into the unity of all things; can we not safely leave the understanding of their essence to a few chosen souls to whom abstract formulas mean as much as do the familiar, inadequate, beloved, noble words of language to us ordinary human beings?

Radiation Balance

The curvature of space provided Arthur S. Eddington, one of the leading theoreticians of astrophysics, with a basis for models of the universe. This Englishman represented the spirit of twentieth-century science in its purest form. Even more ruthlessly than Einstein, he broke with traditional notions. He systematized the innumerable separate accomplishments of spectrum analysis and photometry, and drew the boldest conclusions from them.

His ambition was to create a synthesis of atomic physics and astrophysics, a mathematical system which would simultaneously interpret the macrocosm and the microcosm. And he in fact succeeded in deriving the most important natural constants in both realms from relativity and quantum theory. From the high vantage point thus gained he also criticized philosophical ideas, and became a leader in the modern assault upon causality. As a

writer, his style was forceful and he knew how to dramatize the results of his researches by vivid, humorous comparisons.

Eddington showed the practical scientists that mathematical speculations could still accomplish as much as the most expensive telescopes, and that a theoretician could penetrate even into the interior of stars, if only he asked the right questions.

His first question was of a profound simplicity: "Why does the Sun shine?" The Sun ought not to shine at all, he pointed out. Its light came from its interior, where it was hottest, and therefore had to make its way through matter in order to appear. That matter possessed cohesion; the light must have force in order to break through the gas pressure. The force it employs is radiation pressure, which is also present in the tails of comets. But this pressure is very low; how can it oppose the tremendous force of the Sun's gas pressure? How, then, can stars radiate at all?

Eddington computed the radiation pressure of the Sun and found that it amounted to 3 per cent of the total pressure (gas pressure and radiation pressure combined). It is hard to conceive that pure light, the most ethereal thing in existence, develops a pressure sufficient to overcome the cohesiveness of the Sun's mass, to break through the strata of gas surrounding the Sun's interior.

From his computations of radiation pressure Eddington uncovered a further curious phenomenon. Radiation pressure increases very rapidly with increasing mass of a star. At one hundred times the solar mass it would amount to 4/5 of the gravitation. Under such conditions the light would act with great violence. On the slightest provocation the star would tear itself apart by the force of its own radiation, according to Eddington. Calculations show, however, that such a star could exist by properly adjusting its radius.

If, on the other hand, the star's mass drops to 1/10 that of the Sun, the radiation pressure becomes too weak to break through the opaque matter above; the light no longer can pierce its way from the interior, and the star remains dark.

The significant part of these theoretical computations was that

they roughly agree with actual conditions. Stars range between 1/5 and fifty times the mass of the Sun—within the theoretical limits calculated by Eddington. Astronomers had long wondered why the masses of all stars remained within a relatively narrow range, whereas their other characteristics such as size differ so widely. The heaviest stars are no more than 250 times the lightest ones, whereas the difference in size between the largest and the smallest is as of the whale and the tiny plankton it swallows by the millions. Eddington showed that only masses between 10^{33} and 10^{35} grams are capable of radiation. Stars of smaller mass remain dark; Eddington believed that stars of greater mass would tear themselves apart, and therefore do not exist.

Eddington proceeded to investigate the interior of the stars by ingenious reasoning, and was at last able to give a detailed picture of the conditions inside them.

In the heart of a star, he believed, matter is compressed to one hundred times the density of water, but remains a gas because of its enormous heat. The temperature in the center must be 20 million degrees Centigrade,* no matter whether the external temperature of the star is 20,000 degrees or merely 2,000 degrees. A comparison may convey some idea of what 20 million degrees means. Suppose we could hold a Centigrade thermometer, with the degrees marked in twenty-fifths of an inch, against the outer envelope of the Sun. The mercury would then rise twenty feet. But if our thermometer were thrust into the heart of the Sun, it would have to be as long as the distance from New York City to Baltimore, Maryland, in order to register the temperature.

From this excessively hot core, says Eddington, invisible ultraviolet light radiates. It is passed by stages from one layer of gas to the other, its wave length increasing so that it ultimately leaves the great sphere of gas as visible light, running the gamut of colors from red to blue-white. Throughout, it must fight against the resistance of the star's matter, which would apparently prefer to keep its energy to itself.

* Recent investigations show that the center temperatures differ from star to star, ranging from about twelve million degrees for faint red stars to about one billion degrees for the red super giants.

Thus Eddington's model of a star is a seething, bubbling mass of overheated gases forcing their way to its periphery.

Eddington now asked the question that had been much discussed by physicists before him: what is the source of the radiant energy? The amount of energy poured out by stars in the form of radiation is enormous. It is well known that the Earth, with all its plants and other creatures, is nourished by the energy of the Sun; but this tiny lump of matter takes only a few rays of the vast amount of radiation which the Sun scatters into space.

The physicists of the nineteenth century believed the Sun's energy came from contraction. When a gas condenses, it becomes warmer. A star radiates heat, cools, and in cooling condenses, so that it becomes hotter again, and this process presumably continues until a white giant has become a red dwarf, which slowly goes out like a dying fire.

Eddington contended that this theory was entirely inadequate. He calculated that a star could radiate for no more than forty million years if its energy were derived solely from contraction. It would descend very precipitately from white giant to red dwarf. Yet for at least two billion years, he said, since the formation of the oldest sedimentary rock, our Earth has been receiving undiminished radiation from the Sun. Hence, the Sun must have persisted in its present state for a very long time; that meant a source of energy incomparably greater than the energy of contraction.

As a disciple of Einstein, Eddington had little difficulty finding this source: the Sun's mass. The Sun must consume its own substance, radiate itself. According to relativity theory, the transformation of matter directly into energy should be possible in principle. For the time being, however, the Sun's method of doing this remained unknown. Eddington was able to calculate how much mass the Sun would lose in radiating for an hour: a mass equivalent to the contents of a lake that has an area of 200 square miles and reaches a depth of 270 feet.

How long can the Sun continue to shine if it draws upon its substance so lavishly? The answer is not so bad: in a million years

it will lose only .0000001 of its mass. Evidently, it can keep going
for another ten billion years. A star fifty times the mass of the
Sun could radiate for 500 billion years—which for our purposes
is practically forever.

Nevertheless, Eddington was not content with this prospect,
for the stars would eventually be consumed, their mass devoured.
Even though this was consistent with the theory of the descending
evolution of stars from white giants to red dwarfs, Eddington
drew back from such a conclusion; he had a deep resistance to
any theory of descending evolution.

This subject is linked with one of the most thrilling achievements of our century: calculation of the age of the universe.

Age of the Universe

"The universe is five billion years old"—such a sentence must
inevitably call forth a protest from Occidental men. What arrogance on the part of science to attempt to set up a time scale for
the Creator, no matter how inconceivably long that scale is. What
are five billion years in the face of eternity?

Our modern sensibility demands infinity in time as well as
space, for the Creation as well as for the Creator. For wherever
we set the beginning of the universe, we involuntarily ask: "What
was there before?" We cannot think the "universe" out of existence. Eternity would then be an empty word, with no happenings
to form the content of it. Could the Almighty have been content
with nothingness up to a certain fixed point in time?

But science goes its way without concern for the philosophical
needs of men. Acquaintance with radioactive substances led
physics to some very curious trains of thought. These substances
disintegrate of their own accord, and are transmuted into other
elements—uranium into lead, for example. The process takes
place at a calculable rate. Consequently, the age of minerals can
be determined if their lead content is compared with their uranium content: such and such a span of time must have been re-

quired to transform a given percentage of uranium into lead. In this way the age of the oldest known minerals could be estimated at two billion years.

A similar estimate was made for the entire crust of the Earth; it seemed to be about three billion years old. Meteorites revealed an age of 4.5 billion years. Astrophysics estimated an age of the same order of magnitude for various celestial bodies, and on the basis of a new theory of galactic evolution, for whole galaxies.

The accumulation of evidence makes it difficult to challenge the assertion that the Creation took place between four and seven billion years ago. Let us say six billions; in a ten-place number, a single figure does not matter. The fact that the results unanimously gave a ten-place number was in itself so astonishing that bold conclusions were drawn from it.

If the Earth, meteors, and whole galaxies are of practically the same age, we must assume that all bodies in the cosmos came into being simultaneously. This would mean that the stars of various sizes, colors, and luminosities do not represent evolutionary stages, but bodies which appeared with their given differing characteristics and have persisted unchanged for billions of years.

Eddington, in particular, subscribed to this view. He believed that all the characteristics of a star depend upon two basic factors, its mass and its chemical composition. Purely theoretically, he calculated that the luminosity must be connected with the mass, and he was then able to check this theory by simple statistical comparisons of astronomical observations. Now, he pointed out, it was highly improbable that all the stars should be born with one and the same mass. It was far more reasonable to assume that they occupied the full range of possible masses between 10^{33} and 10^{35} grams. But in that case, the concept of an evolutionary descent from white giants to red dwarfs must be jettisoned. There were giants and dwarfs from the beginning, hot and cool, white, yellow, orange, and red stars. Why assume processes that are not essential? The simpler explanation is the better.

Consequently, Eddington sought for a new source of radiation energy, although he had already found the practically inexhaustible source of the transmutation of mass directly into energy. He

was out to find some method which would not consume the mass of the star. The contemporary reader will at once think of nuclear fission or fusion. But in the thirties, when Eddington grasped at this straw, only courageous physicists seriously considered this possibility. Eddington himself was passionately fond of bold ideas; he once laughingly commented that he was always out-raged at anyone's believing the kind of thing that he did. He therefore set about examining all the elements for their tendency to disintegrate under the conditions within the core of his stellar model. Only a few elements seemed likely candidates—but they alone would suffice to supply a star's energy needs for a billion years without noticeable loss in substance.

Hence, Eddington announced happily, it is not necessary to assume stellar evolution. Every star might have been in its present state since the creation of the universe, and would still continue to radiate white, yellow, or red light, drawing its energy from sub-atomic processes. Accordingly, the stars set up atomic plants long before men thought of them. We can see how wonderfully suggestive this idea must have been to physicists at the dawn of the atomic age. The concept was even more attractive than the notion of stellar evolution.

In 1948, however, the possibility of stellar evolution came to the fore once again. On the basis of chemical analyses of stars, A. Unsöld, astrophysicist at Kiel University, calculated that there are virtual infants in the universe, stars only ten million years old. At about the same time a Russian astronomer, V. A. Ambartsumian, showed that photographs of clouds in the Milky Way indicate that type O and B stars are in the process of being created at the present time. Moreover, the stars in question were white giants, which had posed a problem for Eddington because they radiate so fast that even atomic energy would not suffice to have main-tained them since the assumed beginning of the universe. The new discoveries offered a way out of this dilemma: the white giants we see today are young stars. And those white giants that existed at the beginning of the universe have long since radiated away their energy and become smaller, colored, less luminous stars.

In short, the picture of the birth and evolution of stars, which we sketched in the last chapter, retains its validity in spite of Eddington's stellar atomic plants.

As for the creation of the universe five billion years ago: that, too, cannot be held to be the beginning of all things. We must assume an older period of creation during which the elements themselves arose. For the formation of elements Eddington's stellar temperatures of 20 million degrees Centigrade would not suffice; at least ten times that temperature would be necessary to build up an uranium atom. We therefore see stretching out before the present epoch of the universe another in which altogether different conditions must have prevailed, conditions whose nature we probably can never even conceive.

Infinity in time abides. We must remember that all the discussion of the age of the universe concerns only the present, visible stellar universe.

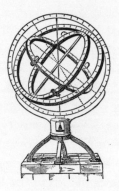

In short, the powers of the birth and evolution of stars which we sketched in the first chapter, retains its validity in spite of Eddington's stellar atomic plants.

As for the creation of the universe five billion years ago that one cannot hold to be the beginning of all things. We must assume an older part of creation during which the elements themselves arose. For the formation of element Eddington's stellar temperature or 10 million degrees Centigrade would not suffice; at least certain that temperature would be necessary to build up uranium atoms. We therefore see stretching out before the present epoch of the universe another in which, alas, the chiller conditions must have prevailed conditions whose nature we probably can never even conceive.

Infinity in time abides. We must remember that all the descent of this age of the universe concerns only the present, visible stellar universe.

BEGINNING OF A
SIXTH BOOK

THE NEW UNIVERSE

The Giant Eyes

I N THE LATEST PHASE of astronomy's development the United States has taken the lead, thanks to the enterprise of George Ellery Hale, the great specialist in solar research. This American Herschel was not content with equipping the richest observatory in the world with the largest refracting telescope in the world, the 40-inch refractor at Yerkes Observatory. He went on to plan the greatest light-gatherers of all time, his famous 60-inch, 100-inch, and 200-inch reflectors, the first two at Mount Wilson and the latter at Mount Palomar.

On the 60-inch he was, so to speak, trying his prentice hand. The cost was borne by Andrew Carnegie, who financed the whole observatory on Mount Wilson. For the next instrument Hale found a California philanthropist, John D. Hooker. This 100-inch reflector, installed in 1917, has become identified with the name Mount Wilson. It proved to be one of the most fortunate telescopes ever built; it is no exaggeration to say that half the discoveries of our century are due to it. During the years 1924 to 1936 it opened up a new universe, that of the extragalactic nebulae. Never has an instrument so well rewarded the care and expense lavished upon it.

Entrusting further research with the instrument to his favorite student, Edwin P. Hubble, the sixty-year-old Hale pondered the possibilities of a third giant eye, with a pupil twice as large. For the purpose he sought out another mountain, Palomar, inasmuch

as the glow of light from the growing city of Pasadena was more and more becoming a disturbing factor on Mount Wilson.

The story of the 200-inch Mount Palomar mirror is remarkable. It began in 1928 with an essay on the possibilities of large telescopes. In this paper Hale pointed out that modern telescopes were still extremely primitive and modest toys. It ought to be possible to build a really efficient one for the bagatelle of eight million dollars, and the annual running costs would probably come to no more than $150,000.

The essay attracted the attention of the Rockefeller Foundation, which agreed to pay for the telescope. But it was one thing to have the money, and another to pour a twenty-ton piece of glass. During the next several years the project ran into such ill luck that Hale must several times have been on the point of abandoning it. The General Electric Company poured the glass disc out of quartz, at a cost of half a million dollars. In cooling, it cracked. Experts opined that a disc of glass that size could not be made.

Hale decided to try Pyrex instead of quartz. Corning Glass then undertook the job, and advertised its part in the grand project so heavily that a horde of spectators attended the pouring. But the mold did not withstand the heat, and the mix was spoiled. A hundred technicians spent a year and a half preparing the third attempt. This time a nearby river overflowed its banks to attend the spectacle, and the men on the job barely succeeded in preventing it from watering the mix.

The precious disc of Pyrex was sent to Pasadena on a special train, to the accompaniment of fanfares of publicity. Then followed the quiet, patient business of grinding and polishing. Tolerances in hundred thousandths of a millimeter were required. After the work was done it turned out that the edge was still a fifty thousandth of a millimeter too high, and another six months of polishing ensued.

Meanwhile, the 500-ton mounting was being built, and an electronic brain for regulating the movements of the telescope was devised. The installation on Mount Palomar began in 1948— Hale himself did not live to see it.

The observer using this giant eye sits in the midst of the path

of the rays, in a cylindrical cage. It is necessary for him to sight a guide star in the view finder, because even the electronic brain cannot precalculate the ultrafine oscillations of our terrestrial globe.

The Mount Palomar telescope reaches out into space some two billion light-years. On the other hand, it covers so tiny a segment of the sky that it would take 5,000 years for astronomers to make a sweep of the whole firmament with it. Obviously, this super-instrument is not meant for the kind of celestial hunts Herschel reveled in. Only known, selected objects can be photographed with it. Fortunately, the new radio telescopes have been probing the universe and finding objects of investigation for the telescopic eye on Mount Palomar. Nevertheless, there was an urgent need for an additional search apparatus that could survey large areas of the heavens and pick out interesting objects.

This apparatus, sometimes called the magic camera, was invented by Bernhard Schmidt. Perhaps "bred" would be the better word, for he created it by hybridizing the lens and the mirror telescopes in a manner that eliminated the disadvantages and combined the advantages of both types. A lens guide first sifts light to the mirror; in this way the mirror is used to its very edges and can see far to the right and left without aberrations. The result is a telescopic wide-angle camera.

The value of the "big Schmidt" on Mount Palomar is evidenced by its sky survey of 1,800 plates, made in a few years. This sweep extends to a distance of 300 million light-years and records more stars and nebulae than all previous surveys put together. It has been called "the astronomical Bible for the next hundred years."

One Hundred Million Milky Ways

Since 1925 our horizon has enormously expanded once again. We have penetrated into a "third-order" cosmos. The first was our solar system. The second was the Galaxy. The third is the system of galaxies.

Scattered over the entire firmament, revealed mainly by the large telescopes, are tiny nebulosities, round, or oval, or spiral-shaped. Not until 1925 was it definitely decided whether they belonged to our Galaxy, or represented remote island universes, as Kant had suspected. A good many contemporary astronomers were inclined to the island-universe theory.

The most suitable subject for close investigation appeared to be the Andromeda Nebula. It is unusually large—twice the apparent diameter of the Moon—and can be recognized by persons with good eyesight as a spindle-shaped mistiness. Observatories had photographed it innumerable times; on the plates it showed as a slanting spiral, the spiral arms closely wound around the oval white nucleus. In 1889 a few bright dots were observed in these arms. As telescopes increased in size, the number of dots grew to several thousand. Was this proof that the Andromeda Nebula represented a galactic system? Far from it. For if it really lay outside our own Galaxy, the dots were too large for stars; they must be gigantic star clusters or small nebulae at such a distance. And in fact photographs taken with the Mount Wilson 60-inch telescope showed the dots as diffused and irregular in shape.

In 1917 a dot appeared which had not been present before, only to vanish again soon afterwards. Without doubt, this was a nova. Its light was a hundred times feebler than that of ordinary novae; consequently, the nebula must lie far outside the Galaxy. But estimates of distance arrived at by other methods contradicted this conclusion. The question was threshed back and forth until the Mount Wilson 100-inch telescope was enlisted.

Edwin Hubble specialized in the peculiar problems of nebular photography. Soon he was able to produce photographs of the Andromeda Nebula in which the whitish glow was completely resolved into sharp points of varying brightness—in all probability, stars. In 1924 he saw some of these points growing periodically brighter. In other words, these were variable stars—the famous milestones. They read: "900,000 light-years to Earth." This was certainly beyond the boundaries of our Galaxy, whose remotest star clusters extend only 150,000 light-years from us. Clearly, the

Andromeda Nebula was a neighboring galaxy, containing possibly as many stars as our own. Hubble detected frequent flares of novae in it—130 of them within a period of a few years. He was also able to discern star clusters—140, more than there are in our own Galaxy. The diameter of the nebula seemed unreasonably small, but that was due to observational difficulties. Today it is established that the Andromeda Nebula is larger than our own Galaxy. It is also more than three times as far away as Hubble assumed. It rotates in a somewhat complicated manner. The white nucleus of the nebula rotates like a solid disk—the speed of rotation at the edge of the nucleus is 150 miles per second. This speed decreases with increasing distance outward from this edge, in accordance with Kepler's third law. At decreasing distances toward the center of the nucleus the speed of rotation also decreases until it reaches zero at the center. This complex motion has not yet been fully analyzed; it may some day help us understand the motions of our own Galaxy more clearly.

Thereafter, more than one hundred additional nebulae were partially or wholly resolved into stars. Most of them showed novae from time to time. By assuming the same average magnitude for all the novae (a method unreliable in a single case, but statistically valid when applied to a group), Hubble was able to employ these novae as milestones where his ordinary variables were not in evidence. Thus he was able to form a fairly good picture of our galactic environs. There are about a dozen galaxies of all types: spiral, round, elliptical, and irregular. They all lie at approximately the same distance from us as the Andromeda Nebula —which, incidentally, has two tiny satellites, just like the Milky Way itself. At an amazingly small distance from it are the two Magellanic clouds, one large and one small, forming with it a group of three.

The tendency to appear in groups seems to be characteristic of nebulae. Hubble found whole clusters of them, some containing hundreds of separate nebulae. The nearest cluster appears in Virgo, seven times as far from us and from Virgo as the Andromeda Nebula—that is, about 22 million light-years away. This cluster served as a springboard into still greater depths of space, for it

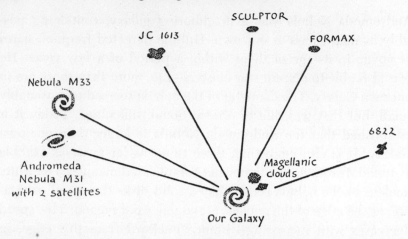

SCULPTOR

JC 1613

FORMAX

Nebula M33

6822

Andromeda
Nebula M31
with 2 satellites

Magellanic
clouds

Our Galaxy

THE TEN NEAREST ISLAND UNIVERSES. ALL THESE GALAXIES ARE AP-
PROXIMATELY THE SAME DISTANCE FROM US AS THE ANDROMEDA
NEBULA (LEFT), WHICH, LIKE OUR MILKY WAY, HAS TWO SATELLITE
NEBULAE.

presented an exemplary collection of all the various types of
nebulae. Hubble was able to compare their luminosities, and
then estimate the distance of any other nebula simply by its
photometric magnitude.

He then proceeded to work out nebular statistics in the Herschel
manner, taking several thousand selected samples, examining
fields of the apparent diameter of the Moon distributed evenly
over the northern sky and half the southern sky. In the course of
these labors Hubble identified 44,000 nebulae. He estimated the
total number within the range of the Mount Wilson 100-inch
telescope—a sphere one billion light-years in diameter. His "universe" contained 100 million galaxies.

The 200-inch Mount Palomar mirror is busy penetrating twice
as far out into space, and it has already become evident that
nebulae extend out to the limit of its range.

In the extraordinarily short span of a single decade Hubble began the exploration of the totality of nebulae, the ocean of island
universes. To the extent that he was able to explore it, its diameter
proved to be about 20,000 times that of the Milky Way, the same
proportion as that between the size of our globe and its orbit
around the Sun. If we imagine the space within the Earth's orbit

as filled with 500 million earths, we can form some concept of the density of population in this new universe. The ocean of space is literally swarming with islands; they are relatively closer together than the crowded Caroline group in the Pacific.

Here is one of the strangest facts in astronomy. Earlier we commented on the frightful emptiness of our sidereal system; now we are forced to exclaim with astonishment over the extraordinary congestion of the nebular system. If stars were the size of pinheads, each would be a few hundred miles from another. If nebulae were the size of pinheads, the space from the edge of one to the edge of the next would be no more than a hand's breadth. In clusters of nebulae, the nebulae are as close together as pins in a pincushion. Thus, suddenly, we find that figures in astronomy cease to be "astronomical." The universe seems quite tiny in comparison to its content, as though the whole process of creation had taken place within the narrowest of spaces. And connected with this curious fact is the most exciting discovery about nebulae which has been made in our century—a discovery whose meaning is still the subject of much dispute.

Is the Universe Flying Apart?

The spectral-line speedometer was naturally applied to the nebulae. As early as 1912, W. M. Slipher's measurements indicated fantastic velocities. After he had accumulated a few dozen figures, he noticed that the movements of the nebulae were, with few exceptions, directed away from us. An astronomer at Strasbourg, moreover, had the impression that the remoter nebulae were receding faster from us. But at that time the distances were still wholly uncertain. Edwin Hubble was the first astronomer in a position to get to the bottom of the matter.

It was a huge task. The light from nebulae is extremely feeble; a nebular spectrum took from eight to ten nights of exposure time. With a specially made objective, it proved possible to shorten this exposure by half. Even so, determining velocities

remained a tricky affair: the spectra were on the average three millimeters long. It was a task of infinite patience to determine microscopic shifts in the lines of such spectra.

Fortunately, Hubble had an associate with the requisite patience, a man who thought it no cross to sit up nights, year after year, keeping the Mount Wilson mirror fixed upon a nebulosity that glimmered far more feebly than a telescopic star. A former muleteer at a lumber camp, M. L. Humason had worked his way up to the post of mechanic at the observatory, then photographer, and had finally won entry into the holy of holies. From the high observer's seat fifty feet aloft within the giant barrel of the telescope, he pursued his great campaign; and under the microscope he deciphered the messages from the universe with the same feverish hunter's fever that had inspired Herschel 150 years earlier when he caught sight of the first faint nebulosities.

Picture after picture showed the expected red shift of the spectra, which meant that the nebulae were fleeing from us.

Picture after picture showed increasing velocities directly proportional to the increase in distance.

The final result was hard to credit. The remotest nebula was racing away from us at 25,000 miles per second, that is, at about one seventh the speed of light. Even astronomers accustomed to astronomical figures could scarcely believe this. Moreover, the too-perfect mathematical relationship between the distance of the nebulae and the red shift aroused suspicion. Perhaps light changed its wave length during such tremendous journeys, losing energy and arriving at our instruments redder than it was when it started. Perhaps the total gravitation of the universe affected the light, and the red shift could be explained as an Einstein effect. And then, light from those distant nebulae has been traveling for over a billion years, one fifth the age of the universe. Astronomers at any given time look at nebulae of such different ages that the question must be raised: have they any right to compare them with one another?

Hubble decided on a complicated *experimentum crucis*. It contained so many possible sources of error, made so many dubious assumptions, that the slightest alteration in a figure

would change a result to its opposite. Nevertheless, Hubble believed that the experiment proved his conclusion: that the red shift actually indicates retreating nebulae; that the extragalactic universe is steadily expanding.

Our universe, then, is conceived as a soap bubble steadily expanding and thinning out. All the clusters of galaxies are separating from one another; in two billion years distances will have doubled. If we wait long enough, all other galaxies will have dispersed, and we will be left alone in our own, surrounded by empty space.

Reckoning backward, we arrive at a period about five billion years ago when all the nebulae must have been united in a single lump, and the universe was only a fraction of its present size—a core of matter, so to speak, which exploded, and the fragments of which are still flying off into infinity. It is an odd conception: that our universe originated in an explosion. How strongly reminiscent it is of the birth of stars as supernovae, with a vast outburst of light and gases spewed out into a cloud that continues to expand before our eyes for centuries and even millennia afterwards. Our universe as a whole seems to have originated in much the same manner, possibly also with a tremendous eruption of light. In any case, something tore the condensed mass apart and sent it rushing outward on a gigantic flight that is still continuing.

Can it go on forever? Is an eternally expanding universe conceivable?

To the mind of Occidental man, it scarcely is. Consequently, an American theoretician, Richard C. Tolman, suggested, soon after Hubble's discovery, the possibility of a pulsating universe alternately expanding and contracting like an accordion. The expansion stage may have stopped long ago, since the movements we see and measure today took place millions and billions of years ago.

In one respect theoreticians have agreed: they considered a change in the spatial content of the universe, whether one-directional or pulsating, quite in order. A static, unchanging universe does not really suit the temperament of modern man, his desire

to see the universe as subject to motion and change. (For this reason, recent postulates of a "steady-state" universe have met with a poor reception by the majority of astronomers.)

One consequence of the new discoveries was revision of Albert Einstein's formulas by others. He was invited to Pasadena; Humason and Hubble discussed the problem with him; and he declared Tolman's equations original and persuasive. There was nothing sacrosanct about his own, he said; and he was quite willing to concede that his static universe was now revealed as a special case of a more general dynamic universe.

Further developments, however, led to even more significant consequences. The general theory of relativity remains the basis of all models of the universe, but certain newer theories suggest special variations. On the basis of the flight of nebulae astronomers are now constructing and examining models of the universe of the most various types, and testing them against observational evidence. The discussion is far from concluded; only recently it has been suggested that it is time to turn to Euclidean geometry again. In short, modern cosmology has been thrown into question by a single series of observations. Everything is fluid once more.

The present state of affairs has been drastically described by Bernard Jaffe as follows: "The theoretician supplements Einstein's principles by functions of his own, adding a new symbol here, removing another there, changing coefficients or exponents, rearranging the formulas when new difficulties appear or new interpretations occur to him. Every line represents the creation of a new universe; every sheet of paper that is crumpled and tossed into the wastepaper basket signifies a universe destroyed. In the morning he constructs and in the evening he tears down, god and demon at once."

This comment suggests that the age of great theorists is over. A highly sober and critical branch of science has arisen, cosmology, which no longer swears by any system, which no longer seeks domination by reasoning alone, but wishes rather to do justice to observation. Modern cosmology recognizes that observations can often be explained equally well by various theories, and that they outlast all hypotheses.

Evolution of Spiral Nebulae

The new nebular universe has not only upset the theories of mathematicians; it has also made astronomy far more interesting to the layman. Once again there is something tangible for the layman to look at and reflect upon.

Previously, the sky did not reveal such a multiplicity of forms. Stars are and remain just dots of light, and it is almost miraculous that science has been able to tell us so much about them. Even our solar system with the Moon and Mars, Saturn's rings and the comets, the Sun's protuberances and corona, seems monotonous beside the variety displayed in photographs of nebulae. The island universes offer, as a species, at least as much richness in form as, in the animal world, the class of Echinodermata. In fact, the nebulae are curiously reminiscent of these remarkable creatures. The starfish is represented, the sea urchin, sea cucumber, and sea slug. On the other hand, there are strange nebulae that cannot be compared to any living creature. In some, spiral arms hang from stems. From a round nucleus two short radii extend to both sides, with white banners of mist extending from their tips and winding in wide curves around one another. Or the radii continue on to a more or less complete oval ring.

This abundance of forms cried out for classification. The nebular specialist Edwin Hubble arranged them in a sequence from the simplest to the most complicated forms: round spheres, flattened spheres, spindle-shaped, and disc-shaped ovals. At this point the ovals divide; the discs acquire spirals either springing directly from the nucleus or attached to bars. In both groups the nuclei gradually dissolve until only the spirals remain visible. At the end of his list Hubble placed irregularly shaped nebulae without visible structure.

Such a sequence inevitably strikes us as a chart of structural evolution. Hubble's generation assumed, perhaps with too much certainty, that development progressed in the indicated direction, that is, that the spiral nebulae constituted a later evolutionary stage. The question was, how did such a development take place?

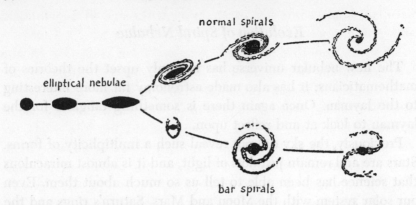

HUBBLE'S CLASSIFICATION OF NEBULAE. THE MORE COMPLICATED
FORMS AT RIGHT, HUBBLE SUGGESTED, GREW OUT OF THE SIMPLER
FORMS AT LEFT.

Why should arms grow out of oval discs, and why should the
arms curve into spirals?

This question could not be answered out of hand. That spirals
should shoot out ahead of disc-shaped structures as the result of
rotation seemed to contradict both experience and theory. There
remained no course but to believe in some unknown force that
scattered a sidereal system in spite of the contracting tendency
of gravitation. It was thought that perhaps the expansion of the
universe, which was causing the nebulae to flee from one another,
was also gradually tearing apart each individual nebula. But
calculation did not confirm this hypothesis; the origin of the
spirals remained an unsolved riddle.

A layman might wonder why Hubble's generation could ever
imagine that spiral nebulae evolved out of elliptical nebulae; to
do so, elliptical nebula would have to rotate in such a manner
that the tips of the spirals ran ahead of the main nucleus, and so
separated more and more from the nucleus. But such a conception
is difficult to grasp. One would think that the nebular nucleus in
its furious rotation is trailing the spirals along behind it, winding
them around itself, drawing them closer and closer, so that in the
end they will fuse with the nucleus. That is to say, the evolution
of these nebulae should take place in a direction opposite to that
in which theorists of the last generation said it did; the spiral

nebulae should come first, contracting at the end to the elliptical and globular nebulae.

The fact that this possibility was not even discussed by the last generation of scientists is a significant indication of the power of the *Zeitgeist*, the spirit of the age, over the minds of men. For the twenties was an era of mathematical exuberance, of abstract theorizing, in which scientists did not see what lay plainly before their eyes. Then gradually observation once more took a dominant position and reshaped our models of the universe by supplying a few new facts.

In 1944 Walter Baade at Mount Palomar made the crucial discovery that white giants are never encountered in the nuclei of spiral nebulae and in globular and elliptical nebulae. They are found only in the spiral arms; consequently, it seemed likely that the arms are younger than the nuclei, and spiral nebulae in general younger than globular and elliptical nebulae. Baade's discovery suggested that the loose spirals may represent the first stage of evolution of spiral nebulae, and that the layman's view may have been right.

Consequently one could then visualize the evolution of a sidereal system roughly as follows:

In a primeval nebula masses condense out, begin to radiate, begin to move. The first stage is an irregular collection of stars something like our neighboring galaxies, the Magellanic clouds. Impelled by the gravitation of some especially dense sector, this collection of stars is set rotating. A maelstrom arises which gradually involves the entire nascent galaxy. The core increases in density, rotates faster, carries the external star clusters along with it; the closer they are to this nucleus, the more its gravitation affects them.

This stage of evolution is represented by the loose spiral nebula M 33 in the constellation of the Triangle: a galaxy consisting of small clusters that reluctantly follow the rotation of the central mass and are gradually arranging themselves in a spiral which at present is just barely discernible.

Nebula M 51 in Canes Venatici shows a further stage: the spirals distinctly marked off, wound around one another several

times, and influenced to their outermost tips by the general rotation of the galaxy. At one tip there still clings a resisting nebulosity.

Nebula M 81 in the Great Bear is of about the same age as the Andromeda Nebula, and fortunately we can see it face-on instead of at an angle. Here the arms have already neared the nucleus; they are, so to speak, on the point of being wound tightly around the spool. The end product of the rotation, then, is a closed, elliptical disc. In the course of an evolution stretching over vast spans of time, it rounds out more and more, until at last it has assumed a globular shape. (See Plates XXXV, XXXVI, and XXXVII.)

After the Second World War the physicists Carl F. von Weizsäcker and Werner Heisenberg presented the requisite mathematical calculations to support such a possibility, under certain simple conditions, of the origin of galaxies. They were able to estimate the duration of the development from spiral to armless ellipse at about seven billion years. According to their theory, the rotation slows steadily, so that the spherical nebulae probably stand still. This theory of galactic evolution represents a return to Herschel's ideas. Herschel looked upon the globular star clusters as the last stage of the evolution of the universe: stars more and more losing their proper motions, clustering together; the rotating galaxy breaking up into isolated globular star clusters. The more recent conception assumes that the entire galaxy contracts into a single sphere. The star clusters, in this view, are only premature examples of the unceasing contraction of galaxies.

If this theory should be confirmed, we will be able to regard the spiral nebulae as fascinating historical documents on a par with the Moon. The Moon, with its craters, demonstrated to us how dark celestial bodies could form out of a cloud of meteors by gravitational attraction. The spiral nebulae may show us the life history of radiating island universes, whirling blazes of light born out of a dark primeval nebula.

But, in the most recent view, the formation of spiral structures from the elliptical nebulae does not contradict either theory or observation. The formation of spirals occurs if dust and rotation are present. It is possible that in the later stages of the develop-

ment of elliptical nebulae dust is formed, and from this spiral arms grow. The spiral nebulae are therefore not necessarily younger than the elliptical nebulae. If a stellar system has no dust in it, then no spiral arms will be formed.

Radio Astronomy

After the Second World War the specialists who had developed radar found a curious application for their valuable and temporarily idle apparatus: eavesdropping on the universe.

The new technique goes back to a curiosity discovered in 1931. At that time a radio engineer at Bell Telephone Laboratories, Karl Jansky, heard on his homemade ultrashort-wave radio set a howling whistle that came through every day at the same time. For various technical reasons, he suspected that the source of the radio waves must be the sky, and he concluded that the whistle returned so punctually every 23 hours and 56 minutes because in that time the Earth turns once on its axis. Thus the rotation of the Earth once a day brought his set into the path of an extraterrestrial short-wave broadcaster. And the direction indicated a point in the Milky Way, in the constellation of the Archer.

From 1945 on the big wire "dishes" of the radar technicians were directed toward this radiation, and the Milky Way was revealed beyond a doubt as a broadcaster of radio waves. There is nothing in itself surprising about this: radio waves and light waves are, after all, closely related. It could be assumed that heavenly bodies radiate other wave lengths besides the spectral colors from infrared to ultraviolet. Most of these, of course, would be absorbed by our atmosphere. But the Earth's envelope of air proved to be transparent to ultrashort waves. A new window was opening out into the universe. Astronomers could employ these radio waves for research much as they had hitherto used light waves.

No sooner was this possibility understood than giant, bowl-shaped antennae were built; they have already grown from thirty

to nearly three hundred feet in diameter. And since radio reception culminates in a loudspeaker, the firmament has been investigated with the ears instead of the eyes. We now listen in on the universe as a doctor listens in on the activities of heart and lungs with his stethoscope.

These noises from the Milky Way are the modern version of Pythagoras' and Kepler's music of the spheres. They are, however, far from melodic; in fact, they are solely the product of the receiving apparatus. But for research purposes they are invaluable because they can be classified by direction and strength. They come from all parts of the Galaxy, and are especially strong from the center of the Milky Way. What is sending them? We still do not know the source of the general short-wave radiation from the Milky Way, but the origin of a special type of wave has been determined.

A Dutch mathematician calculated that the metallic vapors and hydrogen scattered throughout the Galaxy should be preeminent sources of radio waves. Hydrogen atoms, he found, should yield radiation of 21-centimeter wave length. The radar receivers were not tuned to this wave length. But when they had been sufficiently refined, the 21-centimeter waves were heard clearly. Once more theory had triumphed.

From certain places in the sky neighboring frequencies were also heard, likewise of 21-centimeter waves. This was interpreted to mean that several hydrogen clouds moving at varying velocities must lie in these particular directions. And in between there must be empty areas. In a word, the Galaxy has gaps, as a structure consisting of various arms: it is a spiral nebula. The long-suspected but hitherto unprovable spiral structure of our sidereal system has now been definitely established. One of the arms passes close to the Sun, another at a distance of 4,000 to 5,000 light-years.

Thus the chain of proof for the Kantian doctrine of island universes has finally been completed. It is now known beyond a doubt that our Galaxy is but one of 100 billion or more galaxies in the universe. Photographed face on from a proper distance, it would present the same appearance as M 51 or M 33.

Thus radio astronomy, barely ten years old, has already yielded

brilliant results. It has, however, much more to offer. It can, for example, determine the direction and speed of meteors in broad daylight. In this way it confirmed other indications that very few meteors come to us from outer space; virtually 99 per cent of them are remnants of comets of our own solar system.

Even more important are the sharply defined broadcasting areas from which we receive especially loud whistles. One of these is the Crab Nebula in the Bull, the remnant of the super-nova of A.D. 1054. Like other clouds, this nebula consists of gas, but in contrast to others the gas is in furious motion. It is expanding at a speed of 935 miles per second, generating short-wave noises by the violent collisions among its atoms.

The radiation is surprisingly strong. It surpasses that of the Sun by two thousand times. Consequently, the supernova has recently been pinpointed as the cause of cosmic rays. These terrifying rays penetrate through thousand-foot layers of stone; no known atomic process can impart such energies to electrically charged corpuscles.

Radio astronomy has proved of enormous value to the 200-inch Mount Palomar telescope. As we have seen, that giant instrument can only make probes the size of pinpricks into space; it is altogether unsuited for wide sweeps of the heavens. Using the extra-terrestrial whistle tones as guides, Walter Baade was able to direct the Palomar telescope to particular points in space, and discover a number of fascinating facts about the nebular universe. At one spot which broadcast unusually strong radio signals he found a double nebula. These occur fairly frequently, and Baade had long suspected that they were colliding galaxies. Considering the congestion of the galaxies, such collisions would seem inevitable. In nebular clusters all the members must at one time have collided, Baade thought. Nothing much would happen in such collisions, he pointed out. Because of the enormous distances of the stars from one another, two galaxies could pass right through one another as do the two streams of stars in our own Galaxy.

But stars make up only half the content of galaxies; the other half is clouds of dust and gas. And these dark masses actually

collide with one another when the galaxies meet; tremendous maelstroms of gas are engendered, and the excited atoms produce short-wave radiation that sounds as loudly in our radio receivers as the much nearer expansion of the Crab Nebula.

According to Baade, the impact of such masses of gas upon one another tears them loose from both galaxies and hurls them into empty space. After the collision there remain behind gas-free galaxies, swept clean, so to speak, of dust and smoke. Baade had already observed such galaxies in the 200-inch telescope. Ordinary spiral nebulae are full of dark streaks, bands, rings; each shows the well-known layer of dust in the center when it is observed edge-on. But in the nebular clusters are some nebulae displaying no dark spots at all; presumably these galaxies have already been involved in a collision.

The collaboration between observatory and radio astronomy is, on all fronts, rapidly increasing our knowledge of the farthest reaches of the universe.

Space Travel

A new science has sprung into being, an utterly unique one because it consists of research into a dream. The boldest utopian fantasies of mankind are nowadays shaping up as technical projects. The voyage to the Moon, once a fable of Kepler's, is now the subject of earnest mathematical computations by a group of specialists who have whole organizations at their disposal, and who hold scientific congresses. It is hard to decide whether the members at such meetings are astronomers, engineers, or fantasy writers. Astronomy seems to be undergoing another metamorphosis; astrophysics is becoming astrotechnology.

It is startling to hear these scientists declare that space travel in itself is child's play. The only serious problem consists in overcoming the Earth's gravitation; this calls for speeds merely ten times higher than the top velocities yet attained by airplanes. It is, according to the astrotechnicians, simply a question of power;

we already possess the means in the reactive force provided by the combustion of gases: rockets. In fact, it is pointed out, man has already penetrated into space. In 1944 a German V-2 reached an altitude of 110 miles; in 1949 an American Wac Corporal rocket climbed to 250 miles; in 1958 a satellite will be launched to fly around the Earth at a distance of 300 miles or more.

Once a rocket is safely out in space, no further propulsive force is needed. A single impulse will suffice, as Galileo's law of inertia stipulates, to carry it on to limitless distances. For that reason Wernher von Braun, the famous rocket engineer who developed the V-2, suggested building a station in space whose colonists could be supplied by regular commuting rockets. It would circle the Earth as a satellite at a distance of about 1,000 miles and a velocity of approximately 3.7 miles per second—revolving around the globe in two hours. If its orbit were placed almost perpendicularly above the equator, it could keep the entire surface of the Earth under supervision.

Once such a space station were built, a voyage from it to the Moon would be really simple. Any airtight vehicle would do; the shape would not matter. There would be no air resistance to overcome; the spaceship starting from the station would already have a velocity of 3.7 miles per second, so that its rocket motor need not be very powerful; it would be used only for small impulses, and for braking. The trip to the Moon would require five days.

The next goal, Mars, would involve a journey of 260 days. After arriving on Mars, the explorers would then have to wait fifteen months, until the next opposition of Mars, for Earth to approach close enough for their return trip. Thus the duration of the entire voyage would be two and one half years; a small fleet would be needed to supply enough food for the expedition.

Apparently, the outlook is unexpectedly good. We need only the vantage point outside the Earth that Archimedes called for— not to move the world, but to escape from it.

Building the space station should be a matter of no great difficulty. Von Braun and his associates plan a three-stage rocket, 260 feet tall, 65 feet thick at the base. Each successive stage will

taper off in size; the lowest rocket will provide the greatest lift, propelling the vehicle to an altitude of 25 miles in one and a half minutes. This will take 500 tons of fuel, three fourths of the total weight. After this fuel has burned up, the empty shell will fall into the sea, whence it will be reclaimed and overhauled for a new start.

The second stage will continue to blast for another two minutes, and will be discarded at an altitude of 40 miles. The third section, with the crew cabin, flies on at far less expenditure of power in a great arc to its destination 1,000 miles above the Earth. Once that altitude is reached, the cargo is unloaded: 33 tons of building materials for the space station. That is to say, it is simply cast out into space, and continues to circle the Earth on its own inertia. The rocket itself returns to Earth. Its greatest danger on the homeward journey will be friction with the atmosphere; its skin will heat up like a meteor, and will have to be made of extremely tough material to withstand the thermal stresses. The crews' resistance to the physiological stresses of high acceleration are even now being investigated at various institutes of space medicine. It has already been learned that the human body can endure enormous accelerations for short periods of time.

The flight into space and back should be completed in about two hours. Only twelve flights will be necessary to transport all the material for the space station. It will be made largely of plastics, prefabricated, so that it need merely be assembled in space. Mechanics in space suits will move about without difficulty, no more conscious of their 3.7-mile-per-second speed than we are of the Earth's 18-mile-per-second speed around the Sun.

How will the men react to weightlessness in space? Some experience on this subject has already been accumulated. For brief moments pilots in jet planes have seen pencils rise up from the instrument board and float before their eyes. They themselves felt as if they were falling, or rather, as if they were simultaneously moving in all directions at once. Their heads "swelled," they could no longer orient themselves, they felt confused, but they did not lose consciousness.

The greatest unknown in the plans so far is the effect upon men

of cosmic radiation. It is incomparably stronger than radioactive contamination from atom bombs. On Earth we receive it only after it has been enormously filtered by the atmosphere; whether the human organism can endure its full force, and whether any protection against it is possible, remains an as yet unsolved problem.

The future Earth satellite will be equipped with every imaginable technical refinement. It will obtain electricity from solar power; the Sun, in fact, will be its sole source of energy. An air-conditioning unit will supply oxygen thinned with helium, in order to avoid the danger of the dreaded "bends," nitrogen bubbles in the blood. The lack of gravity will be partly offset by centrifugal force; the satellite will rotate rapidly on its own axis.

Another peril may be constant bombardment by meteors. About once every two weeks the inhabitants can expect a missile from space to smash a hole in the wall. Then alarm bells will clang, bulkheads will shut, and the men will get into space suits to repair the damage.

All this sounds eminently reasonable and trustworthy. The utopian dream has already assumed tangible form. Its advocates believe it can be realized within ten years, if the funds can be obtained; their preliminary budget calls for only five billion dollars.

For astronomers, perhaps the most exciting prospect is the possibility of an observatory alongside the space station. Conditions would be ideal: no shimmering atmosphere, no interference whatsoever with the image in the telescope. With "good seeing" twenty-four hours a day, an entirely new and wonderful chapter in the history of astronomy would begin.

To Infinity

This book must come to a close; astronomy goes on. Therefore, instead of "The End" we prefer to conclude with two of the latest sensations in the science—at least one of which points dramatically toward the future. The consequences of one of them

are potentially so vast that even professionals speak of them only in whispers. The other is so "popular" that it is discussed by even the cats on the rooftops.

The popular sensation began in 1947 when an American businessman saw from his private plane a long chain of saucerlike things winding around distant mountain peaks. Since then, flying saucers have been found all over the world; by 1952 the number of sightings had reached 1,700. The United States Air Force set up an investigating committee of two hundred specialists who are said to be still at work trying to solve the mystery. Astronomers and meteorologists, physicists and military scientists, space pioneers and specialists in mass hysteria were enlisted. Questionnaires were sent out and statistics drawn up, on the basis of which a distinct saucer season in July and August of every year was discovered.

After the most egregious cases of deliberate deception and autosuggestion were eliminated, 90 per cent of the cases turned out to be observations of new American research balloons, which are made of thin plastic, climb to heights of 100,000 feet, and are 140 feet wide. In the sunshine they gleam like silver; because they are only partly filled, they can assume every imaginable shape.

When the remaining 10 per cent had been thoroughly sifted, a few well-authenticated cases were still unexplained. The professional sensationalists pounced upon these; soon there had blown up a world-wide enthusiasm for matters astronomical which almost reached the pitch of the stir over Mars during the eighteen nineties. Fighter pilots tried to shoot down or overtake flying saucers; they reported unbelievable speeds and sudden changes of direction that no ordinary plane could follow. Illustrated magazines published photographs of flying saucers; some but not all of these were exposed as trick photography. The trustworthy pictures showed round or oval, cloudy or sharply outlined spots, white by day and by night, often in groups, sometimes in V-shaped flights, some containing as many as twenty "saucers." As had once been the case with Schiaparelli's canals, these observations were considered infallible testimony for the existence of inhabitants on Mars. With their superior intelligence these un-

known beings had presumably built spaceships shaped like saucers which could move at inconceivable speeds, and with which they were now spying upon the Earth.

As for the expositions of the mechanisms of these miracle ships, these were, in their pretentious quackery, highly reminiscent of the outpourings inspired by the "deluge" comet of 1524. The whole arsenal of modern technology was called in: rocket drives, atomic energy, solar radiation. Major Donald Keyhoe topped them all with his electromagnetic fields of force which easily overcame the Earth's gravitation. If we are to believe him, the inhabitants of Mars have already anticipated the latest project of our theoretical physicists: practical exploitation of Einstein's equations that link the gravitational and electromagnetic fields.

The more positive side of the saucer madness was that an army of volunteer star gazers pitched into the task of watching the sky. For their sightings as a rule were actual observations of atmospheric phenomena: ball lightning, unusual meteors, so-called fireballs. Significantly, the saucer season coincides with the period of the densest meteor swarms. Fireballs can assume all manner of sizes, shapes, and colors; they also appear in pairs and flocks and travel for minutes on end in great, sweeping orbits. In Venice in 1836 a glowing disc the size of the Moon was seen in the evening sky; it trailed a shower of sparks after it, and finally burst. In 1863 Schmidt, the selenographer, observed a whole squadron of fireballs. White funnels of smoke and reddish rockets with long tails have also occasionally been reported. But professional astronomers seldom have the luck to observe such interesting meteors. If the public continues to devote time to gawking at the sky, astronomy can only profit.

The second sensation is of considerably greater scientific importance. It concerns the wonderful built-in speedometer that astrophysics has discovered in all luminous celestial bodies. It now appears that we can no longer rely upon it as confidently as we did in the past. The speedometer occasionally plays us false. This does not mean it is now good for nothing; we merely understood it in oversimple terms. Apparently there is a second "instrument," which we have not yet learned to read. In time

astronomers will find out how to distinguish between the two effects.

The speedometer principle was this: a shift in the spectral lines toward the violet means motion toward us, a shift toward the red means motion away from us. In the case of Sirius the lines are shifted toward the violet; Sirius is approaching the Earth at a speed of five miles per second. The tiny companion of Sirius naturally accompanies the movements of its partner; nevertheless, the companion's lines are shifted toward the red. How can we account for this? Eddington explained the phenomenon on the grounds of the excessive mass of the companion of Sirius; it is, as we have noted, a white dwarf whose matter is compressed to 40,000 times the density of water. Eddington argued that gravitation slowed the oscillations of its electrons, causing the atomic clock to run slow, precisely as relativity theory would have it. According to Eddington, this was an important proof of Einstein's theories.

In recent years a Scottish astronomer, E. Finlay-Freundlich, has checked this phenomenon in numerous other cases. His results were upsetting. In the case of some binary stars the smaller partner shows a red shift many times in excess of the theoretical value. On the other hand, some white giants, whose mass is also extremely dense, attain at best three quarters of the predicted value.

In all these cases, moreover, the red shift cannot be interpreted as indicative of a particular motion, for the observed white giants belong to nebulae or star clusters whose own spectral shifts indicate motion different in direction or speed. Finlay-Freundlich then postulated that the red shift had some connection with the temperature. In the case of O stars whose temperatures were about 23,000 degrees Centigrade, it was regularly half again as large as the shift in B stars at 20,000 degrees Centigrade. And a special type of star whose temperature is estimated at 40,000 degrees shifts its lines by ten times the expected amount.

The extent to which temperature diminishes radiant energy and reddens light remains, at present, a mystery. At any rate, it has been demonstrated that there are other influences besides

motion upon the shift of spectral lines; the speedometer readings must be carefully corrected.

It appears at present that these investigations are calling into question one of the most important methods of research, and the favorite cosmological theory, of our century. We have not yet arrived at ultimate wisdom; there will be much for our descendants still to fathom. The mysterious, sparkling world above us has once more dropped a veil across its face, and where our age has seen the apotheosis of the mathematician, the next will probably belong once more to the patient observer.

So astronomy remains a science eternally young. We must not be discouraged if our inquisitive probings are met with new questions instead of persuasive explanations. We ought to rejoice that the search for truth is an undertaking bound to continue to infinity. The spirit of Western man needs to conceive of life stretching on into infinity, if not an infinity of space and time, then of seeking and striving.

In one of the most glorious periods of European culture a very wise man, Gotthold Ephraim Lessing, declared: "If the Lord God held out to me in his right hand the whole of truth, and in his left only the urge to seek truth—I would reach for his left hand."

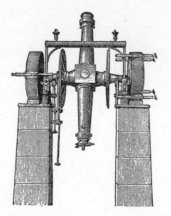

APPENDIX AND INDEX

APPENDIX

SOME ASTRONOMICAL FIGURES
(APPROXIMATE, FOR PURPOSES OF COMPARISON)

Velocities
IN MILES PER SECOND

Earth's surface rotation at the equator	0.25
Sound	0.20
Earth's revolution around the Sun	18.5
Turbulences in galactic nebulae	6–10
Transverse velocities of stars	6–37.5
Surface rotation of stars	30–150
Revolution of "twin" stars	190–380
Rotation of Milky Way at periphery	120
Flight of nebulae	600–40,000
Light	186,000

Distances
IN LIGHT-UNITS (EACH LIGHT-SECOND = 186,000 MILES)

Moon	240,000 miles =	about 1 1/3 light-seconds
Sun	93,000,000 miles =	about 8 light-minutes
Pluto, orbital diameter	7,500,000,000 miles =	10 light-hours
Nearest Star (Alpha Centauri)		4 light-years
Sirius (Canis Major)		10 light-years
Great Bear		100 light-years
Orion Nebula		1,800 light-years
Milky Way (diameter)		80,000 light-years
Nebular universe (diameter according to Charlier)		10,000,000,000 light-years

NAME	PERIOD OF REVOLUTION AROUND THE SUN	DISTANCE FROM SUN IN MILLIONS OF MILES	DIAMETER IN MILES	MASS (EARTH = 1)	DENSITY (WATER = 1)	ROTATION IN HOURS	NUMBER OF MOONS
Mercury	3 months	36	3,010	.056	3.8	88 days	—
Venus	7 months	67	7,580	.82	4.9	—	—
Earth	1 year	93	7,918	1.00	5.5	24	1
Mars	687 days	141	4,220	.11	4.0	24	2
Jupiter	12 years	483	87,000	318.00	1.3	10	12
Saturn	29 years	886	72,000	95	.7	10	10
Uranus	84 years	1,783	31,000	15	1.3	11	5
Neptune	165 years	2,793	33,000	17	1.3	16	1
Pluto	248 years	3,666	4,000?	1.00	—	—	—
Moon	Same as Earth	—	2,160	.012	3.4	1 month	—
Sun	—	—	864,000	330,000	1.4	25–30 days	—

CHRONOLOGICAL TABLE

ACHIEVEMENTS OF THE EGYPTIANS, BABYLONIANS, AND CHINESE

B.C.

4000–500   Sundial and water clock. Calendar: reconciliation of year and month.

Orientation by the noonday shadow. Quarters of the heavens.

Recognition of zodiac as path of Sun, Moon, and five planets.

Displacement of the zodiac (because of wandering of the Earth's poles—precession).

Annual retrograde motion of the planets.

GREEK ASTRONOMY

600   *Anaximander:* The Earth is a sphere.

Pythagoras: Spherical shell universe.

Harmony of the spheres based on numerical harmony of musical tones.

300   *Heraclides* describes retrograde motions of planets as loops.

250   *Eratosthenes* calculates the circumference of the Earth.

Apollonius conceives eccentric planetary orbits to account for irregular motions.

150   *Hipparchus'* measuring apparatus and observations.

Theory of Apollonius discredited.

A.D.

150   *Ptolemy's Almagest.* Improvement on Apollonian theory.

MODERN ASTRONOMY

1500   *Nicolaus Copernicus,* 1473–1543.

The Earth rotates around a north-south axis in one day.

The Earth revolves around the Sun in one year.

The Earth's axis always maintains the same direction: seasons.

The planetary loops are reflections of the Earth's motion (1506).

Giordano Bruno, 1548?–1600
The universe is infinite.
The Sun is a star.
Innumerable earths exist.

1600   *Johannes Kepler,* 1571–1630
1605: Orbits of planets are ellipses.
Velocity diminishes with distance from Sun.
Nonuniform motion can be calculated by the law of radius vectors.

Tycho Brahe, 1546–1601
Precise sighting instruments.
First observatory, Urania.
Underground observatory.

Galileo Galilei, 1564–1642
1610: Telescopic discoveries: Mountains of the Moon. Sunspots. Phases of Venus. Moons of Jupiter. Handles on Saturn. Milky Way composed of stars.
1634: Inquisition trial. Law of falling bodies: falling is constantly accelerated motion. Law of inertia: uniform motion requires no force.

Isaac Newton, 1642–1727
Reflecting telescope.
1666: Motion of Moon explained by falling plus inertia.
1672: Spectrum; theory of colors.
1682: Law of gravitation. Explanation of tides.

French Academy of Sciences
Hevelius: Air telescope.
Picard: Telescope as a measuring instrument.
Roemer: Meridian circle.
Huygens: Pendulum clock. Calculus of probability. Saturn's rings. Saturn's moons.
1672: *Cassini:* Distance of Sun 93,000,000 miles.
1675: *Roemer:* Speed of

light 186,000 miles per second.

1678: *Huygens:* Wave theory of light.

| 1700 | *Mathematicians* | *Greenwich Astronomers* |

Euler
Clairaut
d'Alembert
Lagrange
} Theory of perturbations.

1675: Foundation of Greenwich Observatory.

1701: *Halley* predicts return of comet.

Halley: Motion of stars and acceleration of Moon.

1727: *Bradley* explains aberration of stars because of Earth's motion.

Philosophers

1750: *Wright* recognizes Milky Way as stellar system.

1753: *Kant* describes evolution of universe from primeval nebula.

1761: *Lambert's* cosmology: sequence of higher-order universes.

Pierre Simon de Laplace, 1749–1827

All perturbations periodically balance out.

All motions in the solar system have same direction.

Cosmogony: primeval Sun casts off planetary rings.

William Herschel, 1738–1822

1781: Uranus discovered.

1800: Giant reflector: moons of Uranus.

Binary stars revolve around one another.

Sun is moving toward Hercules.

Probing the universe with stellar statistics.

| 1800 | *Investigation of the Galaxy* | *Investigation of the Solar System* |

1814: *Fraunhofer* lines.

1820: First perfected telescope.

1801: First minor planet: Ceres.

1838: Linear distance of a star first measured.

1845: First spiral nebula in the "Leviathan."

1859: Invention of spectrum analysis.

1863: Photometer invented.

1871: Beginning of astronomical photography.

1885: First supernova in a nebula.

1888: Displacement of spectral lines: stellar speedometer.

1890: Doubling of spectral lines: "twin" stars.

1900

1900: Spectral types: stellar thermometer.

1904: Two opposite streams of stars.

1904: Ca lines indicate Ca clouds.

1912: Variable stars as milestones.

1915: *Hertzsprung-Russell*

1811: Comets' tails: burning gas.

1818: *Encke's* comet; 3-year period.

1833: Rain of meteors from Leo.

1843: Sunspot periods; corona.

1846: *Biela's* comet disintegrates.

1846: Neptune computed and found.

1856: Saturn's ring a mass of small bodies.

1866: Meteor swarms found to be remains of comets.

1873: Map of the Moon ten feet across.

1881: Sun's temperature measured: 6,000 degrees Centigrade.

1888: Canals of Mars.

1892: Photograph of Sun by spectral light at Mount Wilson Observatory.

1900: Comets remain in the solar system. Comets' tails produced by light pressure.

1908: Sunspots are like magnets.

1912: Lunar craters result of impact of meteors.

diagram: giants and
dwarfs.

1916: General theory of relativity.

1918: Nova spectrum: explosion of stars.

1926: Theory of stellar evo- 1925: Sunspots change po-
lution. larity every 11 years.

1941: Quantitative analysis 1930: Planet Pluto
of stars. discovered.

Investigation of the Nebular System

1924: Andromeda Nebula resolved by Mt. Wilson reflector.

1929: Red shift of nebular spectra. Fleeing nebulae?
Expansion of the universe?

1931: Radio noises from the Milky Way.

1946: Nebular research with Mount Palomar reflector begins.

1952: Milky Way proved by wave analysis to be spiral
nebula.

INDEX

A NOTE ON THE AUTHOR

RUDOLF THIEL was born in Kaiserslautern, Germany, in 1899. Interest in astronomy has been common in his family for generations, and he still owns one of the original Fraunhofer telescopes. He began to make astronomical observations as a boy, and went on to study physics at Bonn and Munich. He has written a number of books on various aspects of cultural history. The writing of *And There Was Light* occupied him for six years. Mr. Thiel now lives in Darmstadt with his wife and four children.

A NOTE ON THE TYPE AND PRODUCTION

The text of this book is set in Caledonia, a Linotype face designed by W. A. Dwiggins (1880–1956), who was responsible for so much that is good in contemporary book design. Though much of his early work was in advertising and he was the author of the standard volume Layout in Advertising, *Mr. Dwiggins later devoted his prolific talents to book typography and type design, and worked with great distinction in both fields. In addition to his designs for Caledonia, he created the Metro, Electra, and Eldorado series of type faces, as well as a number of experimental cuttings that have never been issued commercially.*

Caledonia belongs to the family of printing types called "modern face" by printers—a term used to mark the change in style of typeletters that occurred at the end of the eighteenth century. It is best evidenced in the letter shapes designed by Baskerville, Martin, Bodoni, and the Didots.

This book was composed, printed, and bound by Kingsport Press, Inc., Kingsport, Tennessee. The paper was made by P. H. Glatfelter Company, Spring Grove, Pennsylvania.